MW00636937

To Jenn –
One of my favorite long
lost distant Ransom
cousins!

Rhea Seddon

GO FOR
ORBIT

RHEA SEDDON

GO FOR
ORBIT
★ ★ ★ ★ ★ ★
One of America's First Women
Astronauts Finds Her Space

YOUR
SPACE
PRESS

Murfreesboro, Tennessee

For my husband, Hoot Gibson,
and my children, Julie, Paul, Dann, and Emilee

★ ★ ★ ★ ★ ★

"History will be kind to me for I intend to write it."
WINSTON CHURCHILL

For information please contact: Your Space Press, P.O. Box 11898, Murfreesboro, TN 37129.
Email: AstronautRheaSeddon@gmail.com. Visit: www.AstronautRheaSeddon.com

Cover and book design by Roy Roper (www.wideyedesign.net)
Editing by Roy Burkhead, MFA, 2nd & Church (www.royburkhead.com)
Creative/Media Consultation by Stephanie Huffman, Epiphany Creative Services (www.your-epiphany.com)
Front cover photo: NASA. Back cover photo: Astronaut Robert "Hoot" Gibson

Library of Congress Cataloging-in-Publication Data
Library of Congress Control Number: 2015905397
FIRST EDITION
Seddon, Rhea – 1st ed.
Go for Orbit / Rhea Seddon.
Seddon, Rhea

ISBN #:978-0-9962178-1-1   Hardback
1. Biography & Autobiography   2. Women

YOUR SPACE PRESS
          P.O. Box 11898
          Murfreesboro, TN 37129
          Please visit us at www.AstronautRheaSeddon.com

Distributed by Your Space Press
14   10 9 8 7 6 5 4 3 2 1

YOUR
SPACE
PRESS

CONTENTS

★ ★ ★

ACKNOWLEDGEMENTS

★　★　★　★　★　★

This book's journey followed many starts, many stops. Its birth occurred just before Christmas, 1993. December 18 is the date on the first of twelve yellow legal pads. I had completed my third and final shuttle flight earlier that year. We were making our arduous annual holiday drive to Utah to ski, to California to visit Hoot's family, and then back to Houston. My two sons were old enough to entertain themselves, and there was time to write. I began to spew forth what I could remember about my NASA days—my days as a spacewoman. The last entry on the final pad was June 20, 1996. I had a third child by then, and our family had begun the trek homeward to Tennessee.

There the writing stopped.

The papers collected dust as I struggled to raise three children, to support a husband who traveled a great deal in his new job with Southwest Airlines, and to face the white-knuckle round-trip daily commute to Nashville for my new job at Vanderbilt University Medical Center.

Not until 2008 could I see a way forward.

Middle Tennessee State University in Murfreesboro, Tennessee—my hometown—had a creative writing mentoring program called, The Writer's Loft (now known as MTSU Write). Over five semesters I moved my words from handwriting on paper to 1s and 0s on the computer and sent monthly packets to my mentor, David Pierce—a published author and MTSU English professor. David opened an entirely new world for me. He and the program were instrumental in my learning how to turn a chronology of events into a real story. On the night of September 17, 2010—a Friday night—after I read aloud a few of those early words from my manuscript, I earned a certificate in creative writing. Sitting way back in the room paying close attention was a guy named Roy. We didn't formally meet that evening.

Over the next several months I sent a few book proposals to agents recommended by my author friends. None of those agents believed the book was anything new or *revelatory.*

Really?

So the book rested quietly in my laptop.

In 2013 I received a request from Roy Burkhead, now the editor of the Nashville-based literary journal, *2nd and Church.* He had been one of the early masterminds behind The Writer's Loft. He remembered my graduation reading and wondered if I would write an excerpt for the third issue of his magazine. He even offered to feature me on the cover. When he received my passage, he tactfully asked if he could edit it "a little." His work improved my words so much that I asked if he would edit the entire book. He did that and more: encouraging my writing, teaching me how to enhance my phrases, urging me to get the book published, designing my first web site, and polishing much of what I continue to write.

In 2014, Stew Ross of Southeast Business Forums invited me to speak to a group of networking people. Over the next several months, I spoke to several of his groups. After one of my talks someone said I should write a book, and I mentioned, shyly, that I was working on one. Afterward, Stew offered to help. Over coffee he said that a woman in Nashville was helping him with a book. He put me in touch with Stephanie Huffman in May. By mid-2015, Stephanie and her team at Epiphany Creative Services had guided me through the process of building the book and a marketing plan. She and Ally Otey helped me with tasks large and small. I became a brand, venturing into the social media world of blogging, Facebook, and Twitter. We built a sampler of my work.

Through her trusted contacts, Stephanie connected me to the people who made the book come to life. Roy Roper of Wideyedesign took the book cover from a simple idea to a unique work of art. He also patiently laid out the book, skillfully interleaving all the photos and designing the book jacket. Donna Huffman and Norma Shirk proofread the final version.

Lastly, Pollock Printing (a third generation printing company in Nashville) helped me through the decisions required to make words on a computer evolve into a real live book.

There were many others along the way who helped in so many ways.

Friend Steve Montague, when I confessed I was writing a book simply said "How can I help?" and sent me William Zinsser's book *Writing about Your Life*. The voice of experience all along the journey was that of my fellow astronaut Mike Mullane, who wrote a defining book about our 1978 class: *Riding Rockets, The Outrageous Tales of a Space Shuttle Astronaut*. Dr. Rick Chappell was chief scientist at Marshall Space Flight

Center in Huntsville, Alabama and worked on a shuttle flight in Houston with me. He later became director of Vanderbilt's Dyer Observatory in Nashville. He offered his vacation house in Destin, Florida for several of my long *writing sabbaticals*. The Johnson Space Center History Office and especially Jennifer Ross-Nazzal Ph.D. verified I had my facts correct and helped me unearth many of the pictures that grace the pages of the book.

Besides being a wonderful partner and supporter for so many years, my husband, Hoot, let me rummage through all his personal and space pictures then digitized many for this book. Only occasionally did we disagree about what really happened during our astronaut years. And we couldn't have accomplished any of this without our nanny, Joann Powell, who lived with us for twenty five years and made it all possible.

We never know the number of people who will help us or those we will have an opportunity to help. I strive always to pass along the encouragement I have been given.

I happened to give a talk at a conference at which the famous Presidential Historian Doris Kearns Goodwin gave the keynote. At a reception afterward, I had a chance to speak with her. In a room full of tall men, she and I were the only small people who could see eye to eye. I asked her about the presidents she had known and about her writing experiences. I mentioned my background and told her that I hoped to write a book. She simply said "Oh you *must* write your story!"

Thank you, Doris. Here it is.

CHAPTER 1

★ ★ ★ ★ ★

THE LONG ROAD TO SPACE

looked up at the rocket that awaited me, gleaming huge, ungainly and pristine white in the pre-dawn darkness. It hissed and groaned, alive and beastly. Was it Jonah's whale, ready to swallow me down and perhaps never cough me up? Or something more benign, a futuristic bird ready to bear me to the heavens and return me safely home?

Fellow Astronaut Story Musgrave described it as a butterfly bolted to a bullet. The Shuttle itself had a beautiful grace about it as it glistened in the brightness of the huge Xenon lights. It had wings and round, plump edges. The monstrous fuel tank and boosters looked plain, almost brutish, hiding so many millions of pounds of explosive materials.

Space Shuttle *Discovery* awaits launch on April 12, 1985.

"We dare you to come closer, deary!" they whispered.

Not really afraid, but anxious and excited, I had only moments to take it all in. It was the first time I had stood next to a shuttle ready to launch. We had trained for over a year and been delayed twice. We had practiced in simulators and an unfueled vehicle. I knew what to do if everything went right and how to perform when something went wrong. There was so much to learn that I hadn't truly believed that this would all come to pass.

There are moments in each life that change everything. "Will you marry me?" "You've been accepted." "You're pregnant." If I survived the launch of this vehicle I would become one of fewer than ten women in the history of humankind who had ventured into the halls of space. I would learn what it was like to float weightless and see the Earth as a blue marble in the blackness of the void. It would change everything.

The fullness of my life had brought me to this moment. All the unlikely roads taken, the risks addressed, the difficulties overcome had led to this. The ride up the clanking rusty elevator which had withstood the blast of Apollo and earlier Shuttle flights would be my first upward push of that day. Across the narrow orbiter access arm we clamored, brave or feigning bravery, with the bravado of the fighter pilots we were or had come to emulate. We would sit atop the harnessed bomb until its fuse was lit. This was the culmination of years of preparation; there could be no turning back. How in heaven's name had I gotten here?

In 1977, the John Gaston Hospital, or the John as those of us who worked there knew it, was where the indigent of Memphis came for their medical care. It was the chief training hospital for the students, interns, and residents at the University of Tennessee College of Medicine. As such, it matched the best, brightest, and most hard working of young men and women with the poor, the downtrodden, and the just plain bad. It sat across Monroe Avenue from the huge, well equipped, and private 2,000-

bed Baptist Memorial Hospital, yet all the local area's traumatic injuries, burns, and near-dead were routed to the John's Emergency Room—better known as *the pit*. First as a medical student, then as a surgical resident, the pit was my world.

Day and night the ambulances would tear into the back alley behind the hospital. Lights and siren meant someone was *in extremis* in the medical terminology – or fixin' to die in the local vernacular. Friday and Saturday nights near the start of the month were the worst. Government checks had gone out, and the liquor stores were doing a booming business. The knife and gun clubs were mixing it up. It was always interesting to hear the story that went with the wound.

"The patient was walking home from choir practice when some dude jumped out and shot him," I would recount to my senior resident after taking a history from the patient. After surgery, we would discover that the bullet had come from a police revolver and that the patient had been shot during a police chase following a burglary. Then there was the often-told story from young men that they were sitting on their toilets in their own apartments, reading their Bibles, when an unknown assailant broke in and stabbed them. One learned to be a skeptic.

What lingers in my mind so many years later is not of the plethora of patients, not of the countless lives saved and lost, not of the decrepit physical appearance of the place but the overwhelming odor of dirty socks and body odor that struck me as I trudged through the cipher-locked doors. Fancier, more modern hospitals took to calling themselves Emergency Departments, but at the John, it was more of an Emergency Room. There were two major sections: one known as the trauma end and the other as the medicine end. As a surgery trainee, the former was where I hung out. A major portion of the trauma side was one large room that held about six gurneys. Curtains could be pulled between them so that there was some privacy for examining a patient. However, patient history taking, moaning and groaning, screams for assistance, profanity about the unfairness of life and one's current predicament blended into a cacophony that made the practice of medicine stressful and chaotic.

Still, there were moments of levity. One night a drunken man was brought in and put in four-point restraints—a handcuff on each ankle and wrist attached him to the bedrails—so he wouldn't fall off the stretcher and onto the floor before he could sober up. He didn't know where he was but didn't want to be there.

He began his slurred mantra, "Call me a cab!"

Dozing off, he'd awake a little later and repeat his request in a booming voice loud enough to be heard all the way down the hall, "Call me a cab!"

To most of us, it soon became part of the background noise, but one of the interns was getting tired of it. "Call me a cab!" cried the insistent drunkard once more.

"OK, you're a cab!" came the intern's reply.

The interns made up the receiving line in the ER and handled most of the routine problems without the assistance of others. However, when a major traumatic injury case rolled through the door, a call went out from them to the surgical residents to come a-runnin'. The victim was disgorged from the ambulance into the glaring lights of John. As the patient was swung from the ambulance litter onto the gurney in the Trauma Room, he found himself looking up at a myriad of nurses, technicians, and young doctors of varying levels of training. Someone with a bullet hole in the abdomen would find every stitch of clothing cut off his body. Blood would be drawn from one arm, and each arm would have a large-bore IV line shoved into its veins. Then began a swift routine called *a tube for every orifice.* Before even having a chance to say "How do you do," a tube was slid up the victim's nose and down into his stomach. A catheter was snaked into the bladder. If someone was having trouble breathing, yet another hose went down the windpipe. Several people began examining the victim from head to toe. An x-ray was taken to see where the bullet had lodged.

The litany of questions then began.

"Who shot you?"

"Some dude."

"What kind of a gun?"

"A big one!"

"Where do you hurt?"

"All over."

"Had anything to drink tonight?"

"Just two beers."

The medical students believed this last declaration. The resident knew the blood alcohol level would come back showing at least a six-pack. Church-going teetotalers did not often visit our world.

After the entire well-practiced choreography in the ER was completed, the patient was whisked off to the Operating Room. We young doctors who might have been awake caring for patients for the past 20 hours would split open the patient's abdomen from top to bottom (or *xyphoid to pubis* in surgeon language), so that the bullet's course through the innards could be traced. Hopefully, all the shattered parts of the patient's body could be repaired. It always bothered me when a patient who had pleaded with me to patch him up as we prepared him for surgery died on the operating table. Sometimes the destruction was too extensive.

Many of these patients had massive wounds, and we doctors would spend many exhausting hours (almost always in the middle of the night) in the sterile coolness of the OR trying to stem the flow of the blood, leaving enough of the internal organs for continued survival, reversing "some dude's" work. After the operating was done and the abdomen stitched closed, the patient was transferred to the ICU. There, he had to be watched for many more hours lest some unexpected complication make the night's work for naught.

The doctors' lounge was outside the ICU and looked like what someone would expect for a charity hospital. Dusty, ring-stained end tables flanked ancient, cracked, orange Naugahyde sofas. Here, I sat as a resident in the predawn hours in early 1977, babysitting a post-operative patient through the night. Exhausted, I hadn't slept in almost 24 hours and had another whole day ahead of me. I needed a shower, and the last vestiges of the make-up I'd put on that morning were long gone. My scrubs were stained with blood, spit, vomit, and poop. I couldn't help letting my mind wonder:

My parents, Edward and Clayton Seddon during World War 2.

What the heck was I doing in this place?

I hadn't been brought up to be in this grubby spot. I had been raised in a typical, nice upper middle class Southern home in Murfreesboro, Tennessee where my maternal ancestors had lived for generations. My mother was a Southern Lady, and she had taught me to sew, garden, and prepare wonderful party menus. I had taken ballet lessons at Miss

As the first child in the family, I was doted on by parents, a grandmother and a great grandmother.

Mitwiddie's Dance Studio and learned the piano from Sister Alvera and art from Mrs. Ogilvie. I knew which fork to use at a formal dinner and had had a Grand Tour of Europe. My father was a Harvard-educated Catholic

Yankee lawyer, a true oddity in our small town in the south. My mother, born Clayton Ransom Dann, had not liked the women's college she had attended as a freshman. After a lengthy discussion, my grandparents permitted her to transfer to Ohio State University. Her Aunt Alice Dann Means lived in Columbus, so she'd have someone to chaperone her in that far away place. There she met my father, and they married after graduation while he was an officer in Patton's Army in World War II. After the war and law school in Boston, my father brought his wife and newborn daughter named Margaret Rhea Seddon (after her maternal grandmother as was the tradition in the South) home to Murfreesboro where he set up a law practice. My younger sister, Louise (after her paternal grandmother, of course), was born in 1950, and the four of us began a typical 1950s family life. My future would have been a mirror of my mother's – except that I was born in 1947, at the front end of the baby boom. Like many of my generation, I witnessed the growing demands of women for equality, never realizing how this all would

My parents, my younger sister, Louise, and I on a visit to grandparent in Florida

Homecoming at Murfreesboro Central High School with my cheerleader team in 1962. I am the third from the left on the front row.

sweep me along into my own future.

As I entered my teen years it became obvious that I was intelligent and had an interest in science. My father would have preferred that I pursue a degree in law to be able to take over his practice and run his businesses. However, more than anything, he wanted to make sure I could be self-sufficient some day. He had spent too many years looking after several generations of my mother's family—my mother, my grandmother, and my great-grandmother—not to mention helping out many of the little old ladies of the town. He wanted me to be a more independent person. Ever tolerant, my mother wanted me to be happy in whatever I did. She'd often shake her head with a bemused smile when I explained my grandiose ideas to her. It was considered odd in those days for a cute little cheerleader (even a rather intellectual one) from Murfreesboro Central High School to be interested in planning a career in science. I was so lucky that my parents encouraged me and that there were several role models among their friends who helped me.

Dr. Lois Kennedy, a friend of our family, practiced medicine in our town. Tall and imposing, she was soft of heart, delivering many of the local babies. I worked in her office one summer and got to see what the practice of medicine was really like. It was always sad to me that she had never married because she would have made a fine mother. Would I someday have to choose between career and family like she had?

Dr. Florence Ridley was a professor of English at UCLA, and she had grown up with my mother in Murfreesboro. She was a woman ahead of her time, leaving the South to pursue her career on the West Coast. When I began to look around at colleges, Florence suggested several California universities, including Berkeley, which had a fine reputation in the life sciences. I couldn't have known that student activism would begin in earnest on that campus right after my application was mailed in the fall of 1964.

The Free Speech Movement was in full swing at Cal when I arrived there in 1965 at the age of 17. Berkeley had over 27,000 students, which was three times as large as my entire hometown. Rallies were held on Sproul Plaza, and the expletives that were often thrown about made my ears burn. There were tables set up recruiting for the Gay Liberation Front and the Black Panthers. Not only was there the strangeness of new surroundings but it was all so impersonal. No one knew who I was or cared. Soon, I joined a sorority and found friends, but I was still very much on my own. My father's advice was to keep putting one foot in front of the other until I walked out of the rough spot. That's what I did.

Isn't it funny how little things can send you down an important pathway in life? In my hometown, Rutherford County Hospital was opening its first Coronary Care Unit, or CCU, the summer after my freshman year at Berkeley. My father had been on the hospital's board of directors for many years and asked the hospital administrator, Jim Arnhart, if I could find a summer job there. It was all arranged that I would be a summer aide in the new Intensive Care Unit, perhaps to be indoctrinated in the glamorous new field of cardiology. The problem was the unit's opening was delayed, and I was redirected into the surgical suite and fell in love with surgery. I spent every college summer peering into open abdomens and helping fix people up while my girlfriends were at the country club pool.

The University of California at Berkeley in the late '60's. It was a hot bed of student unrest with the Free Speech Movement and anti-war protests.

During my time at Berkeley there were years of unrest with student protests of everything from the Vietnam War to People's Park, a heated battle over plans to turn a verdant green vacant lot into University athletic fields.

My Sigma Kappa sorority house- a refuge from the craziness of campus.

While students at traditional colleges worried about the football team and dates, I worried about throat-burning tear gas raining down from police helicopters or rounding a corner on campus to come face-to-face with National Guard troops in riot gear. Amidst the turmoil, however, new ways of thinking were developing. It was becoming more acceptable for women to plan careers, even unconventional ones. With my particular interests, medicine was an obvious choice, although it was still not a lady-like field as far as my Murfreesboro friends were concerned.

My grades were not terrific in my first years at Berkeley because I was in pre-med, the most difficult and competitive major. There were times when I was sure I could never reach my goal of becoming a physician. I was an immature, small town girl, far from home in what became a place of turmoil. I am not sure how I managed, but I learned that dogged persistence can

On to medical school at the University of Tennessee College of Medicine in Memphis.

often overcome many other shortcomings. It was a lesson I would carry with me all my life, and conquering each obstacle gave me the confidence to face the next one. Once I got into my major in physiology in my junior year, I hit my stride. My overall grade point average improved, and one glorious day in the spring of

I became the only female in my surgery residency program at UT.

my senior year, a letter of acceptance arrived from the University of Tennessee College of Medicine in Memphis. Another friend of my mother's from Murfreesboro, Dr. Frances Riley, a pediatrician in Memphis, probably had spoken to the school on my behalf. She had graduated at the top of her med school class at UT, in an era when few women were admitted. She would become one of my finest mentors, for she had managed to have a successful practice, a happy home, and three wonderful children. In 1970, the year of my entry into medical school, there were six women in a class of over 100.

During my hospital rotations in the second half of medical school, I enjoyed several areas of study, but there was never any doubt that I would go into a surgical field. After finishing a surgical internship at Baptist Hospital in the summer of 1975, I became the sole woman in the General Surgery Residency Program at the University of Tennessee Hospitals in Memphis. That is how I came to be in the doctor's lounge at the John, sitting on an orange Naugahyde sofa in the middle of the night in 1977. Elvis had departed the building earlier that year and there were times I wish I had, too.

After completing medical school, an internship, and half a residency, it was too late to change my mind about a career. There were too many years invested, yet it seemed there were too many miles to go. I think I was at a low point: single, exhausted, dirty, and unfeminine with still no end in sight. Into this time of uncertainty in my life appeared Dr. Russ Greer, a neurosurgery resident.

The only residents who had it worse than general surgery residents like me were the neurosurgery residents. At least when I opened up a belly, I could look in, find what was broken, then repair or remove it. Patients can do without half of what is in there and will thank you very much in a week or so, and go home to get on with their lives. The inside of the skull is remarkably different. Open up the headbone and everything looks pretty much alike – like soupy gray custard. With an injured or diseased brain, it is hard to tell what is salvageable and what is scrambled. It is equally hard to tell what is important for future normal function. Rather than using a scalpel inside the head, neurosurgeons spend hours slurping up brain goo with a suction tip. They kid about someone's speech-producing area getting sucked into the jar. But it is not a joke. One never knew what would remain functional when the patient woke up. Also, the brain has the nasty habit of swelling after surgery. Trapped inside its hard casement, swelling caused pressure that could destroy or impair other brain areas or kill the patient. Many neuro patients spent days or weeks in the ICU. Miraculously, some awoke completely well; others were in a vegetative state forever. Since it was impossible to tell which path a particular patient would take or what complications might occur rapidly, they all had to be watched constantly, day and night.

Russ Greer was at about the same stage of his neurosurgery residency as I was in surgery, but he was a little older. He was keeping a close watch on his ICU patients as I was on mine. He plopped his carcass down across from me in the doctor's lounge. We compared notes about our respective ICU patients and bemoaned our own sorry state. Then he asked me a question that started me down the road to a different future.

"What would you do if you weren't doing this, if you could do anything you wanted?"

It was a simple question. I could have shrugged my shoulders and we would have chatted about other things. What happened from there gave me faith that someone in heaven was looking after me, guiding my path in rather strange ways. I paused while I considered all that was out there for an unattached, well-educated young woman with no obligations other than to make something of herself.

"I'd be an astronaut," I said.

Looking back, what a strange answer it was that popped into my head and found its way out of my mouth. I would be asked thousands of times later in my life how and when I got interested in the space flight program, and I have had a long time to consider my answer. At first, I would say it was the Skylab flights that took place during my medical school and training days. On the first manned Skylab flight, a medical doctor, Dr. Joe Kerwin, was doing studies of how humans adapted to space. How fascinating!

Then my father reminded me that it was earlier than that. He remembered the night that Neil Armstrong and Buzz Aldrin first walked on the moon. We were at Center Hill Lake near my home in July of 1969, spending a few days water-skiing. Like millions of others, my family stayed up most of the night at a motel near the lake to watch Apollo 11 land and to hear the historic words "Houston, Tranquillity Base here. The Eagle has landed." Later, the astronauts emerged onto the surface of the moon, and we heard "One small step for a man, one giant leap for mankind." Standing outside, we looked at the moon with new reverence. My father tells me that I said then that I would like to go there someday. I was 21 and not yet out of college. Did my father think that was ridiculous for a girl? In any event, he didn't laugh.

My interest in space went even further back.

I was like so many children in high school, caught up in the Mercury and Gemini flights of the 1960s. Everything would stop, the TV would be switched on, and we would all—a whole nation—watch the countdown. All of us knew the astronauts' names. We knew their backgrounds, their families. We knew they had gotten special deals on houses in Houston, that they drove fast cars. They had lucrative contracts with *Life* magazine which documented their lives, and we suspected they were all wealthy because of their fame. They were the heroes of the day, and I thought it would be fantastic to be one of them.

But the fascination went further back still.

I was in grammar school when Sputnik 1, the Soviet Union's *spy in the sky*, was launched in 1957. Not yet ten years old, I saw it passing over my house. Even though I went to a three-room, eight-grade Catholic elementary school, the push for more science education had reached us. The United States lagged behind the Russians in technology. To prevent what was perceived as certain future Cold War disaster, our nation had to hurry up and raise a generation of scientists and engineers to save the free world.

Even my tiny school, in my little Tennessee town, got the word and worked to include more science, so our country could win the space race.

The nuns at St. Rose of Lima Catholic School were not well-equipped to teach science. Eventually a science teacher was imported from our community. Science was something brand new for me when it became one of my subjects in seventh grade. The entire country regarded the study of science as a national imperative. It captured the imagination of an impressionable pre-teen. I remember in the spring of my seventh grade year, 1960, we had to write a big report on some science subject that interested us. Mine was about what was predicted to happen to humans if they went into space. I remember copying sketches from a magazine article about the G-forces from the rocket ride and about the possible things that could happen in the weightlessness of space. Humans had not yet ventured off the planet, and there were dire predictions.

So there it was, the start of a thread that wound its way through the history of our generation and so many years of my life. This thread was what prompted me there, in a sleep deprived state in the doctor's lounge at the John, to blurt out that I wanted to be an astronaut when Russ Greer raised the question. It was an odd declaration by a junior female surgical resident. Odder still and eerily serendipitous was Russ's reply: "I used to work for NASA."

The stars began to align.

I don't remember in what capacity he worked for NASA or where, but he had kept in contact with the people he had worked for. A few weeks later as he hurried past me in the hospital hallway, he called out: "Hey, Rhea, my friends at NASA say they're going to take a new group of astronauts soon for the space shuttle program."

"Hey, Russ. How do I apply?"

"Don't have a clue. Gotta' run!"

It was almost like a dare: "You've said you'd like to fly in space. Prove it!" But where to apply? And how? What sort of person were they looking for? It had been almost ten years since the last astronaut selection. There had been ten years of affirmative action in the interim. Had the Women's Movement gotten through to the world of rocket science?

I knew that astronauts lived and trained in Houston, Texas at some NASA facility there. I addressed a letter of inquiry to "NASA, Houston, Texas" and hoped it would find its way into the right hands. How long would it take to get through the double bureaucracies of the post office and NASA, or would it ever get to the right place at all? It didn't take long at all. In two weeks I received the information I needed.

How strange fate can be. NASA was soliciting applications for a new astronaut class to begin in July of 1978, and my residency would be completed at the end of June that year. For the first time they would have two types of astronauts – pilots and scientists. As in all previous years, the pilots would be chosen from the best of military test pilots, with a requirement for at least 1,500 hours of high performance jet time.

Now, on the other hand, a new breed of astronauts, called mission specialist astronauts, would come from the science and engineering communities. The requirements were not too stringent: at least a bachelor's degree in science, math, or engineering; preferably an advanced degree; and/or work experience. I supposed an MD degree and four years of surgery experience would qualify. Since there was no surgery planned for space that I knew of, perhaps NASA would be more interested in the fact that I had been moonlighting in emergency rooms up and down the Mississippi delta (against our residency program's rules). Also, I had become interested in nutrition and had done extra research in that field. Surely NASA was concerned about unexpected emergencies in space and the nutrition of its crews.

Beyond career backgrounds, there were health requirements. Normal blood pressure, vision requirements, height between 60 (whew, made it by 2 inches!) and 76 inches , and no major medical problems.

Anyone interested who felt they qualified could write for an application from Mr. Duane Ross in the Astronaut Selection Office at the Johnson Space Center. It was after requesting and receiving the forms that I determined that the application process itself was the real test of the desire to have the job. Anyone who could fill out the reams of paperwork required for the civil service position (since I was not military) and another set designed to allow the selection board to choose the best candidates to interview must have really wanted the position. There were birth certificates, transcripts, and copies of various diplomas to be sent in. There had to be three recommendations from people who knew me and could give an assessment of my job performance. *Right,* I thought. *I'm going to walk into the office of the Chairman of the Department of Surgery and tell him he might receive a call from the NASA Astronaut Program asking for an assessment of the performance of one of his not-exactly-stellar residents?* Had I lost my mind?

Dr. James Pate was the silver haired, mature, and experienced surgery chairman who had seen many classes of residents do a variety of things with their training. Luckily he had a sense of humor. He was amused when I told him about the application for this outlandish position, but then he figured I was a strange sort of woman to be in a surgery residency in the first place. Dr. Pate knew I never intended to be a general surgeon. He had advised me that he thought it would be difficult for a woman to be successful in that field. This was the 1970s, and he was probably correct for that time. Few men would go to a woman surgeon to have their hernia repaired. Many women still wanted a strong father figure to take charge of their operation. I had applied to the general surgery residency, planning to go on to a plastic surgery residency later. I guess he figured if I made it into the astronaut corps, it wouldn't be like the world was losing a good general surgeon. He promised if NASA called, he would say nice things.

My second recommendation came from my flying instructor, Jose Guma. Toward the end of medical school I decided that one day I might be a rich doctor and buy my own airplane. So I decided to learn how to fly. I guess I also thought that it might someday help me to get into the space flight program, but that was a far-fetched idea. My ever-tolerant father agreed to give me flying lessons as a graduation present from medical school.

Jose had come to the United States from Cuba, was a little older than I was at the time, and loved nothing more that being up in the air. He was a patient flight instructor and was happy to have a reasonably intelligent student. Jose would have loved being an astronaut himself, so he didn't think I was nuts for applying.

Who else to ask? It needed to be someone who had known me for a while, perhaps someone who knew my family, who could vouch for me personally. I chose Jim Arnhart, the administrator of Rutherford Hospital who gave me my first summer job. After I talked to him about needing a recommendation, I'm sure he went home and said to his wife, "Ed Seddon's daughter is crazy – Berkeley, medical school, surgery, and now the NASA Astronaut Program!" Years later, sitting on the Astronaut Selection Board, I found it interesting to see which people in the applicants' lives they chose to provide their recommendations. I was a small-town girl who didn't know anyone famous, but I don't think I could have ever chosen finer people. Each knew a different aspect of my life and must have given passable reports on me.

The most welcome part of the application information were the words "affirmative action." NASA wanted to accept women for the first time. That was a most fascinating thought for me. How would women fit into this all-male organization? Having been the sole female in my residency program and one of a few women in my medical school class, I knew there were good and bad things in store. Vivid in my memory was the sexist rule I encountered during my internship at Baptist Hospital in Memphis. No women were allowed in the surgery doctors' lounge. I would wait between operative cases on a folding chair in the nurses' bathroom, hoping that someone would remember that I was there when it came time to start the next procedure. I learned that there were several approaches to dealing with this kind of barrier – put up with it, attempt to change it, or get away from it. The chairman of the department refused to address the issue. I switched to the UT program for my residency. They didn't have rules like that.

I also remembered the comradery that I enjoyed with the young men in my medical school class and in my residency program. We all worked as a team, supported and helped each other, partied together. I never was invited to go quail hunting or to play golf with the professors the way the males were, but I never felt short-changed when it came to assignments or responsibilities. There was more than enough work to go around. Could I become a successful female astronaut? Would the same team spirit directed at a difficult goal overcome differences in gender? What hurdles would there be for women becoming part of space missions? What an opportunity, what an adventure!

Applications were due by June 1977 and I completed the paperwork early. I didn't mention to any of my friends or colleagues that I was applying, since I knew I'd be kidded and laughed at. Besides, I figured I would receive a nice, thin letter from NASA saying I hadn't been accepted. On many occasions in my life, I have cast my fate to the wind and attempted something I thought was far beyond my reach. If NASA didn't want me, it wasn't meant to be, and it cost nothing to try. One time I told my father that nobody from a small country town could ever do anything exciting. He told me, "Rhea, you can go any place in the world from right here in Murfreesboro, Tennessee." I had been rejected for positions before. In those instances, I always figured that wasn't what fate had in mind for me and that there was something else out there for which I was better suited. I had no idea by what means the selection would be carried out or when, so I sent in the completed forms and began waiting.

A resident's *New Year* begins in July, and in July 1977 I started my third year as a resident on the surgical wards at the Memphis Veterans Administration Hospital. Dr. J.J. McCaughan was the head honcho in surgery at the VA. Tall and lanky, he had been at the VA for many years and had trained a boatload of residents. He was leading rounds one July morning. Along with several other residents and students, we were in the hallway outside one of the clean, efficient wards when one of the nurses pulled me aside to tell me I had a long-distance call holding. I excused myself from rounds and scurried to the nurse's station.

It was a fellow named Jay Honeycutt calling from the Johnson Space Center in Houston.

"Dr. Seddon, are you still interested in applying for the Astronaut Program?"

"Yes, sir," I said, trying not to sound overexcited.

"Could you come for an interview the last week in August?"

"I'll have to take some leave, but yes, sir, I think I can get away."

"Then you can expect to get tickets and information in the mail."

I had a million questions: "What will the week entail, sir? Who else will be there for interviews?"

"There will be briefings about the space shuttle and what the crew positions are. We want folks to know what they will be signing up for. There'll be an extensive physical exam and psychological testing to make sure you're fit. Remember to bring running shoes and exercise clothes, since there's a treadmill test. You'll have an hour and a half interview with the selection board, and you're invited to a social event on Thursday night. There'll be about twenty of you being interviewed that week, all life scientists. You'll finish late in the day on Friday."

"Will there be any other women?"

"Yes," he said. "Eight of you."

What else to ask? With my heart pounding in my throat, it was hard to think and hard to talk. "How many will be interviewed altogether?"

"About 200."

"And how many will eventually be selected?"

"Thirty to forty."

Not great odds, I thought, *but not impossible.*

"And how many applied?"

"Counting all the guys who applied through the military, over 8000."

WOW! What a terrific honor to make the top 200 out of 8,000! After thanking Jay for the invitation, I went back to join the others making rounds, trying hard not to look both elated and astounded. Afterwards, I asked Dr. McCaughan if I could take a week of leave in August to go for a job interview.

"A whole week?" he asked. In their final year, residents took off a day or two at a time to interview for specialty programs, but nothing ever took a full week.

"Yes, sir, that was the request."

"From whom?"

"Well, uh…NASA."

"For what position?" he asked, his stern brows furrowed.

"Um…to become an astronaut, sir." I said, with a whisper. "I'm sure I won't get the job, sir, but it would be a real honor just to be interviewed."

"Well," he said. "I suppose it can be arranged."

"Thank you, Dr. McCaughan!" I said, hurrying back to my patients.

So I waited for my ticket and information to arrive from NASA. In the meantime, I tried to figure out how to get in shape for a run on the treadmill. My job left me precious little time to work out. Ordinarily up at 5:00 a.m., I had to be at the hospital by 6:00 a.m. to check all my patients before starting surgery at 7:30 a.m. On good days, I got home at 7:00 or 8:00 at night. Every third or fourth night, I stayed at the hospital all night, taking care of all the patients on the wards and admitting any new ones. My only option for exercising was to get up at 4:00 a.m. if I hadn't spent the night at the hospital and run around the large pond at my apartment complex. You do what you have to do. So that's what I did, although it was walking at first. I worked up to running (well, okay, jogging) by the time I left for Houston.

Houston Intercontinental Airport was a huge place, like Houston itself. Located 20 miles north of town, it is still inside the city limits. On the other hand, the Johnson Space Center or JSC is about 20 miles south of downtown, and also inside the city limits. On arrival at the airport on Sunday, August 28, 1977, I had to find my way to the commuter airline serving the Clear Lake area, where JSC is located. It felt strange to have to take an airplane to get to a place in the same town – but then, this was Texas. While waiting at the Metro Airlines lounge, I wondered if any of my fellow passengers were interviewees. Some were young, fit, and intelligent looking. Several of them were sizing me up, too. Was this the competition?

It was mid-afternoon when the small Metro Airlines plane touched down in Clear Lake. Several of the other passengers and I found a van waiting to take us to the Kings Inn Motel near the center where we were to stay for the week. In the shimmering heat of a Texas summer, the place didn't look high tech. At the turn onto NASA Road 1, there was a dilapidated old building with a sign that said "Rusty's Radiators." Tenacious old weeds grew along the road. We drove about a mile until it looked like we might have made it to civilization. We could see some gray, industrial looking government buildings in the distance as we turned into the parking lot of the motel.

An orientation meeting was scheduled for 7:00 p.m. No one was late and everyone was more than a little nervous. As it turned out, the twenty of us were the third group of candidates to be interviewed. We were all life scientists (MD, PhDs or some with both degrees and one DVM), and we were the first group to include women. There was a rumor that the press had raised the question of whether NASA was serious about interviewing women for the astronaut corps. The first two groups who had been in Houston in the prior weeks had been "same-ole, same-ole" male jet pilots.

The two people who stood out to me most that evening were George Abbey and Sam Pool. Mr. Abbey was introduced as the Director of Flight Operations, which I assumed wasn't anything important because he was such an unprepossessing person. A round, dark, crew-cut man, he mumbled his way through a welcome and a short explanation of what the week would include. Most importantly, he told us to bring to our interview an essay explaining why we wanted to be astronauts. Sam Pool was a physician and in charge of all the medical and psychological testing we would undergo. He outlined in detail a busy schedule, but, for me, it was wonderful to have a whole week with no night call. I was interested in seeing what the thorough medical tests would tell me about my own health. I don't think the others were looking forward to the exams.

All the interviewees introduced themselves and told what they did and about their degrees. Oh, what a sinking feeling! There were several with both MD and PhD degrees and many with extensive pilot time in addition to their advanced degrees. Some had even been doing NASA research. I figured NASA had made a mistake when they invited me. Well, I figured I'd better enjoy my visit, learn some new things about space, and maybe meet a few *real* astronauts. I might even get to know some of the people in my interview group. Who knew, some might be a part of the new astronaut class and get to fly in space someday, and I could say I had interviewed with them.

After the briefings, I met Jay Honeycutt, with whom I had spoken on the phone. He told me that there would be a lot of press interest during the week because of the women in the group.

"Would you mind speaking with a few reporters during a break in your schedule in the morning?" he asked.

Me, who had never spoken to a reporter in my life? Did I dare decline?

"Well, no, I wouldn't mind." I was too naïve at that point to know any better.

Then, at the end of the evening, we were given our individual schedules for the week. Talk about bad luck! My interview was scheduled for Monday morning. Since this was Sunday night, it meant my essay had to be written before morning. Here I was, a young woman who was interested in the space program, but not knowledgeable about it. I came to Houston to find out about the space shuttle and what the crew's responsibilities would entail. Now I had to write an essay about why I wanted the job before I knew anything about it.

About 9:00 p.m. at the motel, I agonized over what to write in my essay. I thought of doing something cute and unique, like saying "You tell me why I would want to be an astronaut." I knew nothing about the selection board and whether they had a sense of humor. *Would something meant to be funny go flat with those people?* I didn't even have any proper paper. At this hour of the night, sequestered in a small hotel, I had the notes pages from the back of my daily schedule calendar. I gave up. If the Astronaut Selection Board was going to give points for a well-thought-out, well-written, well-prepared essay, I was going to lose that round. No style points, no points for technical skill, no points for anything. All I could come up with, written on two pages of 5 by 8 inch lined note paper was:

"Just about any reason I could give for why I want to be an astronaut are

[sic] bound to sound trite when spelled out on paper. I suppose it has been a secret dream since my childhood.

Space is one of today's new frontiers – and one which I am enthusiastic to explore in terms of my own areas of expertise – medicine, physiology, and nutrition. I also think it is time that women be allowed into the program – not only because they have a great deal to offer – but because it is time that we knew how they will fare in space – and what special problems they will face there.

In particular, I am looking for something special to devote myself to. I will complete my surgery training next June – and have been offered several positions in the field of surgical nutrition – but I can think of no more exciting and challenging an undertaking than studying, and being a part of, the human animal's first steps off the planet."

Monday morning was an eye-opener in many ways. As the bus delivered the 20 of us to the Johnson Space Center, the women were attacked by a gang of media people. Cameras, microphones, notebooks, jostling, scrambling, tripping over one another: the press was at its worst. I found the whole incident mildly disturbing, mildly exhilarating. I guess the men in the group thought it was disgusting and demeaning that they were for the most part ignored. It would be the first of many run-ins like this that would occur in the next few years. There was time to say a few polite words to the reporters before we were whisked into the Flight Medicine Clinic to begin our medical tests.

I ended up getting myself into trouble in my first real interview with the press later that morning. NASA decided it would look good to have me do the interview in the area where the treadmill tests were done. They had me wear shorts and rigged me up with some electrodes to look like I was instrumented for the exam. Unfortunately, the pictures were taken with me breathing on an ugly looking mouthpiece. How lovely! I knew I would get ribbing from friends back home if they saw it. But the worst thing was the trick questions from the media after the pictures. A couple years later, I would take a course on how to recognize and avoid this kind of query. But on that Monday morning in the summer of 1977, I was pretty green. One reporter asked me why NASA had not interviewed women before. Not knowing why they hadn't, I said I didn't know. Then the reporter said "Don't you think it is about time that NASA interviewed women?" I gave an honest answer and said "Yes." I should have known that the newspaper quote the next morning would be that Rhea Seddon said that it was about time that NASA interviewed women. Well, if the essay didn't win me any points that quote surely would get me negative ones.

So I showed up for my late morning interview feeling stupid and off-balance. I was asked to sit down in the waiting room as my non-essay was carried into the inner sanctum, and the door was closed. Moments later, I heard peals of laughter emanating from behind the closed door, presumably at the stupidity of my writing. I wanted to be allowed to slink back to Memphis and pretend this had never happened. Would they be blunt enough at the end of the interview to tell me that I was dreaming if I ever thought I had a chance of getting this job?!

Finally, the door opened. I took a deep breath and swallowed hard. The big surprise was that the Astronaut Selection Board was chaired by none other than George Abbey, whom I had written off the night before as someone inconsequential. Members of the board who were there that day included John Young who was Chief of the Astronaut Office and, of course, a famous person. I recalled that he was a veteran of Gemini and Apollo flights and was one of the dozen men who had walked on the moon. He would command the first space shuttle flight. Joe Kerwin, from a Skylab flight, was there, too. The first physician in space, he was one of my heroes and someone I had hoped to meet. There was Joe Atkinson from the Equal Employment Opportunity Office, presumably to keep the others honest. Thank goodness there was one woman on the board. Dr. Carolyn Huntoon, a bona fide scientist, was head of the Biomedical Lab. *Maybe she is here to keep all the men from beating up on the women interviewees,* I thought. There were several others, but I didn't catch their names.

I don't remember being scared. I had no way of faking any of my answers. I had no idea what questions they would ask or what answers they were looking for. I wasn't entirely sure they knew what they were looking for in women astronauts. Perhaps some were hoping they didn't have to take any.

I was the first woman they interviewed for the mission specialist position. (The National Academy of Sciences had screened and sent forward the names of the scientists selected as astronauts in 1965, so there were some non-pilot astronauts.) I believe the board wasn't sure what to ask me or even how to ask. So there we were, sparring and searching, they trying to come up with good questions, me trying to come up with good answers.

I was asked to describe my residency and my particular areas of interest. I realized most of them had little background in medicine, surgery, nutrition, or emergency care, so I started out slowly. I did think some of them needed to know the depth of my knowledge, so I directed to Joe Kerwin a more detailed description of what I was doing. I noticed he got a rather blank look that let me know he had been away from the practice of medicine long enough to not have any idea what I was talking about. So I tried to speak in simple terms and briefly. I guessed it didn't matter how good I was in my chosen field if they didn't understand what I was talking about.

They asked about my flying experience, and I was happy to tell them I had my private pilot's license and a lot of flying hours – at least a hundred. The pilots in the group had a good giggle about that, but at least it let them know I had done more than sequester myself in a hospital.

After covering some basic background information, the questions got trickier. "What do you do with your free time?" *What free time,* I thought.

"Well, I like to read and travel." Hey, maybe that was a good answer. Astronauts travel a lot, right? "I have been to Europe, the Caribbean, and North Africa."

"What do you do to keep fit?" someone asked. I exaggerated a bit when I said, "I run, and I lift weights." *Please,* I prayed, *don't ask me how often or how much!* I was then asked what I thought of cigarette smoking. What an odd question that was out of the blue. It was Mr. Abbey who asked it. *Did I see a smirk on his face? Was it some kind of joke?*

"Cigarette smoking has been shown to be dangerous to your health," I said, feeling like I was sounding like the Surgeon General. "It is a pretty nasty habit." There was laughter all around the table, and I know I blushed a deep red. What was so funny about that? I learned later that Joe Kerwin was a smoker, and they were kidding him. However, at the time, this little game made me squirm, not understanding their humor. I would learn that this was vintage George Abbey.

Then the questioning took another bizarre turn. "What do you think of the Panama Canal Treaty?"

It went through my mind that this couldn't have anything to do with being an astronaut. Was this another joke or were they testing how I responded to stress? Again, I responded somewhat obliquely: "Well, it seems that there comes a time in a country's history where the people clamor for independence."

Again, mortification as laughter broke out. *What was so funny about that?* I was getting paranoid at this point. I should have realized that these guys were from a military background and were very conservative and against the treaty. It was not the last time I failed to know my audience. In speaking to the other interviewees later, we figured out that this was the "current events question" du jour. It was designed to show whether or not we were keeping up with what was going on in the world and whether we could give a non-inflammatory, yet eloquent opinion. So much for my eloquence rating.

Perhaps the dumbest question came near the end of the hour and a half interview. Someone said, "What if, on the plane going back to Memphis this weekend, you meet the man of your dreams and he asks you to leave your medical career, give up the chance to become an astronaut, and go away with him?" That didn't sound politically correct, and I was a little surprised anyone would ask that kind of question or would phrase it that way. But it was 1977, and these folks had little idea how to find out whether the women they interviewed were serious or not. I answered honestly, that he wouldn't be the man of my dreams if he wanted me to give up everything I cared about. I thought they would dig deeper, but that seemed to be a satisfactory answer, and we left the subject. Soon the interview was over and they thanked me for coming.

It was early Monday morning, and I still had no idea what the job of mission specialist astronaut would entail. That is what I had come to Houston to find out. I didn't see how I could make much sense to anyone on the selection board. As for correct answers or what characteristics they were looking for, I wasn't sure they even knew in the case of women. I simply had to be honest and forthright and hope that was the best thing to do.

After the essay, the press fiasco, and the interview, everything else was easy. I was put through all the kinds of tests that I often ordered on my own patients. I gained a new perspective on what it was like to be on the receiving end of those body invasions. Blood draws, 24-hour urine collection, the treadmill, lung functions, poking and prodding, brain waves testing, and a battery of psychological tests.

There were two long interviews with the psych doctors, one with a "good" guy and one with a "bad" guy. The "bad guy" was a rather dark, foreign looking man who asked uncomfortable questions. "Have you ever been sexually assaulted?" "Have you ever contemplated suicide?" "Do you fear death?" After I answered them, he stared at me for a long time as though he suspected I wasn't telling the truth. It would have been funny if the circumstances hadn't been so stressful.

The "good" guy was Dr. Terry McGuire. Again, there was no way to know what the "right" answers were. Having had the requisite psychology and psychiatry training in college and medical school, at least I recognized the purpose of many of the questions.

"Are you more creative or more organized?"

"What is your relationship with your parents like?"

"Have you ever had personality conflicts with people at work?"

Dr. McQuire also asked some rather open-ended questions.

"If you could be reincarnated as any animal what would it be?" Of course, all the pilots he had interviewed wanted to be eagles or lions or something strong or fast.

"I'd like to be a dolphin" I answered.

"Why?" he answered, puzzled.

"Well, they are very bright, happy, and playful. That is how I would like to be."

"If you had to write something on your sweatshirt so that someone could identify you in the distance, what would it be?"

"If you knew you were going to die soon, what would you ask your family to put on your tombstone?"

I don't remember how I answered those questions, but I wondered what they could tell him about aspiring astronauts.

After the formal interview, he asked me if I had any questions. I wanted to know if he had done these interviews with previous astronaut classes. "Yes," he said. "All of them." I had a million questions.

"Do most of the pilots have similar personalities?" I asked. "Are the male scientists like the pilots or different? Are they looking for the same traits or different ones, or do they even know, in the women they are interviewing?"

Terry was happy to share a bit of his perspective, and we spent a pleasant half-hour over lunch, just shooting the breeze. I later learned that the psych exam was pass/fail – either you were crazy, or you weren't. I was pretty sure I had passed.

Of all the tests, the most bizarre was the Personal Rescue Enclosure. It didn't take too long to decipher what they were really testing. We were told that NASA had invented a system to transport the crew of a disabled space shuttle to another shuttle that had come to the rescue. Two crewmembers on each flight would have suits that they could do spacewalks in. The other members of the crew would have to somehow be transported to the rescue vehicle. They had developed a hollow ball, some 34 inches in diameter, made of space suit material, into which the stranded astronauts could be zipped for the ride between shuttles. Could we try them out and write an engineering assessment afterwards? That sounded okay to me.

So I plopped down in the middle to this cloth ball for the test. I was given an oxygen bottle and mask since the ball would be completely sealed. They put electrodes on me to monitor my heart rate. I sat in a cross-legged pose and bent my head over while the ball was pulled up and zipped over the top of me. Inside it was dark, quiet, cozy – very cozy. I realized that they hadn't told me how long I had to stay inside. I worried a little that they were going to do something to frighten me, but soon this little interlude got pretty boring. I have no idea how long I stayed in that cramped space because I think I dozed off. Then, there were people around, unzipping me and giving me a pen and paper to capture my thoughts on their design. *Was that it,* I thought? As I was jotting down what I could think of to say about the experience, it dawned on me what they had been testing. Claustrophobic individuals would have been extremely anxious in a set-up like that, and their heart rates would have shown it.

We had numerous briefings on what the shuttle program was all about. The first launch was planned for sometime in 1979. There would be several orbiters, and they could be refurbished after each flight. The flight rate might be as high as 50 flights a year, almost one a week. The large cargo carrying capacity of the shuttle would allow NASA to recoup all their launch costs by charging paying customers for taking their satellites into space. NASA was dreaming big. Did they believe what they were telling us?

We were taken out to visit nearby Ellington Field, formerly Ellington Air Force Base. It was home to NASA's fleet of two-seat T38 jets. Our tour guides showed us around the planes and gave us a chance to sit in one. "Think you'd like to fly one of these?" I was asked. To tell the truth, I couldn't even imagine that. I'd make sure to take a picture of this plane back to Memphis for my flying friends to see, figuring they'd be jealous that I got to sit in it!

I especially enjoyed meeting the other seven women in my group . Several were MDs like me, so we had many discussions about our shared experiences in a still mostly-male field. There was Anna Fisher, an emergency physician from Los Angeles, who had changed her wedding date so she could come for the interview. She had gotten married the Tuesday before we arrived. Her husband, Bill, had also applied and would be interviewed in a later group.

Shannon Lucid, a biochemist from Oklahoma, was the only mother in the group. She had three children, and we all marveled how she managed. She reported that she was asked by the board, "What would you do if you were an astronaut and decided to have another child?" I'll bet none of the men were asked questions like this.

Nitza Cintron was a biochemist of Puerto Rican extraction. Danielle Goldwater had done NASA research for a number of years. Millie Wiley was doing research on bone chemistry, an important subject for long term spaceflight. The others were equally well qualified. I didn't stand a chance.

The men in the group were stellar. Jim Bagian was an impressive physician. Bright, fit, out-spoken, and self-assured, he looked like a shoo-in. All were fascinating to talk to. We wondered about everything we did: *Is this a test? Was NASA bugging our phones, watching what we selected for lunch, and observing our every move?* Soon it became a joke among us.

The next "test" was on Thursday night. There was a cocktail party and dinner where we would have a chance to visit with members of the Astronaut Office and Dr. Chris Kraft, the JSC Center Director, in a less formal setting. Even I knew that Dr. Christopher Columbus Kraft was a legend. He had been featured on the cover of *Time* magazine in 1965. As the first Flight Director of the Mission Control Center, he had been given the task of figuring out how to make spaceflights happen. In the early days of the space program there was no way to track the spacecraft, communicate with the astronauts, recover the nose cones in the ocean, manage Mission Control. He had had to figure out what all the unknowns were and address them. He lived in fear of the *unknown* unknowns – it was all so incredibly new.

As a smart, tough, and outspoken Center Director, he was much admired. I was delighted to find him friendly and outgoing. In fact, I had never been in a workplace where all the people seemed to be so straightforward, energetic, and enthusiastic. Toward the end of the week I began to think that not only would the work at NASA be fascinating, but also the people and the environment would be great, too.

Then it was Friday. We finished all the interviews, briefings, and tests and, for the first time, I agreed to go with some of the other interviewees to a local pub for happy hour. In fact, it was the first time all week that I had dared to have a drink. At other dinner get-togethers and at the Thursday night social, I hadn't dared to imbibe for fear of saying the wrong thing. There were a lot of NASA folks at that Friday night gathering. Maybe everyone was relieved that this group of interviews was over, and they could let their hair down and relax. I was introduced to Bob Crippen, who it was rumored would be John Young's pilot on the first shuttle flight. Meeting him would be something to tell everyone about back home! As the party came to an end, I decided to go back to my room at the motel, which was just down the street, since I had a flight out the next morning. All the interviewees wished each of the others well, and we all wondered if any of us would be "real astronauts" someday. As I was about to leave, Mr. Abbey appeared and offered me a ride.

"Oh, no, that's okay," I said. "It's just a short walk."

"No," he insisted, "I'll run you over there."

What could I say? As we got into his car, he asked me if I would like to see some of the neighborhoods where many of the astronauts lived. "Sure," I told him. Then I got to thinking. It was pitch-black night outside, so how was I going to see those neighborhoods? He had obviously been drinking. He probably had a lot to say about whether I was going to be selected or not. I began having second thoughts about whether I should be out riding around with this guy. I sat there, clinging to the door handle of the car while he played tour guide around the local area. Between name-dropping and house pointing, he asked me whether I had enjoyed my week at NASA.

"Have you gotten a good picture of what the job of being a shuttle mission specialist would be like?"

"Well, yes, I think so."

"We want to make sure that the people we interview understand what they are getting into before they think of leaving promising careers," he said. I was flattered that he would ask my opinion.

"Yes, sir, I think the people who briefed us were pretty straight with us."

"Well, then," he asked me, "are you still interested in the job?" That was the first hint I had that I might still be under consideration. Was he was just being polite or was this something he asked everyone? Surely, most of the others were better qualified.

"Yes, sir," I said. "I'm still very interested."

We finished our tour, and he dropped me off at the Kings Inn. I left for home the next morning loaded down with souvenirs since I figured that would be my first and last visit to the Johnson Space Center. What a thrill it would be when I got to be an old lady, to tell my grandchildren that I had been interviewed for the Astronaut Program.

So, back to Memphis, the VA Hospital, and the old 100-hour-a-week grind of taking care of the sick and dying. There was little time to think about much else, let alone the space flight program. I had been told that the astronaut selection would be made by Christmas. I thought my chances were slim to none, so I went about some other job-hunting for what I would do when I completed my final year of surgery residency.

I had started out to do a residency in plastic surgery. For a variety of reasons, I had changed my direction and wanted to do further studies in nutrition. I thought perhaps I might run a nutritional support service in a large hospital someday. Since intravenous feeding and continuous tube feeding had become possible, it was a brand-new field, and I found it exciting.

I had treated badly burned patients who might have starved because they couldn't take in enough calories. When given adequate nutrition, they gained weight, healed their skin grafts, got well, and went home. Cancer patients receiving radiation or chemotherapy tolerated the full course of treatment and did better if they were well nourished. Post-operative patients went home sooner and felt better. I received offers to study in Boston and San Francisco, and I told the program directors there that I would let them know by the first of the year.

Early December came and went with no word from NASA. I managed to get a few days off for Christmas vacation and left my phone number at every place I thought NASA might call looking for me. I even read through newspapers every day of my vacation, assuming that whoever was selected would make it into the news while a slim rejection letter would be sitting in my mailbox when I got back to Memphis.

New Year 1978 came and went. The people in Boston and San Francisco to whom I had promised answers about nutrition fellowships began calling, needing my answer. *How could I tell them I still hoped to be an astronaut?* All I said was that I was awaiting an answer on "another position."

The second week in January brought a strange phone call. I was back at the VA when Jules Bergman, a correspondent from ABC News , called and asked if I would agree to do an interview with him. Naturally, I asked him why. He said he was interested in speaking with some of the women who had been interviewed for the NASA Astronaut Program because he had heard that the selections were soon to be announced. Not knowing much about newsmen and interviews (or Jules Bergman) I said okay, but that I did not have much time. He agreed to come to the hospital on Sunday, January 15 with a film crew and we would talk for a few minutes on camera. *Strange,* I thought. I figured this was one interview that would end up on the cutting room floor.

Sunday arrived, and I took a break from seeing patients and met the film crew at the front of the hospital. We went into a quiet exam room and started our interview. There were the usual questions about my background and why I wanted to be an astronaut. Then came the big surprise. Jules asked me what I would say if he told me that it was going to be announced tomorrow that I had been selected as one of the new astronauts. It was, I thought, a hypothetical question, so I answered it as such.

"Oh, I'd be thrilled because I really was excited about what I saw at NASA."

"No, you don't understand. Your ARE going to be selected tomorrow," Jules said firmly.

I'm going to look like a fool if this guy is pulling my leg and I get all excited, I thought.

"Gee, Mr. Bergman. I honestly can't get too excited till I hear that news from NASA. But it would be an honor and a surprise." Cut, end of interview.

"Really, they are going to call you," Jules said.

"How do YOU know THAT?" I asked.

"I have my sources in Houston," he said. "Would you like to be on *Good Morning America* on Tuesday? We could fly you to New York tomorrow night."

Jeez, my thoughts were swimming. This was too much to take in. I was overwhelmed, but I wasn't sure I could trust this guy. Let me outa' here!

"Uh, could we talk tomorrow if this thing really happens?"

"Sure, we'll call you tomorrow," he replied as they left.

What do I do now, I thought? *Is my life about to change so radically?* A live interview on a big morning TV show? No, that was crazy. I decided to go back to changing dressings on surgical wounds and writing pre-operative orders for tomorrow's surgery patients, followed by a drive home to fix a late supper. I did call my father that night. I knew that he had mixed emotions, having just finished supporting me through medical school and helping me through the almost four years of training since that. I was sure he didn't understand why I wanted to make this unusual change in careers. *Why not go be a rich doctor? Why not choose a safe job?* I knew he would support me, though. My mother had passed away suddenly in 1976, but I imagined her in heaven, still shaking her head in amusement at the crazy things I did.

Falling asleep that night, I had to wonder if I would say yes if I was offered the job the next day. Would the choice be irrevocable? Would a "yes" start me down the road to fame and glory or lead to my demise someday in a fiery conflagration? Could I pass whatever tests they had waiting for me? Who else would be selected to go on this journey? Would there be other women—and would we have a bond of sisterhood through a shared trek—or would we be caught up in an ugly competition? Would I forever end my chance of having a happy marriage and children? Ghosts of past and future haunted my dreams.

I did not have early surgery the next day, Monday, January 16, 1978. It was 7:30 a.m. when I pulled into the hospital parking lot. Oddly, my beeper went off, telling me to check with the hospital operator. I walked to the front desk of the hospital and asked the operator what she had for me.

"A call from NASA in Houston, Dr. Seddon," she said. Word had gotten around that I was waiting for a yes or no for the space program, so the ladies sitting behind the reception desk were all watching expectantly.

"Hello, this is Rhea Seddon."

It was George Abbey. In his typical low monotone he asked, "Are you still interested in coming to work for NASA?"

I had the sudden creeping awareness that I might be about to jump off a cliff...to leave the world of medicine, the world of being DOCTOR Seddon, the smell of hospitals, the coolness of operating rooms, the white coat. For what? The unknown, the unique, the first, the development phase of the space shuttle. But I was young and single, with no one to think of but myself. I had no real ties at this point in my life, and that allowed me to consider lots of options. I could do what I darn well pleased, no matter how crazy or risky, both physically and professionally, the choice might be.

"Yes, sir!" was all I could get out.

I would learn what these notification days were like for all the interviewees. The head of the Astronaut Selection Board called the "winners" and got to hear how they handled their excitement. The other members of the board divided up the "losers" who, of course, were not losers at all in any sense of the word. The board members got the rotten task of telling those poor people how wonderful they were and how much the board had enjoyed talking to them, BUT...they hadn't made it.

I was sure that everyone who was being selected that day tried to sound cool and collected while about to jump through the roof. I was! I turned away so the operators couldn't hear.

"How wonderful! When do we start? Who else was selected? How many women are there?" There were six women in the class of 35, which was more than the women in my interview group thought they'd choose. Mr. Abbey asked me not to say anything until about noon, when the press release would go out with all the names of the selectees on it. He also warned that there might be some press interest.

There were to be twenty mission specialists and fifteen pilots. Later I heard rumors that there were originally twenty of each, but NASA Headquarters in Washington had balked at having that large a class. It was said that some of the pilots who were selected in the 1980 class were ones that were cut in 1978. I never knew whether this was true or not.

My first call was, of course, home to my father. He was flabbergasted. Had I really been offered the job and was I sure I wanted to do this?

"Yes, to both questions, Daddy." He knew he had raised me to make independent decisions about my life, so he joined me in my elation. Next, I needed to tell Dr. McCaughan. He showed very little reaction. I suppose this was not something that happened every day, having one of his residents running off to fly in space.

Then I called the VA Hospital administrator to let him know about the possible press interest part. He wasn't someone a young resident talked to every day. He was, of course, happy to have some positive publicity for his hospital. He referred me to the people who handled community and public relations for the VA. It was not often that they could draw a crowd of reporters for a good news story. I was reminded to say wonderful things about the hospital.

As predicted, shortly after noon the press began to call and arrive at the hospital in droves. The VA Public Affairs staff set up a press conference. What a circus it was! I learned about the click-wheeze of the camera motors every time I looked up and smiled. I tried not to say anything about subjects I didn't know anything about or that it was "about time NASA took women." I tried to be more tactful in my remarks, avoiding the mistakes I had made when I had faced the onslaught in Houston. It was the beginning of a new learning curve.

The call from Jules Bergman came as promised. I could take a late plane to New York and be on *Good Morning America* the next day. A live interview on a national channel was about as scary as flying in space itself at that point but it went well. I learned that TV hosts, like David Hartman who interviewed me that morning, earn their pay making their guests comfortable enough to be able to talk on TV.

Of course, having my face on the front of newspapers and on television meant my week was filled with calls day and night from old friends wanting to congratulate me. It was wonderful to hear from a lot of them. I was glad to be able to show those of them who didn't think I'd amount to much that I had made something out of myself. Then strangers began to call me at all hours. I learned one of the downsides of being "famous" and had to get an unlisted number.

In February of that year, something else happened that would be the beginning of another new phase of my life. The Astronaut Candidates were all invited to Houston for an orientation which was part-indoctrination, part house-hunting trip. We would all get a chance to meet one another and start figuring out what kind of group we were. Of course, I had gotten to know Anna Fisher and Shannon Lucid who were part of my interview group. I had read news stories about Kathy Sullivan, Sally Ride, and Judy Resnik (the other women in the group), and I was looking forward to meeting them.

After I arrived in Houston, the phone in my hotel room rang.

"Hi, Rhea? This is Judy Resnik. You got any Tampax?"

I was to learn that this was classic Judy: no small talk, no bull, blunt,

The Thirty Five New Guys in the first Space Shuttle Astronaut Class. I am in the middle of the front row. Though I didn't know him then, my future husband is seated right behind me.

and to the point. She would be like that until the ill-fated *Challenger* carried her away one morning in 1986.

Sally looked like the quintessential Stanford graduate student, which she was, of course. With the exception of some deference to dress code protocol on a limited number of occasions, she looked that way until she went back to California academia in 1987. Kathy Sullivan was one of the smartest people I had ever met. Strong-looking and self-assured, she seemed interested in and knowledgeable about everything.

The 29 men were a mixed bunch. Military types, academic types, all outgoing with the same look-you-in-the-eye straight forwardness that for me characterized almost every astronaut I ever met. All were fit and trim, even the academicians.

What would happen to all of us, I wondered? *Would we all stay with NASA? Would we all get to fly in space? Who would be my friends? Who would fly first? Would some be killed?* I knew this was the beginning of the first chapter in a book of unknown length, the unfolding of a fascinating story.

We all mixed and mingled during our briefings and meetings, trying to put names with faces. Everyone was friendly. A bunch of us went out for

The first six women astronauts in the history of the American space program – me, Anna Fisher, Judy Resnik, Shannon Lucid, Sally Ride, and Kathy Sullivan.

drinks after the formal part of our visit was over. I recognized two of the men who were part of the group and went over to say hello.

"Hello, I'm Rhea," I said, extending my hand.

"Hi. I'm Mike Coats, and this is Hoot Gibson."

I was impressed with how good-looking they were. Mike was dark-haired with amazingly blue eyes. Hoot had sandy hair and a gorgeous blond mustache and eyebrows. His blue eyes twinkled when he talked. I was a little disappointed to learn they were both married. Well, they would still be fun to have as friends.

As it turned out, one would be much more.

CHAPTER 2

★ ★ ★ ★ ★

ASCANS

---

n Monday morning, July 10, 1978 we became Astronaut Candidates, ASCANs for short. We called ourselves the Thirty Five New Guys or TFNGs. We were the most diverse group ever to be selected, from crusty old (a relative term since the oldest of us was 39) Vietnam-experienced attack and fighter pilots to young whippersnapper astrophysicists fresh out of graduate school. Sitting at our first all-hands meeting with the 27 astronauts from the Apollo era, it was apparent that the oldest of "us" was younger than the youngest of "them," and we outnumbered them. For the first time there were female, Asian, and black faces. (African-American Robert Lawrence was selected to be in the Air Force's Manned Orbiting Lab program in the 1960s but died in a plane crash before it flew.) I'm

The official patch designed for the Astronaut Candidate class (ASCANS) of 1978 or The Thirty Five New Guys.

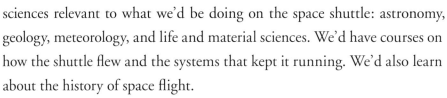

sure most of us looked—and were—pretty green. What did they think of us and how would they treat us? We didn't know.

Our training would be different, too. We'd do NASA's own flight training for the T-38 jets. We'd hear lectures on the various sciences relevant to what we'd be doing on the space shuttle: astronomy, geology, meteorology, and life and material sciences. We'd have courses on how the shuttle flew and the systems that kept it running. We'd also learn about the history of space flight.

Before we could start flying, however, we had to learn how to handle emergencies in the jets. The T-38s were equipped with ejection seats and we needed to know how to use them. If something went wrong with the airplane—the engines both quit (a T38 couldn't do a "dead-stick" or engine-out landing), a fire started, or some critical part fell off—by lifting two handles on the sides of the seat, small rocket motors could blast the seat clear of the plane. An automatic system then would kick the flyer and parachute free of the heavy seat. At the appropriate altitude, the chute would open and the flyer would drift to the ground.

All of the above should happen in theory if everything worked properly. But there were a multitude of things that could go wrong, and we had to be aware of all of them and remember how to react quickly and appropriately. There were sobering statistics about how many people ejected from aircraft, how many survived, and what the deaths were caused by. If we ejected too low, the chute wouldn't have a chance to open. If the jet was going too fast, our arms and legs would flail so badly that we'd die from our injuries. If we were in the wrong position for ejection, we'd break our necks. If...if...if. The numbers didn't look too great, and most of us hoped we'd never have to bail out.

One of the big "ifs" was the possibility of an over-the-water ejection, which brought its own dangers. Since a lot of an astronaut's time was spent flying between Houston and Cape Canaveral in Florida, we flew many hours over the Gulf of Mexico. So the non-military folks in our group were sent to water survival training at Homestead Air Force Base in south Florida. I had no idea what this would entail, but I became a little apprehensive when we were advised not to wear white tennis shoes because it would attract the sharks in Biscayne Bay where the training would take place. I hadn't been comfortable in the water since my teens when a friend held me under water "for fun." I'd inhaled a bunch of water before I managed to pull free, so I sometimes had anxiety attacks when I had to spend time under water.

I began to wonder if this was our first trial by fire – in this case, by water. Unlike some of the pilots, the rest of us did not take risks just for the thrill

Sally and I at a briefing for our water survival class in Florida in August, 1978.

PHOTO COURTESY OF NASA

of it, especially the women. Was that somehow a product of having two X chromosomes or were young males encouraged to take risks and gain experience until they were more comfortable with them? I was willing to take calculated chances if they got me closer to a coveted goal, but I wasn't sure how much punishment I would have to take in this quest for space.

Of course none of the ASCANs wanted to look (or act) like wimps, certainly not the females. While the women never discussed it, we were aware that we were being watched for signs of weakness. All of us adopted the bravado of the pilots whose favorite saying seemed to be "Better dead than look bad." Through it all, I was never sure whether there would be a show stopper for me, some task that would be impossible. But if it meant going to space, I was willing to try anything they threw at me.

It was a good thing I was game enough to give it a go and that the instructors at survival school were patient, kind, and professional. After some lectures in the heat and humidity of August in south Florida, it was into the water. We had to learn how to position ourselves to keep our faces out of the water, so if our parachutes were pulled by the wind, we could breathe long enough to release the fittings to free ourselves.

First we were taught the proper positioning for an over-the-water ejection. Then we got rigged up in a parachute harness and were dragged through the water tied to the back of a boat: once on our faces, once on our backs. It wasn't easy, but with a little practice we could do it.

Another task was to swim to the edge of a large floating parachute, swim under it, and make our way across to the other side of the parachute by following one of the seams that went from one side to the other. Apparently, some fliers have drowned because their chute landed on top of them, and they panicked and swam around in circles until the chute sank with them still underneath.

The most interesting experience, however, was the para-sailing. The in-

Sally, Judy, Anna, Kathy and I celebrating our survival.

structors kept reminding us that on many tourist beaches people paid for the chance to indulge in this sport. On the deck of a flat-topped ship, I donned a parachute harness. Then a big deflated orange and white parachute was pulled up behind me and the straps fastened to the shoulder buckles of the harness. The chute was then flung up against a mesh wall to help it inflate. A long tow rope was attached to the chest strap of my harness, and the other end was fastened to a speed boat idling in front of the ship. Some rapid-fire instructions were provided while all this setup was performed.

"When the boat takes off, start running. Don't trip or fall because the deck is rough to keep it from being slippery, and it will scrape up your hands and knees. Run off the front of the ship, and the chute should get you airborne. After the boat has pulled you out a ways and you're up to the full length of the rope, the boat will stop. When a guy in the back waves a flag at you, reach out and hit the metal bar in front of you and that will disconnect the rope. Go through your checklist as you drift down toward the water - check canopy, discard facemask, inflate life preservers, deploy life raft. Steer your chute into the wind. Put your hands on the buckles ready to release the fittings, but whatever you do, don't release the parachute until you're in the water. Got it?" said the young military man.

"Yep."

"Remember how to keep your face out of the water if you get dragged?"

"Yep."

"Any last words for your folks back home?"

"What? Uh… no. Ha. Ha."

"Ok, get going," he said as he gave a thumbs up to the boat driver.

I took off running down the deck as the speedboat jerked the rope on my chest. *Lord, don't let me fall! What if the chute doesn't work?* For once in my life I was glad I was small because I was almost immediately lifted off the deck and into the air - higher and higher. In those few minutes as I was hoping I didn't get killed, I was once again wondering if this was really what I wanted to be doing. I was raised to be a fine Southern lady whose scariest moment should be whether the soufflé for the dinner party would puff or not.

Then the boat stopped.

I was up as high as I could go, so high in fact that the people in the boat were mere specks down on the water. Was the guy

Practicing hanging suspended under a parachute during land survival in Enid, Oklahoma.

PHOTO COURTESY OF NASA

waving the flag? Should I release now? How quick would the fall be? Could I remember all the steps I needed to perform? I took a deep breath and hit the metal release bar that popped up and almost hit me in the face. But I was floating peacefully down.

Go through the checklist, my brain was telling me. Pop off my face mask. Make sure the life preservers are okay. Grab like crazy behind my thighs for the handle to release the life raft. Done - with time to spare.

I figured I'd better remember some of this, even enjoy it a little. It would be another tale to tell my grandchildren about, parasailing into Biscayne Bay. Hands on the releases; then, the water reached out and grabbed me. Of course, hitting the water knocked my hands off the release fittings, so I had to fish for them again. Luckily, (or do they plan it this way?) the wind was blowing enough so that my chute didn't land on top of me, but not strong enough to drag me across the water. So I managed to pop the releases.

We'd all heard the scary tales of downed fliers who became entangled in their parachute shroud lines and drowned as it sank, so I didn't kick my feet. This was also why we carried a knife in our flight suit pocket, in case we needed to hack ourselves free. Right away, the speedboat was at my side to gather the parachute and me up.

"Good job, ma'am," said my rescuer.

"Thanks," I said, trying to sound fighter-pilot cool as my legs trembled climbing into the boat and my knees knocked standing there on the ride back to shore.

By far, the most bizarre aspect of our water survival ordeal was the fact that the press followed us there. I often wondered why it wasn't made off limits to them, but for whatever reason, it wasn't. There was a busload, then a boatload, rushing around trying to get some quotes and pictures. Several of the ASCANs swore the press were the "bad guys" and should be shunned. But most of the press people were just doing their job trying to figure out whether this new mixed group could make it as astronauts. There was a big fiasco when one of the military boats zoomed by the little press boat and their wake almost swamped the smaller boat and ruined a bunch of camera gear. Some of my colleagues thought it was pretty funny to see sputtering, soaking wet reporters shaking their fists at the working troops. I was sorry that an accident on the military's part ended up being collateral damage for the civilians.

My friends back in Murfreesboro got a great kick out of the resulting article in *Time,* complete with a colorful picture of their hometown hero. Little ole Rhea Seddon in a baby blue flight suit reclined in an orange life raft, holding a flare sending out billows of red smoke. Daddy was amazed—and I'm sure Mother turned over twice in her grave.

Of course, not only did we face the risk of parachuting from the T-38s into the water, but also onto terra firma. So once we had survived Florida, we were off to sweltering Enid, Oklahoma. We practiced graceful parachute-landing falls by jumping off low platforms. The instructors warned us about all the variations of land we might end up on—things like forests, high power lines, and swamps—and the best body positions for falling into them. For instance, if it looked like we'd be landing in trees, we were told we'd need to keep our feet together so we wouldn't straddle the branches and be split in two. That sounded like a pretty awful way to die, so I remembered that piece of advice.

At the conclusion of the practice falls and the lectures, we were once again hooked up to a parasail - this time attached to a truck. Up I was jerked over the monotonous flatland of Oklahoma. I felt myself rising in the wind like some ungainly kite attached to a hot rod pickup truck spewing black smoke. The choking dust almost obscured the poor fellow in the truck bed who was keeping an eye on me. All of a sudden there was eerie silence as the truck cut its engine and I started a slow and pleasant drift downward. Then, there was a WHUMP as I tried to do the roll I was supposed to do at the end of the fall. I came home with a bruise that went from the side of my left knee to my waist from the landing. I swore Oklahoma had the hardest dirt in the world.

We began our flight training. NASA's fleet of two-seat trainer jets, the T-38's, were small and simple for the guys who had been flying big supersonic fighter aircraft like the F-14, but were quite a step up for those of us who had been flying little propeller planes. They could climb to 50,000 feet and go supersonic in a dive. Best of all, they were "forgiving" aircraft.

I strap into the backseat of a NASA jet for my first flight.

DANGER

EJECTION
SEAT

PHOTO COURTESY OF NASA

There was enough redundancy and capability so that if certain parts didn't work, they wouldn't fall out of the sky.

In the past, NASA had put all new astronauts who weren't jet pilots through the Air Force flight training so they were fully rated and could fly independently in jets. But for our group, they decided they'd do their own syllabus and train us to be "back-seaters" in the planes. There would be no starting out in small planes, then working up to multi-engine jets. We would get specific training in the T-38's.

When someone called the Federal Aviation Administration about how we should log our flight time, they didn't have a label for people who had no license at all, but were flying jets. Who would do a thing like that? So NASA logged it as "Mission Specialist" time. Those of us who had private pilot licenses as I did could log co-pilot time. My pilot log book started with about 100 hours of single engine Cessna time, and then began counting co-pilot multiengine jet time.

A T-38 flies over the western mountains at 41,000 feet

The T-38 was a sleek little plane, weighing about 12,000 pounds fully loaded. It could reach Mach 1.2 (that's over the speed of sound) and cruise at 45,000 feet. From its underside, it was shaped like a Coke bottle with little delta wings. The NASA ones (the Air Force had some, too) were a classy white with a blue stripe running their length and a NASA insignia on the tail. One thing that always made me smile when looking at them was that they have a black tongue-shaped antenna protruding under the nose of the aircraft that reminded me of a puppy's tongue. But it seemed apropos to think of these planes as eager puppies ready to jump and play, panting at their masters as we trotted out to the flight line at Ellington Field where the planes were housed.

On the morning of my first T-38 flight from Ellington Field near the Space Center, one of the NASA instructor pilots, Dick Laidley, and I first briefed what we'd be doing. He and I walked to the equipment room, grabbed our parachutes, and I picked up my shiny new flight helmet (University of Tennessee orange—my choice) and headed out to the flight line in the shimmering heat of a late summer Houston day. The "old guys" weren't sure whether they were supposed to help the women carry all their gear. A chute, helmet and helmet bag, kneeboard, checklist, and flight boots amounted to about 20 pounds of extra stuff. But no, we needed to learn to manage it ourselves.

I soon learned that my biggest problem as an astronaut was not being female: it was being small. As much as NASA wanted to open the astronaut ranks to smaller and taller people, there were some things that couldn't be retrofitted to accommodate the differing sizes. My first evidence of this was the steps on the side of the T-38. There were two little bars that could be pulled out of the side of the plane. Dick showed me how easy it was to step up onto one, then the other, and then into the plane. When I tried it, it was obvious that someone 5'2" tall with short legs would never be able to just step up onto that first step. It poked out level with my waist. After much contemplation and many failed attempts that day, I figured out my own unique way of pulling up, hopping, and scrambling up the side of the plane. It wasn't pretty, it wasn't graceful, but I made it into the cockpit. It was the first of many work-arounds I had to learn to fit into a taller world.

There were also equipment problems that I didn't recognize. If they hadn't been caught, they could have cost me my life. One day I had put on my chute and fastened the chest strap before walking out to the plane. As the pilot and I ambled out to the flight line I saw that he was watching me with a puzzled look on his face.

"Is that parachute slipping off your shoulder a little?" he asked.

"Yes," I said. "Even the small ones are a little wide in the shoulder for me."

"Let's go back to the equipment room," he said. "If you bailed out of the plane and were head down when the parachute opened, you might come right out of it."

"Oh", was about all I could think to say. It was not the last time that there were things NASA hadn't figured on with small women using equipment designed for larger men that put my life in danger.

On that morning in August 1978, I was semi-prepared for my first ride. Strapping into the airplane and learning about all the radios was not easy. First, I'd attach the parachute to the seat pan which contained survival gear then fasten myself to the chute. Next I'd buckle myself to the ejection seat using a five-point harness, remembering to insert a gold clip into the buckle of the lap belt which inflated the parachute if I ejected at low altitudes. Then I'd don a cloth skull cap to help absorb the sweat. There was lots of that in Houston's weather when the glass canopy was closed, making the cockpit a greenhouse. On top of that went my flight helmet with attached oxygen mask. Then the mask hose was attached to a fitting on the chute, and the airplane's oxygen supply was snapped into the other side. Fastening my chinstrap, plugging in the communication line, putting on flight gloves and a kneeboard to hold my checklist, and—finally!—I was ready to go for a ride.

But why dress up in a long-sleeved flight suit of fireproof Nomex, heavy boots, helmet, and mask and heavy gloves? We got the pleasure during our training of looking at pictures of people who had jumped out of burning airplanes who had not been wearing this type of gear. A pilot who pushed up his sleeves ended up with blackened arms. There were incinerated hands from neglecting to wear gloves. Even forgetting to turn up the back of the flight suit's collar could leave a badly scarred neck. Although the chances of a fire were slim, the horrid results for those who didn't wear this bulky, hot attire convinced us to wear it all, even in 100° heat. When people said how glamorous it must be to be part of the "jet set," I'd smile and think of myself sweltering on the end of the runway, sweat running off me in rivulets.

My instructor pointed out a few things on the control panel that looked a little like Cessna instruments and showed me how to turn on and adjust the communications gear, so I could hear him and the ground controller. We taxied out to the end of the runway and received clearance to depart, and I closed the canopy. We were ready to go. No guts, no glory. I watched the air speed indicator as we started our take-off roll. As we left the ground at 160 knots which was over 180 mph, I realized that was the top speed for the only other plane I'd flown. I heard the whir and thump of the landing gear retracting as we nosed up into the sky. Galveston is about 30 miles south of Ellington, but before I'd even gotten used to the feel of the airplane, Dick dipped a wing, so I could see we were over the island. Out over the blue waters of the Gulf of Mexico we went, past barges headed toward the Houston ship channel, past sailboats and oilrigs, faster and higher.

Up, up we climbed.

I watched the altimeter go past 20,000 feet, past 30, past 40. We had to climb slowly above 40,000 feet because the air feeding the compressors in the jet engines gets pretty thin up there. Too quick a move on the throttles or too rapid a turn, and the airflow wouldn't be enough, and an engine could quit. (Of course, we would be able to start it again if we went back down into the thicker air, and the other engine was plenty to get us home, but pilots don't like to admit they "flamed out" an engine. Not cool.) In no time we were up to 50,000 feet. I could see the curvature of the Earth and soon the sky began to turn black. Getting that first glimpse of the edge of space gave me goose bumps.

We wasted no time lollygagging around up there in the thin air at high altitude. Dick nosed the plane over into a steep dive to let me *break the sound barrier* for the first time. I watched the airspeed indicator. We'd been doing about .8 mach (or 8 tenths the speed of sound) in our climb, but as we barreled headlong down toward the blue water, I watched our speed crawl past .9, .92, .96, and the airplane began to shudder.

"Oh no, it's going to shake its puny little wings off!" my brain was saying.

Dick came over the intercom to tell me this was the transonic buffet, where the airplane is pushing into a bow-wave of noise. Then almost miraculously, the needle passed 1.0, and the ride was smooth again. I went from sheer, heart-pounding terror to pure elation.

Hey all you barges and boats down there, I thought. *Did you hear my first sonic boom?!*

As the altimeter whizzed below 30,000 feet we slowed our descent, and Dick wanted to show me what "G's" felt like. He knew we'd get up to 3G's in the shuttle and experience them during some maneuvers in the jet. So he started a level turn. As he tightened up the radius of the turn, I felt myself being squashed down into my seat. I watch the G-meter go from 1 to 2, to 2.5, then to 3. That was the maximum sustained G-force in the shuttle. It was a bit uncomfortable, but not bad. There was more.

Four T-38s in tight formation

I'd been taught if the G forces were pushing from my head to my feet, blood had a hard time getting up to the brain. Eventually, my visual field would start to narrow, then I'd "gray out" or see gray. I would still be able to hear, but if the force increased, I'd "black out" or go unconscious. To prevent that from happening, I knew to perform what's called the anti-G straining maneuver. I'd tense my legs and abdomen, hold my breath, and bear down hard. This would increase my blood pressure enough to force blood flow to my brain and keep me conscious. As the pilot pulled harder and harder into the turn, I learned that by straining I could handle 5 G's pretty well, at least for a short time.

"Wanna see zero G?" Dick asked.

"Sure, why not," I said. We soared up a few thousand feet higher. Then he pushed the jet over the top like a roller coaster. All of a sudden my pencils were floating, my arms were floating, and I was coming up out of my seat against my seat straps. Yuck - my stomach was in my throat. No one had told me what to do if I needed to vomit. My major focus now became how not to throw up. I didn't want to be considered a sissy, and I knew it might somehow count against me if I was labeled as someone who got airsick, so I said nothing.

As we headed back north, Dick began his tour guide pitch: "There's Galveston Island and Scholes Field Airport."

"Yea." I said. *What did I have for breakfast and would it all fit in one of my gloves if it came back up?*

"Here's Galveston Bay, the bridge at Kemah, Clear Lake. Really beautiful." *If I use my helmet bag, will it leak and be all soggy?,* I thought while he continued: "There's the Astrodome, downtown Houston, Intercontinental Airport with our alternate landing field if we can't get into Ellington."

"Great," was all I could say. I thought maybe if I closed my eyes and sat real still, the nausea would pass.

"OK, we'll do the approach into Ellington, and you can see what a landing is like," he said, and we headed back to the south. *Oh yes, that's what I need, wheels on the ground.* I toughed it out as he droned on about altitudes, airspeeds, approach fixes, housing developments. When the wheels hit the pavement, my stomach went back to its normal, healthy location, and we were HOME!

I checked the clock. We'd been in the air less than an hour and a half. I learned that we had burned about 3000 pounds of gas, which didn't mean a lot to me. Who measured gas for their car in pounds? Later I learned that a gallon of gas weighs six and a three quarters pounds, so our little tour— and each hour and a half of flight time that went into my log book—had burned about 450 gallons of jet fuel. I was impressed with the money NASA was willing to pay to make me a good flight crewmember and to keep its pilots well trained. Those flight hours and the training I got in the air made it inconceivable that sometimes the question was asked, why not do away with the T38s? Somehow I couldn't imagine the American public wanting a person flying the country's most expensive flying machine, the space shuttle, not having made any takeoffs and landings in a real airplane that year.

And I didn't see how back-seaters, those of us who couldn't pilot the plane, could know about being a crewmember for the flying part of spaceflight if we'd never had a chance for some hands-on flying and served as a real navigator and communications handler, and learned to perform calmly and competently in an inflight emergency.

My first flight was an introduction to jet flying. Since NASA was in charge of our orientation to flight, they asked several of our fellow ASCANs with flying experience to teach a ground school for the rest of us. We had a series of introductory lectures that taught us about the basics of flight, navigation, and communication. The classes were held in the astronaut library, a small room with dusty books and voluminous NASA documents on crowded shelves. I noticed there were pictures of several men and a few mementos on one of the shelves, looking almost shrine-like. When I asked who they were, someone told me they were astronauts who had been killed, some in T-38 accidents. Later I found out that some of the older guys called this place "The Dead Astronaut Room." I paid closer attention to the lectures.

After ground school all the back-seaters were required to get 15 hours of flying per month, just like the pilots. That was hard to accomplish. Pilots could book an airplane when there was an empty space in their schedule, after work when the weather was nice, or on the weekend. Also, the pilots had jobs or training that required flying. But we back-seaters had to find an open seat whenever we could find time to fly. The problem was somewhat compounded by a few pilots whose wives didn't want them to fly with the women. Another problem was the darned inefficiency of the flying. I would go to Ellington early in the morning, plan the flight, brief, fly, come home, shower, change clothes, and go back to work in the afternoon but I would only log one hour of flying time. Since we all had lectures and other jobs, I found it frustrating until I figured out that some of the ASCANs were doing a lot of flying for their job assignments, like being on the team that would shepherd the shuttle into its first landings. Pilots Jon McBride, Dave Walker, Hoot Gibson and Dick Covey got to be good friends.

The initial flying syllabus included a variety of aspects of flight, which I ran through quickly. Having never liked stalls or acrobatics in small planes, I didn't like them any better in jets. The most interesting and disconcerting flight regime I participated in was formation flying. I guess I had never thought about it when I'd seen two airplanes flying together, but it takes a good bit of skill and training to make it work out right.

Suppose you were the wingman, or "wingie". That meant your "leader" took off first, and you needed to "join up" on him. As the wingman, you'd go zipping down the runway, the lead airplane in sight, just getting airborne. He'd slow down a bit, but you'd keep your speed up until you got close, then you'd modulate your speed until you caught up with, but didn't fly past, him. Then, you'd both climb up to your assigned altitude and continue the flight together. The first time I flew a formation flight, I was sure I'd left grip marks in the armrests in the airplane.

Zooming along at 300 knots, we'd come screeching up beside the lead airplane and plant our wingtip at what seemed like inches from his wingtip. Then we'd both push our speeds up, and soon we'd be at .9 mach and 39,000 feet still wingtip to wingtip. Over time, I got used to this kind of flying because our pilots were so good at it, but the literature was full of stories of mid-air collisions during formation flights. There were even some terrifying video clips of them, and one of the guys in our office lost a son in such an accident. That was never far from my mind when we were drilling holes in the sky this way.

The T38s weren't the only aircraft we came to know and love. During this timeframe, we were also introduced to NASA's KC135, the aptly

The infamous KC135 "Vomit Comet" climbs to altitude before diving to create moments of weightlessness.

named "Vomit Comet." A beefed up Boeing 707 with almost all the seats removed, the walls of the remaining open space were well padded. Its primary purpose was to generate brief intervals of weightlessness. It did this by flying a parabolic flight path, going up and down, up and down like an airborne roller coaster, between 30,000 and 40,000 feet over the Gulf of Mexico. On a good half-day flight, the plane would do 60 parabolas. The great thing was the 30 seconds of zero gravity as the plane got to 40,000 feet altitude and pushed over into a dive and everything inside became weightless. I could stand on the ceiling and see what the airplane interior looked like upside down. I could do awesome gymnastics, like multiple somersaults in mid-air. I lifted huge pieces of equipment with no strain at all. Then the crew, headed by Bob Williams, would yell "Down!" as a signal to get back down on the floor. As the plane reached the bottom of its path, it began a 2-G pull out for about 30 seconds. That's when I could lie on the floor and pretend to be a worm. Up and down, up and down, one ride and you understood the plane's nickname - sometimes all too well. I learned that I could enjoy the flight only if I took a concoction the flight surgeons gave out. A mixture of scopolamine to prevent the motion sickness and Dexadrine (an amphetamine) to counteract the drowsiness from the scopolamine worked wonders for me.

While ASCANs got a "dollar ride" for orientation, meaning they didn't have a job to perform, all other flights of the KC135 had more business-like purposes. There are numerous experimental protocols carried out on the airplane. Crews could practice any in-flight procedure that could be broken up into 30-second segments. Or various pieces of hardware could be given a zero-G tryout.

One of the experiments going on when I got to NASA was one that was trying various treatments for a form of motion sickness, called *Space Adaptation Syndrome* by our medics, which affected many space travelers. NASA had an intense interest in understanding what caused it and how to best treat it. They also wanted to figure out if there was a way to predict who would have trouble in space (not always the same people who got motion sick on the ground) and how to prevent it altogether.

One of the early KC135 studies of motion sickness I witnessed involved spinning college students in a rotating chair during the weightless portion of the flight to see how long it took them to be sick. Then various medications or training could be used to increase the time necessary to produce symptoms. On one of my flights I asked about the poor blindfolded souls who were spinning, then burying their faces in a barf bag, and was told that it was the Bible College Kids. When I looked puzzled, it was explained to me that at first they'd recruited at several different colleges. But it became obvious after a while that the data obtained from some of those students was confusing. Placebo or sugar-pill drugs on some days worked better than real drugs. Some days a subject would be resistant to the motion, the next day susceptible. Finally, one of the subjects, when talked to at length, admitted that he used such recreational drugs as alcohol, marijuana, and so on. He knew others of the subjects and knew they were into drugs, too. So NASA

I am practicing how CPR or cardiopulmonary resuscitation might be performed in zero-G.

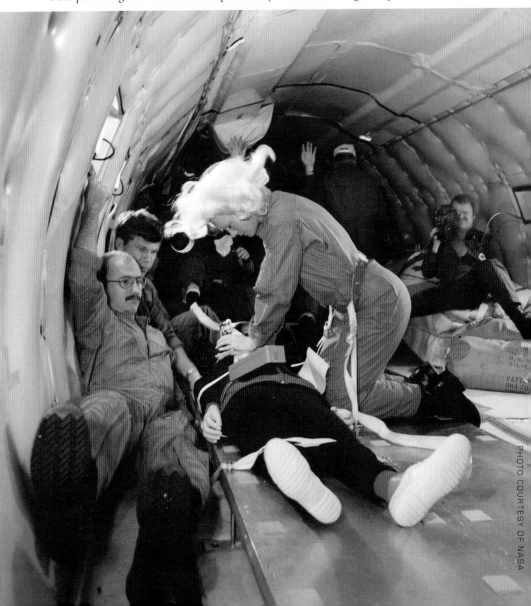

Lifting heavy objects without gravity- even your future husband- is easy!

trekked to church schools in the area where drinking and drugs were strictly forbidden, and the data was more reliable. Unfortunately, these tests, while teaching a lot about motion sickness in the KC135, didn't find a way to predict or prevent space sickness.

I was assigned to try the new food packages for the shuttle era, but it took a little training to get the food out of the package without spilling the stuff. Until we had perfected our technique, the other passengers on the flight who weren't feeling well had to contend with Parmesan cheese-coated strands of spaghetti floating by and the smell of stale peanuts.

The most challenging tests I participated in on the KC were of the space toilet, or Waste Containment System (WCS) in NASA parlance. The U.S. had never had to design a urinal for women, and they weren't sure what the problems would be. The urinal they came up with was a vacuum hose that pulls air into it, including the urine that's in the vicinity. Women can't aim their urine the way men can, and a funnel on the end of the hose had to be designed so that it could be held up against the body. It had inlet holes on the sides near the top to draw the air through. Several designs were tested on the Vomit Comet. One of the main problems was that each woman could, at best, test only two urine funnels per flight. We'd get out to Ellington before the flight and start drinking a lot of liquid as flight time neared. Then once the plane got out over the Gulf and the parabolas began, with our bladders filled to capacity, we'd start cycling through the WCS area, trying to get situated and ready to pee at the onset of zero G. Sometimes the weather wasn't cooperating, and the flight would be bumpy. There would be squeals and giggles from behind the curtain which enclosed the toilet area as we tried to keep our wastes going down the ill-fitting funnels. After the first visit to the toilet, we'd run to sit in the back of the plane and start drinking again, hoping to be able to urinate again before the end of the flight. Sometimes there weren't quite enough parabolas, and we'd have to suffer with a full bladder on the ride back to Ellington.

The plane the pilots loved best was the *Shuttle Training Aircraft*, or STA. It was a Gulfstream II business jet that had been modified, so it could fly the steep glide slope that the shuttle did. One side of the cockpit had regular airplane controls, and the other had a shuttle cockpit and control stick. An instructor pilot and a pilot astronaut flew the shuttle's approach path from about 35,000 feet to a few feet off the runway. Computers took inputs from the astronaut's side of the cockpit and made the airplane react like a shuttle. Pilot astronauts got hundreds of simulated approaches at the three possible landing sites in the U.S.: Edwards Air Force Base in California, the Kennedy Space Center in Florida, and the Northrop Landing Strip in White Sands, New Mexico.

In the midst of the fast-paced world of airplanes and flying, we also spent a great deal of time in the classroom, where we learned all about the space shuttle and all its various flight phases and systems. I tried hard to listen to endless lectures on hydraulic fluid and redundant power systems and tire pressures, but it didn't make a lot of sense to a humble physician. I had developed the bad habit during my sleep-deprived residency of falling asleep during uninteresting lectures, so I nodded off during many of these sessions. All the classes had detailed handouts, so I spent my Christmas vacation that first year going back over the information. The big picture came into focus with a little help from patient pilot friends who answered all my naïve questions.

More interesting to me as a scientist were the lectures in various space-related sciences. Since astronauts would be expected to observe the Earth from space, there were lectures in geology, oceanography, and meteorology. Most of the pictures from space back then were from the Skylab missions. The most fascinating lectures were in geology. Dr. Bill Muehlberger from the University of Texas trained us on basic landforms, then showed us the perspective from ground level and then on the scale seen from 200 miles up. We even had the chance to go on a field trip to Taos, New Mexico to look at rock formations and mountains up close to compare them to what we'd see from space.

Equally as intriguing were Dr. Bob Stevenson's lectures on oceanography. Bob had been a B-17 navigator in World War II, worked at the Scripps Institution of Oceanography in California, and had instructed astronauts in *space oceanography* since the Gemini days. It was gorgeous to see ocean currents swirling around islands, to understand the importance of plankton blooms off coastlines, and to ponder the scale of movements of water around our globe.

Since we'd not only be looking Earthward from space but skyward, we also learned about the stars and astronomy. I was surprised to learn that the unchanging stars were still being used to navigate our spaceships in much the same way as voyagers of old used to. Mission Control could track the shuttle from the ground and uplink a message to its computer to give it a precise location and speed, but the ground couldn't discern which direction the nose of the spacecraft was pointed. The shuttle had two Star Trackers to decipher this. With the forward-pointing tracker aimed at a known star and the upward-looking tracker aimed at a star about 90° from it, the orbiter could align its navigation platforms. However, should the platforms get "lost in space," (for instance, if the computers had a glitch), it would be up to the astronauts to find star pairs about 90 degrees apart in constellations they recognized, to do a rough alignment with an imprecise manual visual instrument, and then do a fine alignment with the Star Trackers. I envisioned the sailors of the 15th century with their mariner's astrolabes (which in Greek meant star trackers) heading out, as we were, into worlds unknown.

All of this meant we had to spend several hours with Dr. Carolyn Sumners at the Burke Baker Planetarium at the Houston Museum of Natural Science. Reclined in well-padded chairs, we'd stare at an overhead projection of the night sky's stars. Starting from recognizable constellations, like the Big Dipper or Orion, we'd trace our way around to the patterns of stars mapped out by the earliest of civilizations. What a joy to ponder looking at the tracings of Scorpio, the Gemini twins, Pegasus: *all that had been there to delight our earliest ancestors.* We also got to know strangers from the southern hemisphere's sky, like the Southern Cross that appears on Australia's flag. There were specific stars in many of these constellations that were our navigation stars. I couldn't wait to see them from a higher vantage point.

We also had lectures on subjects that were expected to be experiments on future flights, such as life and material sciences. Although I found the medical lectures—what was known about how living things change in weightlessness—the most interesting, it was now the turn of most of the pilots and engineers to doze off.

Then, there was more physical training. Astronauts trained for space walks, known as Extravehicular Activity (EVA), by practicing the work in a huge water tank, in suits weighing almost 300 pounds. Safety divers outfitted with SCUBA gear were in the tank. If for some reason a space walker's suit flooded, he or she could open the face plate and buddy breathe with the diver until a hoist could pull him or her out of the water. That meant that all of us had to do SCUBA training in order to be comfortable in the water and not panic in an emergency. Bill Moran, a seasoned SCUBA diver, tutored us twice weekly in the pool at the Clear Lake Recreation Center.

The first tasks were basic swimming. Bill was patient but firm. We had to be able to tread water for 20 minutes, swim the length of the pool and back under water, retrieve a brick from the bottom of the deep end of the pool, and haul it to the surface before we could begin using the SCUBA gear. I wasn't a strong swimmer, so it didn't sound easy.

In attempting to tread water, I lasted about three minutes, flailing, and wearing myself out. Hoot Gibson, a classmate who'd surfed all his life, would say "Just relax and float. Your head will be above the water, and you can breathe easily." He showed me how to do it. I stopped flailing and sank up to the top of my forehead. "Oh, that's strange," he said. I could tell I was going to have to develop more efficient arm and leg strokes to get my head up. Twenty minutes began to look like an eternity.

At first I could make it about a third the length of the pool under water before I started getting panicky over not being able to breathe. I'd come up gasping, and cling to the edge of the pool. *How in the world would I make it to the far end and back?*

I couldn't even dive down close to the bottom of the deep end, much less retrieve something heavy. I surely couldn't haul a weight back to the surface. How did that relate to space suit training anyway?

I was embarrassed to be such a weakling in front of all my classmates. I went home and cried out of exhaustion and frustration, thinking this might be how I'd be washed out of the Astronaut Corps. Was it a physical limitation that I was facing or a mental roadblock? Was I not brave enough or not capable enough? Was it my body or my spirit that wasn't up to the challenge? Should I admit defeat and give up or, as I had done before in times like this, figure out a way to get through it?

When I had time to think clearly, I got mad at myself and realized that this was just a physical task. This was NOT going to be my undoing. The pool was open for the community late every afternoon, and I became a regular. The mothers with dogpaddling children and the athletes swimming laps must have thought I was some sort of nut case. Who would hyperventilate at one end of the pool then swim like a crazy person as far as possible underwater then surface and do it again, over and over? Each day's goal was to go a little farther. The lifeguard soon learned that I wasn't drowning in the far corner of the deep end: I was trying to tread water. Each day I got more efficient at it and didn't thrash and splash as much. I could soon swim down, touch the bottom. Then I managed to grab a rock and hoist it up to the surface.

I didn't tell anyone I was doing this kind of practice, but I'm sure Bill Moran knew what was going on. It wasn't long before he was heaping praise on my improvement. Finally, I could perform all the required tasks. The SCUBA equipment part was easy after that. It was later that I found out that I was not a candidate for space walks because they couldn't fit the smallest of us in the EVA suit. But the confidence I gained from doing what I had thought at first impossible was worth the effort.

We started making the rounds of the other NASA centers. We were a rather massive entourage with 35 ASCANS and a few "keepers," sometimes traveling in several NASA corporate aircraft and T38s, other times by commercial airline. Imagine a rowdy group of pilot-types all sitting in one section of the airliner, drinking beer and harassing the flight attendants.

It was a surprise to see all the places around the U.S. where NASA employed people and commissioned work. Unfortunately, the people at these places all felt obligated to fill our two- or three-day trip with visits to every section of their organization. The people and what they were doing were fascinating, but everyone seemed to measure their worth by the size of their computer banks, so much so that it became a joke. Our group smiled in unison when each location started their ritual of reviewing with us a detailed organizational chart, followed by a tour of their huge cold rooms packed full of gray lockers with massive computing capacity.

The center we all found most fascinating, of course, was the Kennedy Space Center (KSC) in Cape Canaveral, Florida. (At one point, the Cape was renamed Cape Kennedy, but there was an outcry from the locals, so just the Space Center got the Kennedy name.) If you look at the eastern coastline of the state of Florida, it is easy to see how the site was chosen for flinging rockets into the sky. The cape itself juts out eastward from the coastline several miles. Since it is most efficient to launch things east (thus getting an additional boost from the rotation of the Earth) and as close to the equator as possible, Cape Canaveral, the southernmost cape on the U.S. coast, makes a good place. Of course, it hasn't ever been wise to launch stuff to fly over populated areas because of the occasional blow-up. East Florida had distinct advantages over, say, Houston or southern California.

At KSC we were treated to tours of old launch pads where U.S. manned spaceflight began and the pads at Launch Complex 39 where Apollo flights originated and where the first shuttle flight would begin. We were let in on the rather odd history that because an Apollo tower was being used, the shuttle would sit on the launch pad with its tail pointed to the south and would have to roll around its axis after launch so it could

The Kennedy Space Center in Florida is where all of America's human space flights are prepared and launched. The Vehicle Assembly Building and the attached Launch Control Center looks out to the coast where the launch pads are located.

arch upside down due east out over the Atlantic. Because the Cape is at 28° of latitude north of the equator, launching due east makes its path 28° tilted or inclined to the equator. That meant that unless the shuttle rolled even further and flew up the East Coast (which it could do but which required more propellant or less payload weight), it would fly a path 28° north and south of the equator.

We also got to see the crew quarters at KSC. This is where astronauts could stay while they worked or trained at the center and where crewmembers would be quarantined before their flights. Far from being luxurious, it was a pleasant but Spartan dormitory with a dozen or so bedrooms and six communal bathrooms. These, a couple of offices, a big kitchen and dining area, a conference room, and a gym were located upstairs in the Operations and Checkout (O&C) building where shuttle elements like Spacelabs were built up and tested prior to flight.

The queen of crew quarters was Nancy Gunter. I had the feeling when first we met (which proved true over the many years I knew her) that Ms. Nancy ruled her domain with an iron hand. She was the kind of person one didn't mess with. If she was on your side, anything was possible. If you did something to cause her or upper management grief, getting things done could somehow become a monumental pain. She had many years of dealing with astronauts and their bosses, the good - the bad - and the ugly, and she wasn't about to take any guff off any of them.

With our visit, the folks at Quarters saw change coming. It would no longer be a "Men Only" club. We'd have to figure out how to live in a coed dorm, sharing the same bathrooms. As a joke, someone put Judy Resnik's name on one of the doors and pink satin sheets on the bed. JR was not amused.

We also got to meet Eunice Allen, our godmother there, who for many years would see that we were well fed, that the place was ship shape, and that our laundry was done during our stays. She was a wonderful lady, anxious to please and excited about the projects we'd be involved in. Everyone at the Cape wanted to be flying again after the hiatus that followed the Apollo and Skylab programs.

Next we went to the awesome Vehicle Assembly Building, a building with the largest interior space in the world. It is 525 feet tall and 518 feet wide. While it's visible from miles away, it is so huge that its massiveness from a distance was incomprehensible. It has a flag painted on an upper corner that an entire space shuttle could fit on with room to spare.

All the components that make up a space shuttle in its launch configuration—the orbiter, the External Tank, and its two solid rocket boosters (all together called the stack)—would be wheeled into this building horizontally, hoisted to vertical, strapped together, and placed on a mobile launch platform. It was amazing to imagine the size of a building required for the task, and it was an awesome sight to behold, standing inside looking up at the ceiling with our voices echoing off its metal walls. When *Columbia* was first strung up like this inside that building, the newspaper headlines read "She's Up on Her Toes!" which I thought was wonderfully apropos.

Even then, it seemed to me that there were ghosts hanging out around the place: ghosts of past rockets, of past workers and flyers, ghosts of tragedies, ghosts of past glories. Tragic in its starkness was the launch pad where the 1967 Apollo 1 fire killed Gus Grissom, Ed White, and Roger Chaffee. The launch tower dismantled down to its concrete pedestal and abandoned, it was a bleak reminder that when tiny equipment failures were added to poor management decisions, they could put astronaut lives in danger. While driving along roads and seeing glimpses of launch gantries silhouetted against backdrops of blue sky and sea, there was a feeling of otherworldliness, of being part of something bigger than the self, something exciting, challenging, almost creepy. To think, I might become part of its history. Would there be other accidents, other skeletons of flights uncompleted, places of sadness and friends lost?

The small, nearby town of Cocoa Beach had a history of its own, too. This sleepy laid-back beach town became a boomtown at the beginning of the manned space program in the early 1960s because of the space business. Along with most of the surrounding towns, Cocoa Beach housed the thousands of workers necessary to assemble the myriad rocket pieces and prepare them for launch. The managers had to be in touch with people all over the world for hardware deliveries, astronaut training, launch preparations, launch tracking, and so many other things. The press swarmed all over the place. Gathering places and traditions sprang up and became established. When we visited in late 1978, the human spaceflight program was in a lull. The Skylab and Apollo/Soyuz flights had been completed three years earlier, and the shuttle program was dragging along, with no definite launch date. But we new era astronauts were evidence that the shuttle era was beginning in earnest.

We were trotted out to the old hangouts like The Mousetrap in its current reincarnation. In its cool darkness, smelling of alcohol, cigarettes and history, astronauts in bygone days went to drink and meet the locals (and, we gathered, the groupies). We were a bit disappointed to find in 1978 that there were a lot of older men in leisure suits and middle-aged ladies with too much makeup hanging out there hoping to meet astronauts or celebrities. It was my first and last visit to this once-famous place. Our generation would find hangouts of our own.

A memorable event was a relaxed lunch at the Patrick Air Force Base. This base, south of Cape Canaveral, was home to the Eastern Test Range, where the military managed unmanned rocket launches for the United States Department of Defense. The officer's club was on the beach, and its dining room looked out on the water. I was in the midst of animated conversation with a fellow ASCAN when I looked out the window to see Hoot Gibson, dressed in coat and tie, wandering down the beach looking out to sea. What a melancholy sight! When I asked a friend of his if something was wrong, he told me that, yes, his wife had obtained a separation decree and had asked him to move out. I knew he had a young daughter at home and that he must be heartbroken. But that memory of him, solitary, with the background of beach and sand and sea, was engraved in my mind, and my heart went out to him.

The *Florida Today* newspaper was one of Central Florida's institutions. The paper had always been supportive of the space program. When astronauts arrived in town or launches occurred, they were front-page news. The owner of the newspaper, Al Neuharth, was a real mover and shaker and would later help start *USA Today*. He had a huge house at the Cape, and his wife, Lori Wilson, was state legislator. He threw a big party for the 35 of us and our entourage. One could imagine it was like the big wingdings of the past, with local celebs and dignitaries glad-handing each other and the soon-to-be famous rocket riders. I think we all wondered if this was what our lives would hold. Strange enough, it was an anachronism, something from the past, a transition. After the first few launches of the shuttle, this sort of hoopla ceased. The big celebrations in town were those of contractors who got their satellites into orbit or astronaut relatives whose family members made it into space.

I would know the Cape well in the years to come. The expanse of ocean would be a catalyst for many deep thoughts. I'd come to know the special bond between those at the Johnson Space Center who'd send their astronauts all eager and bright, training completed, checklists in hand, down to launch and the folks at the Kennedy Space Center who'd scrambled over the rocket and cargo for months taking care of the chariots that would carry them heavenward. I never felt that the other centers shared in that special bond, not HQ, not the Center in Huntsville, Alabama, not the Ames or Goddard or Langley or Lewis NASA Centers. They were players, often extremely important players, but the life and death stuff, well, that was Kennedy and Johnson, perhaps a tribute to the presidents who put so much of their hearts into the space program's birth.

The other side of the continent also provided us a lot of insight into our new jobs, but in a different way.

Our trip to California was to last an entire week. One leg of that trip was logistically and financially difficult. Rockwell was the prime shuttle contractor, and it had a huge plant to fabricate parts in Downey, near Los Angeles. The challenge was to transport us from Downey all the way to NASA's Ames Research Center near San Francisco. So NASA managed to bend its rules a bit. In the strange world of government ethics, the rules said no NASA employee could accept anything from a contractor, especially one with as important a contract as Rockwell. A civil servant might be influenced in the decision-making or at least give the appearance that someone was being "bought" if any tokens of appreciation were accepted. This was an odd notion for me coming out of the medical world where drug or medical equipment sales people were always wining and dining doctors to entice them into buying their products. That was viewed as capitalism at work. But the government was different. I would soon learn that I had to be above reproach, especially in the highly-visible job of astronaut. Even my small, part-time job working as an Emergency Room doctor on weekends would come under close scrutiny to ensure I wasn't receiving special favors or money under the table.

In the early days of human space flight, astronauts had been allowed to accept lucrative contracts with *Life* magazine and had obtained special low home mortgage rates and all sort of stuff. But when one Apollo crew took envelopes to the moon and cancelled them with a special postage stamp with the intention of selling them to a German artifact dealer for big bucks, the ax fell. It was easiest for the government to make a sweeping rule that said we could not accept any private gain for our public position, and that was that. We rankled a bit that it seemed like an "ABC (Anyone But Congress) Law" since members of Congress were allowed to make money for appearances and speaking engagements. Nevertheless, it was the rule, and we abided by it.

On a few occasions, however, the Holy Fathers at NASA Headquarters granted special dispensation. On our West Coast trip, it was decreed that we were allowed to be ferried to Northern California on a Rockwell business jet. We visited the Rockwell plant in Downey, but *Columbia* had already been shipped to their Palmdale, California facility. So, we just heard the story of its manufacture.

At Ames near Sunnyvale south of San Francisco we were shown that spaceflight wasn't the only thing NASA did. Aeronautics research is another aspect of the mission, or as they said, "The first A in NASA is for aeronautics." Ames had enormous wind tunnels where various aspects of aerodynamic flight could be tested. A scale model of the shuttle was tested there. It should have increased my confidence that the engineers understood the characteristics of the vehicle all the way to space, but there were some things beyond the capabilities of wind tunnels that they could only figure out "by analysis," that is, on paper and by computer until data could be obtained by the orbital flight tests. So many unknowns.

We got up to our usual shenanigans on the west coast trip. It became a tradition on these forays that one of the ASCANS, after a long evening of drinking, would call Mr. Abbey, our boss, to let him know we were all okay. Looking back, no other boss we had at that level would have tolerated a call at 2:00 a.m. from a group of boisterous, inebriated partiers, but George, an inveterate partier himself at the time, seemed to be flattered by it. Jay Honeycutt and Carolyn Huntoon, who *chaperoned* our trips, soon learned if they weren't part of the party, they'd be called or visited at their hotel room and invited to join us once the party started going. This seemed to be the way the military fellows carried on, so the rest of us felt compelled to participate. Alan Bean, who had been saddled with the overall responsibility of our training, also got roped into these get-togethers.

One of my more memorable moments of this trip was sitting next to Al on one leg of the California trip. Al had flown the Apollo 12 mission and walked on the moon. He had also commanded a Skylab mission in 1973. He was an accomplished, well-respected pilot and commander in this high tech world, but I think he was beginning a transition in his life. He had always painted as a hobby, but he was getting into it more seriously, trying to capture on canvas some of the beautiful sights he'd seen on the moon and from space. Along with delving into art, he also seemed to be exploring inside his head, often waxing philosophical rather than focusing on purely technical topics. He was willing to talk to some of us, as novices, about the personal histories of astronauts he had seen evolving over time. I asked him whether being an astronaut prepared a person for any particular type of job later in life.

His answer gave me food for thought: "No, but having been an astronaut will open doors for you to do whatever you want to do in the future."

I realized that at some point in time I'd have to decide what my next career would be. There were no clear-cut, well-established paths, certainly not for a woman, but I might be given the opportunity to do whatever I wanted. This was a comforting thought, one (as it would turn out) I would have many years to ponder.

Along with flying, lectures, trips, and making new friends, there was the responsibility of settling into a new home and getting used to living in Houston, Texas. The Johnson Space Center is located halfway between Houston and Galveston. The history of how it came to be located there seems to have been due to some good old Texas wheelin' and dealin'.

With President Kennedy's directive to put humans on the moon by the end of the decade, America began to plan a new Manned Spacecraft Center. In 1961 a site selection team went looking for a location. It had to include proximity to water since large pieces of equipment would need to be barged in, and a good airport nearby was a must-have. Preferably, it needed to be near major universities because academic exchange would be desirable. A mild climate would permit year-round outdoor work. At least a thousand acres of land had to be available. The NASA administrator was to lead the small group that would pinpoint the site.

After considering multiple qualified sites, Houston, Texas was one of the finalists. Here is where things got a little fuzzy. Lyndon Johnson was vice president at the time and headed the Space Council that advised President Kennedy on space policy. In February, 1961, he had named James Webb as NASA's second administrator. Webb swore that politicians did not influence the final decision but acknowledged that Congressman Albert Thomas from Houston may have pulled some strings. President Kennedy had proposed $60 million to begin work at the future center and knew that the budget required congressional approval. Albert Thomas was the chair of the House Appropriations Subcommittee on Defense which oversaw the NASA budget. Which of these men would have talked together?

How were Rice University in Houston, Humble Oil (then Texas's largest oil company), and the Brown and Root Company involved? Thomas and George Brown, head of Brown and Root, had been college roommates at Rice after World War I. Brown and Root financed many of Johnson's campaigns. Thomas, Brown, and other influential Houston businessmen including the head of Humble Oil belonged to the exclusive Suite 8F Group which met regularly at the Lamar Hotel.

Humble Oil owned a large amount of land around Clear Lake near the proposed site of the space center which wasn't good for oil drilling. In the late 1950s they donated 1000 acres to Rice University hoping to entice a federal research facility to locate there. In May of 1961 when JFK announced the moon program, Rice offered the land to the government. On September 19, 1961, a public announcement was made that the spaceflight center would be located south of Houston on that donated land.

The early site of the Manned Spacecraft Center south of Houston, Texas.

Rice University would have the prestige of working with the scientists and engineers who would build the nation's space program. The center would be a boon to Albert Thomas's congressional district. Humble Oil and its Friendswood Development Company owned choice packets of land in the area where new houses and support contractor buildings would spring up. Brown and Root would get the contract to build a large portion of the new center. The people of Houston enthusiastically welcomed the newcomers with Texas hospitality. One day their city would hear its name in the first words Neil Armstrong transmitted from the moon, "Houston, Tranquility Base here. The Eagle had landed." In 1973 one month after LBJ's death, the Manned Spaceflight Center would be renamed the Johnson Space Center.

So, Clear Lake City was born, and everybody was happy except for maybe the people in other parts of the country who lost out to the wily Texans, as well as the employees of Manned Spacecraft Center who in years to come would have to endure the heat, the humidity, and the bugs of this fair part of the world.

I had come to the area with my father during an ASCAN meeting in April of 1978 to look for a place to live. I was lucky enough to find a nice new townhouse in the right price range out the back gate of the center. The salary I was to be paid was not great. I'd joined the government as a civil servant with a grade of GS11 at about $22,000 a year. At the time it was about two or three thousand more than I made in Memphis, counting the $12,000 I made per year as a resident and the $8,000 I was making moonlighting. My dad agreed to help me with the down payment, but my NASA income was about $3,000 less per year than I needed to qualify for the mortgage loan.

"Surely," my father said, "they'll take into consideration that you are a physician, have always moonlighted, and will do so in Houston and are an astronaut."

I guess we got a rude comeuppance about how much being an astronaut would buy you in Clear Lake, Texas: nothing. University Savings &

Loan controlled the financing for the townhouse I wanted, and it refused to lend me the money without my father's co-signature. So much for being somebody important. I guess it never occurred to me that it might have something to do with being female.

Once I moved in July, I got to know the steamy environment of Clear Lake intimately. While there was no specified fitness program to follow as an astronaut, there was considerable peer pressure to be fit. The small astronaut gym at the back of the center was outfitted with work-out equipment. A new ladies' locker room had been added. There was a circular running track in the shaded back yard. Most of the ASCANs were runners, especially those from the military who'd had to pass periodic fitness exams. Running in Houston was a challenge. About nine months out of the year were incredibly hot. I would get up early to run in the "cool" part of the day. One hot summer, at 5:00 a.m., the temperature was 85 degrees and the humidity was 95 percent. It tested one's dedication. I was soon up to five miles in 45 minutes on a good day and daily vigorous exercise became a lifelong habit. Southern ladies weren't supposed to sweat, but I learned how.

Next, I had to go through all the hoops necessary to practice a little medicine in Texas. I had worked about a hundred hours a week at my residency and still managed 24-48 hours a month in ERs up and down the Mississippi delta. If the NASA job was 50 or 60 hours a week, it seemed like I'd have a little extra time to practice medicine. Besides, I wasn't too sure the astronaut job was going to work out. Suppose they made it so miserable for women that I would hate it? What if I flunked the physical exam next year? What if I couldn't do the work or chickened out? I'd invested a bunch of years learning to be a doctor. I didn't want to "unlearn" medicine. And with a new Corvette sitting in the garage of my new townhouse...well, I could use the money.

Though NASA gave lip service to wanting us to maintain our scientific expertise, it became clear that practicing medicine would have to be on my own time and at my own expense. No, they couldn't help me pay for my Texas license or malpractice insurance. No, I couldn't have time off during the workweek. No, I couldn't even practice medicine without approval from all the way up at NASA Headquarters. Terrific! So, it took me six months and another loan from my dad to get my license, pay for a full year of malpractice insurance, and sign up with one of the big ER scheduling groups.

I learned quickly, however, that emergency medicine was changing. Most of the good hospitals were hiring their own emergency room physicians and specifying their own standards for physician qualifications. After months of being sent to many different hospitals—some not so good, some frighteningly bad—I happened to meet a fellow female physician, Dr. Diana Fite, at a medical conference in Galveston. She was a member of a two-physician group covering Sam Houston Memorial, a small community hospital in northwest Houston. She and her partner, Leo Creip, were looking for some extra help on weekends, and I was invited to join them. I liked the idea of practicing in one hospital where I felt I had some say in how the ER was run, so I joined their little group. I practiced there until they closed their doors some twelve years later when I moved to Spring Branch Hospital, where I practiced until I left Houston.

In each of these positions, I had to specify that I was not advertising that I was an astronaut to attract business. I also had to state that my salary was the same as other physicians and that I was actually doing the work. I had to get periodic reapprovals from headquarters. It was never easy. Despite the hassle and loss of some free time, it constituted a back-up plan in case this new space adventure didn't work out. And it paid about twice as much per hour as I made as an astronaut. Then again, I wasn't an astronaut for the pay.

There were lots of social activities in our early days as a new group. The military folks were used to partying together as a way of getting to know new friends and as a main source of entertainment on remote military bases. There always seemed to be a happy hour on Friday nights, and we got to know the places that were pleased—or not so pleased—to see a group of 50 or so, including spouses, come crowding into their drinking establishment. Lots of the activities were either in a large group or involved the young folks without children, or they were a singles crowd that included Ellington pilots and other NASA employees. Some of these other employees were referred to as "freeze dried" astronauts. They had interviewed with our group, had terrific qualifications, but had not made the cut. NASA invited them to work at JSC in hopes of getting them involved and encouraging them to reapply. Many of them did and were later accepted into the Astronaut Corps. I admired their persistence.

After six months of general training, in the first part of 1979 we were assigned to work alongside a senior astronaut to see what technical assignments were like. These were tasks astronauts worked on when they weren't wrapped up in training for their own flight. They were much like what the military people did back in their service careers, but they were new to me. I was assigned to Fred Haise, one of the pilot astronauts, who I followed around for awhile. He was working on some shuttle system or another, and I sat through several meetings that didn't make much sense to me. I would learn that, like medicine, NASA and the engineering community had their own acronyms and euphemisms to express certain concepts. For instance, in medicine things are graded 1+ to 4+. If someone has a little swelling in his ankles, he has 1+ edema. If he has elephant-like lower extremities, he has 4+ edema. On the other hand, engineers used statistical measures, and if something was way outside the norm, it was referred to as 3 sigma (that is, 3 standard deviations from the mean) as in, "It was a 3 sigma bad day." In medicine, if the patient is dead, euphemistically he was "without vital signs," or, if he has a bad result, "he suffered some morbidity." If your plane crashed into a smoking hole in the ground, that's a "hull loss" in the airplane world. If someone set off a nuclear warhead, that was an "event." I once heard a smoldering fire in wires in the orbiter referred to as "some pyrolysis" of the wires. Learning to understand and then to speak the NASA language was also part of the task of our ASCAN year. What in the world was "SSME CCB – OV102 SSME MEC SW Delta" on a meeting agenda?? I would look at presentation schedules with so many acronyms that the sole readable thing to the uninitiated was the date on the page.

In the spring when it came time for us to be assigned our own technical assignments, it became clear that there were among us...*a selected few.* The ASCANs who were given tasks as CAPCOMs in Mission Control, assigned to follow the development of the Remote Manipulator System mechanical arm, or assigned to space suits were given the jobs that would prepare them for early flight assignments. They'd have the chance to learn about an important aspect of the shuttle that would make them valuable on a crew. On the other hand, I was assigned to follow the food system. Rather than take it as some form of sexism, I rationalized it by telling myself I had some background in nutrition, and it would allow me

I became an expert on the Space Shuttle galley and food systems. Here is a tray with food packages, condiments and utensils.

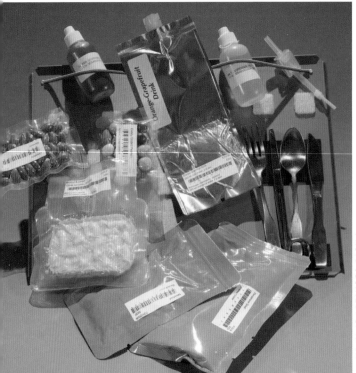

PHOTO COURTESY OF NASA

time to learn more about the shuttle on my own time and at my own speed. But still, it was not a plum assignment, and I feared what it boded for my future. I was determined to do the best job possible, however, and learn how the galley and its ancillary equipment worked. Beyond that, I'd learn for myself all about the electrical and fluid loops on the middeck. There would be other, better opportunities down the road. There was an old poker saying that it wasn't about what cards you were dealt, but how you played them.

We also began to do public relations work for NASA. Having been invited to speak at a number of places before I moved to Houston, I was comfortable with it. We were also given a course on how to handle tough media questions. Early on in the shuttle program, the audiences were friendly. It was later when the existence of human space flight was in doubt that the questions became hostile.

One life lesson I learned from this training was the concept of "ethos" or personal attitude and behavior. While on camera or in public view, we should always appear to be the national heroes the public expected us to be. Don't tell off-color jokes, no roll of the eyes when someone in the audience asks a dumb question, never be seen inebriated. Many public figures had lost credibility when they said something inappropriate when near an open microphone. How was one to know when the camera was on them, the microphone was recording or someone was watching? I decided it would be easier to be a person of good character all the time, to incorporate the high standards expected of me into my own everyday ethos.

I always enjoyed speaking to the public about NASA, what we were doing in space, and what it meant for people on the ground. About the time I'd get bogged down at work with projects that weren't progressing, programs that got canceled, or people who were difficult, I'd talk to some group of important and accomplished people who all thought I had the best job in the world. It's hard to feel bad about your job when there are a bunch of people who'd give anything to trade places with you.

Did I get misquoted or trivialized in the press? Yes, often, like the time I had an intelligent repartee with a female reporter who then wrote her article about my clothes and makeup. I found that reporters got things wrong, and I learned ways of improving my chances of getting my real point across. There were people in the office who detested public appearances and interviews and avoided them. (And I often wondered why NASA sometimes thrust those very people into positions where they would often be in the public eye.) There were others who thrived on it, and some seemed to be feathering their nests for future careers from the outset by doing a lot of speaking to companies or communities where they hoped to work someday.

Toward the end of our first ASCAN year (there were originally to be two), I was assigned to go to the Paris Air Show with a NASA delegation. Two astronauts were always sent, and the other that year was to be Deke Slayton. At the time Deke was manager of the Orbital Flight Test Program. Almost as old as my father, he had flown in World War II. The two of us came to be known as "the odd couple" which we were. Deke had come to NASA with the first group of astronauts for the Mercury program. He had developed some form of heart rhythm disturbance and had been taken off flight status before he ever had a chance to fly. He took over as chief of the Astronaut Office and, from what all of we new guys had heard, had done a terrific job. He had been there during the "Right Stuff" days when turf battles were being fought among NASA constituencies. Astronauts were treated like "the man in the can" at first and had to fight for such piloting necessities as a manual steering capability and a window in their capsules. One could imagine from the lore that was passed down to us that some of the battles were hard fought, but ended with astronauts being thought of as important members of the flying team.

Like many of the Mercury pilots, Deke was a pretty crusty, rugged individualist. Although he was always nice, I got the feeling he wasn't any too sure women belonged in space. Of course, his experience was with early space vehicles and huge clunky equipment, and doing pilot's work in ones, twos, or threes. On the other hand, the shuttle meant seven people in close quarters, doing more varied tasks than driving a spaceship to space and back.

After his heart problem was finally cleared, Deke got to make a space flight aboard the Apollo-Soyuz flight in 1975. The last of the flights to use Apollo hardware, their capsule went up and docked with the Russian Soyuz capsule. NASA chose the absolute epitome of All-American guys when they sent Tom Stafford, Vance Brand, and Deke on that flight—all tall, strong, and straight with blue eyes and light hair. The cosmonauts on the flight all looked Russian—small, dark, squat, round-faced men. It was an interesting mission, but when we got to NASA in 1978, some people said that the U.S. hadn't made a very good deal on it. We had given the Soviet Union a bunch of our technology since ours was a civilian program, while they, in a military space posture, didn't (or wouldn't) give us much more than a handshake in space and some borscht. Many of us remembered this lopsided deal years later when the Cold War ended, and we were once again ordered to work with the Russians.

The Paris Air Show was a happening place in the summer of 1979 - a place where aerospace companies from all over the world peddled their wares. It was one of the few good deals astronauts could get, trip wise. Held at the Le Bourget Airport outside Paris, the various companies rented reception areas called chalets overlooking the airfield. In 1979, astronauts were still pretty important people, and a lot of folks were anxious to meet the famous Deke Slayton and to see what a female astronaut looked like.

The usual government prohibition against astronauts receiving gratuities, including meals, from contractors, was waived so we were treated royally. There were fantastic luncheons at the chalets where important company officers were wooing important customers who were impressed with being able to sit next to an astronaut. There was French wine and cheese served while watching the latest aircraft strut their stuff out the chalet's picture windows. The French Mirage and the United States F16 were dueling over who could do the most awesome flying. The British Harrier would do an amazing stunt, sweeping low across the field toward the windows of the chalets, only to slow down and come to a halt in front of our eyes. Then it would execute a slow pirouette in mid-air and zoom away out of view.

One spectacular evening we were invited on a trip down the Seine. The boat was a luxury barge upon which a sumptuous feast was set. We complimented our hosts on the fantastic full moon they had arranged above Notre Dame Cathedral as we drifted by.

But by far one of the finest evenings I'd ever spent in my life was in the Burgundian wine country. We all set out across the French countryside to the city of Dijon. A magnificent dinner was to be hosted by a group of the wealthy vintners of the local chapter of the Chevaliers du Tastevin, the Knights of Winetasting. Several hundred guests arrived at the Clos de Vougeot, the chateau where dinner was to be held. It was a formal affair, and every two years they honored the NASA entourage, particularly the astronauts. The dinner courses were all named after stages of a flight to the moon. Fine vintage wines from the region were served with each course. The food was fantastic in the French tradition, and it was all carried off with such effortless grace. Dozens of waiters moved about serving and retrieving courses, the correct place settings magically appearing. Wineglasses were never empty. The most miraculous course to me, who had often struggled to have dinner parties where all the food was ready on time, was one that included two perfectly poached eggs on each person's plate. These wonderful people must have thought getting to the moon a most difficult task, but I will never understand how they could poach several hundred eggs to just the right degree of doneness to serve all at once.

At the culmination of the meal Deke and I were inducted into the society. We each had to say a few words. For once I was pleased I had taken French in school, so I could speak without a translator. Unfortunately, I couldn't speak in this foreign tongue extemporaneously, so I had written my little speech out in English, and then had it translated by our embassy staff. I had it pretty well memorized, so I was pleased when it went over well with the audience. The problem was that they thought I could understand French spoken excitedly, so I was swamped after dinner by droves of well-wishers, only part of whose conversation I could understand.

We also had the opportunity to meet President Valery Giscard d'Estaing when he visited the U.S. Pavilion at Le Bourget. Luckily his English was better than my French, so we exchanged a few pleasantries.

The NASA display at the U.S. Pavilion that year focused on the space shuttle, and Deke and I gave several presentations about the machinery. I talked about the diversity in the new group of astronauts. It was newsworthy back then to have women and minorities in space suits. Of course, in the summer of 1979, we thought the first launch of *Columbia* was just a few months away. Little did we know...

It was my first exposure to a big public relations event. Gene Marianetti, our NASA headquarters coordinator, practically killed himself keeping everything straight, arranging cars here and there and making sure we knew what to do. He kept telling me he appreciated my being on time when it was time to leave the hotel for the event. While spending a great deal of time waiting for Deke, who was chronically late, Gene told me plenty of juicy NASA stories – but also had a lot of tips for a novice in the world of mingling with the press and dignitaries.

The most frightening event that happened on the trip occurred at Le Bourget as we were going from one event to another. Deke had brought a bunch of crew-insignia stickers from his Apollo-Soyuz flight in which his U.S. capsule docked with a Russian one in 1975. He had the strange habit of sticking them all over things in Paris. He slapped them in elevators, on restaurant doors, everywhere we visited at the airport. I'm sure every men's room in the area had one. As we walked out of one of the chalets one day, the narrow roadway was clogged with traffic, and a long black limousine sporting a diplomatic flag blocked our path for a moment. Deke, with a devilish grin, reached in his pocket, pulled out a sticker, and applied it to the lower windshield of the car. Immediately, a large burly driver jumped from the front seat and came around to see what had despoiled his beautiful vehicle. He stared at the sticker with a ferocious look on his face, and I was sure there was going to be a fight. Then, amazingly, the scowl turned into a grin, and he started jabbering away in Russian. He stuck his hand out to Deke and insisted that we meet the Russian dignitaries he was transporting. I don't even remember who they were, but they were excited to meet Deke who was well known in their country. I was glad to have escaped witnessing a murder scene.

In all, the trip to Paris was a great culmination to the first year of astronaut candidate training. I was honored that NASA trusted me enough to send me to this important event. I found that there would be a few glamorous things we got to do that made up for the hours of hard work that we had to put into our jobs.

In August of 1979, our bosses decided that one year of being ASCANs was enough rather than two; we had passed the necessary training. No one had washed out, not even the "girls." At a ceremony with our fellow, older astronauts, we were each presented with a silver pin with the astronaut symbol on it. Only after we had flown in space would we receive a gold one like it.

CHAPTER 3

★ ★ ★ ★ ★ ★

BUT WILL IT FLY?

During my year of training, the building of the first real space shuttle, *Columbia,* was not going well. The *Enterprise* flew the landing tests in 1977: it had been built as an engineering model and much had been learned from it, but it was a shell with no heat shield tiles and no real space propulsion system, so many parts were still in development. We seemed to be learning lessons slowly as *Columbia* was built up. Every week there was some new surprise.

The heat shield tiles that covered the orbiter's underbelly were advanced technology, and consisted of a jigsaw puzzle of 31,000 individual black pieces, not all of which had been installed. In March of 1979, NASA decided that the vehicle should be shipped from Rockwell's Palmdale facility in California to the Kennedy Space Center where the remainder of the 7800 tiles could be applied while other work was completed. There was terrific fanfare as this new machine was towed out of her hangar and down the road to NASA's Dryden facility at Edwards Air Force Base. Street and traffic lights had to be taken down to let her drive by. What a spectacle! This black and white machine, unlike any previous airplane or space vehicle, was a hybrid built to fly like both. It had stubby wings and no visible propellers or jet engines. Could it possibly fly itself back from space? It was ungainly looking, not sleek like a rocket. How could it drag itself into orbit? Yet it was the proclaimed promise of a reusable spacecraft for NASA's future – and mine. Crowds lined the roadways waving American flags. It was a glorious day.

And then --

Having loaded the orbiter onto the back of the NASA Boeing 747 carrier aircraft, the piggyback flight to Florida began, as well as trouble. The tile designers' worst nightmares came true. Tiles began falling off in the relatively mild airstream of the airplane flight. Not only did individual tiles come off, but also there was a *zipper effect*. A hole left by one missing tile disturbed the airflow around the neighboring tiles, and more were pried loose. Whole rows of tiles were torn away. Columbia left Palmdale looking like a magnificent black and white, gleaming flying machine, but she arrived at Cape Canaveral looking like a sick bird after a severe molt, the greenish aluminum skin under the missing tiles exposed. Perhaps it was a harbinger of things to come for this vehicle. There was much work to be done on the tiles. Soon, a whole army of young college students were

Space Shuttle Columbia while being ferried across the country from Palmdale California to the Kennedy Space Center in 1979 lost some of her tiles. These tiles, crucial new components for a reusable spacecraft, were designed to protect the vehicle from the heat of reentry.

recruited to spend the summer of 1979 learning to glue on thermal tiles as the push to launch continued. Hundreds of fingerprints were put upon that vehicle before it made it off the ground.

I learned a new expression during those days. The piece of hardware that was the last thing to be completed was called the *long pole in the tent,* the thing that was holding everything up. While we thought it would be the tiles, it was a race between the tiles and the shuttle's main engines.

The wickedly dangerous cocktail of liquid hydrogen and liquid oxygen was not new, and had fueled successful rockets in the past. However, the newly designed engines for the launch phase of the shuttle were more powerful, and they kept exploding on the test stand. There were lots of reasons why the shuttle couldn't handle exploding engines. For one thing, the boost from all three engines and the Solid Rocket Boosters (SRBs) was needed to make it to orbit and not fall back into the Atlantic. Another thing was the close proximity of the three main engines in the back end of the shuttle. An explosion of one engine could take out the other two and blast the whole back end off the orbiter.

And so it went. Problems were studied, fixes designed, schedules rewritten. There were at least two people who seemed to be getting a good deal out of the delays. At NASA, the astronauts who were to be aboard the next space shot were known as the prime crew, i.e.: very important people. If someone referred to an astronaut as part of *the crew,* it was understood that he or she was next up and had a great deal to do with the decisions that were being made about the manned space flight program. The prime crew for *Columbia's* first flight, was named as soon as it looked like the flight was getting near. Before our class's arrival in 1978, John Young and Bob "Crip" Crippen had been named. A veteran of two Gemini and two Apollo flights, with a walk on the moon under his belt, John was the most senior astronaut in the astronaut corps. He was the current chief of the Astronaut Office.

PHOTO COURTESY OF NASA

On the other hand, Crip was one of the most junior having been brought aboard in the Class of '69, the last class before mine. He was regarded as a whiz kid in the realm of the Data Processing System, which included the five computers that ran everything on the orbiter. The space shuttle incorporated the "fly-by-wire" system of the latest aircraft of the day. That meant that the computers told the airplane what to do. In old machines, the control stick, throttle, and rudder pedals were linked mechanically to the aerosurfaces—the ailerons and rudder—and to the engines. In the newer model aircraft, as well as in this new spacecraft, all the things that the pilot touched were like a giant computer game. Push the left rudder pedal, and it sent a message to the computer. The computer looked at both how fast the vehicle was going and other inputs; then, it calculated what message to send to the rudder. The system decided what it should move or fire to make the vehicle go to the left.

In even more modern aircraft, the mechanical dials and tapes that displayed things like fuel quantities and speed had been replaced by computer screens. In the early orbiter days, many of the old airplane displays were still there, but there were also computer display screens on which pilots could call up information on all the orbiter systems: environmental control, electrical power, guidance, navigation, propulsion, and so on. The vehicle was a hybrid of old and new technology.

Bob Crippen was knowledgeable about how the computerized parts worked. John Young always said Crip was along to keep him out of trouble. Someone once asked John if he was going to be scared when the shuttle started to lift off. He answered that if a person wasn't a little scared sitting on top of several million pounds of rocket fuel that someone was about to light, he didn't understand what was going on.

The STS-1 crew. John Young had flown on two Gemini and two Apollo flights and had walked on the moon. This would be Bob Crippen's first spaceflight.

As the prime crew, Young and Crippen were like featured matadors in an important bullfight or star players on a Super Bowl team. Thousands of people, including most of the astronaut office, worked on getting them and their game ready to go. Later in the shuttle program when several flights a year were flying, people were lucky to be prime crew for a month or two. Young and Crippen held the record at the time for being the prime crew the longest, the crew that trained the most for a single first-of-a-kind, two-day flight.

There were many things to be worked out. First, there were the plans for the ascent phase, the time from launch to arriving in orbit. For the first four flights, called the Orbital Flight Test program, there would be ejection seats on the flight deck, and the two crew members would wear Air Force-type partial-pressure ejection suits. Everyone understood they'd get fried if they ejected anytime the boosters or main engines were firing. Above a certain altitude survival wouldn't be possible even with the suit. So the ejection seats were there for use if the space plane was under control and gliding back to Earth at an altitude below 100,000 feet.

The plan for a successful launch day, for the collaboration of all of those millions of pieces and parts, came together…in theory.

The crew would be awakened several hours before launch, taken out to the pad, and strapped in. Then, they'd spend several—perhaps many—

hours lying there waiting for everything to get fueled up, powered up, and checked out for launch. If all went well, the count would proceed. At six seconds before launch, the main engines would start, gulping half a million gallons of liquid hydrogen and oxygen. With booster ignition there would be over seven million pounds of thrust—making the shuttle's liftoff quicker than that of the Apollo. By the time the tail of *Columbia* cleared the launch tower, it would be going over 100 miles per hour. With the boosters blazing away and the main engines running at full power for the early part of the flight, the maximum aerodynamic pressure of the air going by (termed "max Q," a product of speed and air density) would be too great, so the engines would have to be throttled down at the right time and then throttled back up again. There was some worry about these balky high performance creatures executing this maneuver. When an engine was throttled down appropriately, it was in the "throttle bucket." Many failure scenarios involved one or more engines "stuck in the bucket" or at less than full power.

If all went well, the boosters would burn out at two minutes or so and the main engines would be powering the vehicle. Designed as a huge, lightweight, expendable gas carrier, the external tank had to be strong enough to carry the loads of the burning boosters attached to each side and the huge bird that it carried on its back. The first few external tanks were a gorgeous gleaming white until someone found that the white paint needed to make them so pretty weighed almost 600 pounds. Later, NASA opted for the all-natural shade of sickly burnt umber, so it could use that 600 pounds to carry something more useful than paint to orbit.

As the boosters ran out of fuel small explosive packages would separate them outward to clear the sides of the rest of the stack. Each booster would then fall out of the sky from about 150,000 feet down to 15,000 feet where three huge parachutes would pop out from their pointy ends, and they'd drift down into the Atlantic about 140 miles off the coast. Into this area NASA deployed its entire Navy consisting of the two booster recovery ships, Liberty Star and Freedom Star. The boosters would be towed back to Cape Canaveral and be refurbished for later flights.

At least a few people had some concerns about the whole booster separation sequence. T.K. Mattingly, known around the office as a stickler for detail, gave Hoot Gibson one of his early Astronaut Office assignments to see if the boosters really would get away from the tank and orbiter correctly. If they didn't or if they came off asymmetrically, the rest of the vehicle would tumble out of control. Hoot brought back good, concise engineering and safety data that everything was well designed and tested. T.K. kept asking "Why?" to every piece of data presented, and Hoot became frustrated trying to explain everything in finer and finer detail. Finally, to one question, Hoot replied, "Just because that's the way it is." End of discussion.

After the boosters blasted free, the main engines would continue pushing the orbiter and the external tank into space at ever-increasing speeds for another six and a half minutes. Toward the end of that time, the engines would again be throttled back so as not to exceed three G's. The orbiter could have been designed to be strong enough to be undamaged at higher G-loads, but that would have required a lot more structure and thus, more weight. That, in turn, would have reduced the amount of cargo that could be carried into orbit. As it was, the orbiter was originally planned to weigh around 180,000 pounds at landing, and many of its systems, like tires and brakes, were designed for that weight. As with all space vehicles, however, the weight grew. Average orbiter weight at landing zoomed to over 200,000 pounds. Heavyweight flights that didn't deploy anything and returned to Earth with the entire cargo (such as a Spacelab) would weigh in at 225,000 pounds or more.

The three G's experienced at the end of powered flight for the shuttle was mild compared to the seven G's that Apollo flights achieved. But still, spending 30 seconds or so feeling like an elephant was standing on your chest promised to be uncomfortable. Breath would come in short gasps. Moving an arm to throw a switch, especially on the overhead panels, would become a weightlifting chore. Talking would be close to impossible.

And then something remarkable would happen.

At the proper point in space and at the correct speed, the main engines would shut down. During our practice in the simulator the indications that this had happened were three little lights lit on the instrument panel. In space, the lights would be a secondary clue because once the shuttle reached "Main Engine Cut Off" (or MECO in NASA terminology), everything would be weightless. Having survived the fiery baptism of powered ascent, the crew could finally claim to be spacefarers.

But this was only if all those millions of pieces and parts worked.

In planning shuttle flights, the flight designers had to consider all the *what-ifs* that could happen. When the decision was made to use solid rocket boosters, they wrote off the first two minutes. If the boosters did not perform correctly, there was nothing that could be done. As was said around the office, once the SRBs lit, the stack was going somewhere for two minutes, and you hoped it was in the right direction. Even if all three main engines for some reason shut down shortly after launch, there wasn't much to do until the boosters burned out. The boosters were steerable by *gimbaling,* or moving the nozzles on their aft ends, but they could not be throttled down or turned off.

Assuming the boosters did their thing, there were still a myriad of things that could go wrong. Each one of the possible scenarios had to be considered, analyzed, and planned for and checklists written down. Crewmembers and Mission Control had to know exactly what to do. The software that controlled the shuttle had to be programmed.

If one or more engines malfunctioned early, the flight couldn't make it to orbit. If the failure occurred early in the launch profile, a Return to Launch Site (or RTLS) was possible. This was why the weather at the Cape over the Shuttle Landing Facility had to be good at launch time, so the runway could be seen if an RTLS was required. Although all of the fine engineers at NASA said it was possible, an RTLS would still be a pretty sporting maneuver. The shuttle would be going outbound from the Cape at many of hundreds of miles per hour and an engine would quit. "RTLS - Abort!" the CAPCOM in Mission Control would declare. The Commander would reach forward, turn a rotary switch to the RTLS position, and press the ABORT button—telling this behemoth to go the other way. Depending upon how far from Florida the shuttle happened to be when this happened, the vehicle might fly outbound a while longer to burn off fuel. At the appointed time, the boosters would be jettisoned. The shuttle would be upside down, having pirouetted shortly after launch, and then arched out over the Atlantic Ocean with the tank on top.

After the boosters were gone, at a certain point the whole stack would pitch its nose toward the sky to burn more fuel, belching fire out the remaining main engine or engines, standing on its tail. The interesting thing was that the shuttle would still be headed east, having built up tremendous outbound momentum. Eventually, the energy would be used up, and the forward velocity would fall to zero. The shuttle and tank would then pitch over and head back toward Florida. Not long after this, the computer would command a pitch downward, and once established, the main engines would be shut down and the orbiter would separate from the tank. Hopefully, the shuttle would then be able to begin to swoop upward while the tank continued downward so they wouldn't crash into one another.

If the on-board computer calculations were correct, and the machine was still in one piece, the flight into the landing strip could commence. The shuttle should have enough energy (it would now be a glider) to swoop into the Cape. It always seemed incredible that it would work; it was too complex for this ungainly bird. I often had dreams about how strange it would feel to be approaching the Florida coast from the wrong direction, a space-age Wrong Way Harrigan.

As bizarre as that scenario was, there was another that was about as crazy, called a Transatlantic Abort Landing, or "TAL." There was a point on the shuttle's eastward trajectory when the CAPCOM would tell the crew "Negative Return." After this point, there was no capability to get back to Florida. In this scenario, after the boosters were jettisoned, if a main engine or two were lost the only option was to continue across the Atlantic.

The commander would turn the abort rotary switch now to TAL, push the ABORT button, and head for someplace in Spain or Africa, depending on how far to the north the flight path was. There were several places prepared to have a space shuttle descend on them: Rota or Moron in Spain, Ben Guerir in Morocco, Dakar in Senegal, and Banjul in the Gambia. Less than five percent of the citizenry of the United States had ever heard of these places, but the locales had long runways. Astronauts would be sent to some of them for every launch to make sure everything was ready in case their fellow astronauts needed to drop in.

Getting to those landing sites in a space shuttle was not so easy. Upside down, blazing across the ocean, the little red *engine-out* warning lights on the pilot's panel would illuminate. Oops! The crew would feel a lurch that meant that the shuttle wasn't accelerating as fast as it used to be. They'd tell the computer to abort to the proper transatlantic site. On the remaining one or two engines, the entire shuttle/tank combo would execute a half-roll so that the orbiter was now on top and the tank underneath. After that, everything would supposedly be easy. Get close to Africa, swoop down, pop off the tank, pull up, and glide into a strange runway in a foreign country. Florida to Africa in about 35 minutes. I never believed it could be done, but crews spent endless hours in the simulator practicing it. Our passports had to be stamped with visas, and our shots had to be up to date before leaving home for flight so we could exit those countries after landing. It was never too clear how we'd get our spaceship back home. I suspect it would have become a great museum piece in a foreign land.

At least the engineers with sharp pencils said those aborts were possible, in theory. The things called "Contingency Aborts" were another matter. In these, the shuttle couldn't make it to a runway and the stack would be flown as far across the Atlantic as it could go. The Contingency Abort cue card procedure's last step was something like, "Line orbiter flight path up parallel to waves and land on water." After splashdown, the astronauts were supposed to blow out the overhead windows on the flight deck, throw out the life raft, jump out, and wait to be rescued. No one believed that could be done. Everyone knew the payload in the cargo bay would break loose on water impact and come smashing through the crew compartment. But I guess everyone had to have something to do while waiting to hit the water. *You don't want to die tensed up,* the old military adage goes.

I hated practicing those aborts in the simulator. No one ever died during a simulator run. However, a poorly-flown practice run could almost make me feel sick at my stomach seeing the displays on the instrument panel lurch one way, then the other, then begin gyrating wildly as the simulated shuttle spun out of control. I always had to close my eyes and sit calmly while the simulator cabin banged back and forth until someone called a halt to the training run.

Then there were the failures that would allow an Abort Once Around, or "AOA." In this case, the shuttle couldn't make it to orbit, so the craft would return and land at Edwards on the first revolution. At least the crew would have a little time to think about this one, since it took a little over an hour. The last abort type was the Abort to Orbit, or "ATO," meaning the

PHOTO COURTESY OF NASA

Young and Crippen in the Shuttle cockpit give a thumbs up. They had trained for a long time for this flight and were ready to go.

shuttle could make it to a safe, but low, orbit, then assess the situation with Mission Control before the decision was made whether to boost the spaceship a little higher using the orbital engines or return and land.

The procedures for all these scenarios had to be worked out prior to the first flight, along with ones to handle any failure in any system anyone could imagine. Then the procedures had to be mastered by the crew in the simulators. Then Mission Control had to be tied in to the simulator so they could practice monitoring the systems and help handle the problems or combination of problems. Members of the Astronaut Corps trained as Capsule Communicators (CAPCOMs) in Mission Control. From the early days of spaceflight, CAPCOMs were always astronauts who had undergone the same training and spoke the same language as the crew in space. They had to learn to relay instructions and explanations from Mission Control flight controllers to the crew in crew shorthand.

Others of us had plenty of time to practice our own particular positions for the first flight. A chase team of astronauts and NASA pilots and photographers was pulled together. Two members of my 1978 class were designated as "Chase 1." Jon "Big Jon" McBride as the pilot of a NASA T38 jet was to intercept the shuttle as it descended through 35,000 or 40,000 feet coming into Edwards Air Force Base and help cross check the airspeed and altitude of the shuttle. George "Pinky" Nelson in the back seat would be in charge of getting historic photographs. Several of the other pilots were training for later shuttle flight rendezvous.

A rendezvous of these two disparate vehicles was a difficult task. A 10,000-pound T38 jet, sleek and needle-like, didn't want at all to fly like a 100-ton broad-in-the-rear glider. So the NASA pilots and engineers figured out a way to hang enough stuff out the bottom of the T38 to make it sort-of fly like a brick. This permitted the chase activities during shuttle landings and allowed pilots to fly simulated shuttle approaches using the T38s, which were readily available.

The job of the chase plane and its backup was to work with United States Air Force controllers to reach the exact spot in the sky at the exact time *Columbia* began her final descent into Edwards. The shuttle would blaze across the California coastline at over 100,000 feet altitude going around Mach 4 or four times the speed of sound. She would be dropping like a rock and decelerating like a massive truck hitting a snow bank. The chase plane would be flying a lazy racetrack pattern near the runway until the shuttle appeared. If the controllers watching their radars and directing the jets figured out the timing correctly, Chase 1 would see their target and shout "Tallyho on *Columbia.*" Then, the pilot would say, "I have a Judy on the target," meaning they were taking the responsibility from the controllers to conduct the rendezvous from there. After racing over to catch the orbiter, the jets had to get into their proper configuration so the sleek little T-38 would fly like a shuttle. That meant pulling the nose abruptly upward to get the T-38 speed low enough to safely throw out the landing gear, and lowering the flaps. Then the jet had to dive down to catch the orbiter and fling out the modified, heavy-duty speed brakes as needed to slow down enough to match the orbiter's tremendous deceleration rate.

The T38's didn't like this speed up, slow down, speed up, slow down flying. Sometimes the airflow going into one of the two jet engines would be blocked enough that with a hiccup, it would quit running. Not a big problem; a T38 flew fine on one engine as long as you got it down to an altitude below 25,000 feet. But one day, I was in the back seat of one of the T-38s at Edwards with one of the backup pilots doing these maneuvers chasing the Shuttle Training Aircraft for practice, when we had a more serious problem. Up near 40,000 feet we spotted our pretend target and pulled up and lurched left to keep the target in sight. My first indication that something was wrong was that it got very quiet. No engine noise. Then I realized that I was having trouble breathing. At that altitude the engines generate the cabin pressure, and when they aren't operating, the pressure will start to fall. This alerted the oxygen system to provide oxygen at a higher pressure so I didn't become hypoxic. But this forced air into my lungs with inhalation and made it difficult to exhale...and talk.

Luckily, my pilot that day was Chase 2, the backup chase pilot for STS-1, who would be the lead chase plane pilot for STS-2. I had flown many times with Hoot Gibson and felt he was one of the best pilots. Besides that, he was always calm in a crisis and considerate of rookies in the back seat. I had learned in my training that losing both engines was not necessarily a major malfunction. They could usually be restarted once the jet got down to a lower altitude where the air was thicker, but for me, it was heart-pounding time. The T-38 could not land "dead stick," that is without operating engines. It needed the whirring of the engine blades to create pressure in the hydraulic systems to drive the flight control surfaces—ailerons, horizontal stabilizer, and rudder—that maneuver the airplane. One could dive at the ground fast enough to keep the blades spinning, but upon pulling out of the dive for landing, the plane would be uncontrollable. One of the Edwards pilots had reportedly managed to dead stick a T-38 to the expansive dry lakebed at Edwards once. He used what hydraulic pressure he had at the end of the dive to set his control surfaces at one point and then let the jet settle to the runway as it ran out of speed. Had he miscalculated that set point a little, he'd either have crashed or swooped upward only to crash seconds later. But dead sticking was not recommended and something I knew Hoot would never risk, especially if someone else was in the airplane with him.

As I realized that both engines had quit, Hoot's calm voice from the front seat said, "Both engines are out. Why don't you pull out the emergency checklist and talk me through the procedure?" I knew he knew it by heart, and this was something to keep me occupied. As the plane dove lifeless out of 40,000 feet, we calmly talked about how to get an engine started again. It was remarkable how long it seemed to get from 40,000 feet to 25,000 feet where an engine restart was possible. Hoot even had the presence of mind to ask me if I remembered my ejection procedures if we couldn't get the jet running again. We talked through the ejection litany: sit up straight, knees and elbows close to the body, head back, pull up the handles, and squeeze the triggers. Once hanging under the canopy of an open parachute, check that it is fully deployed. Pull the cords on the chute to steer into the wind. (No point in being dragged across the desert facedown after making it that far.) Hands on the chute releases and prepare to do a parachute landing fall on contact with the ground. Then release the chute. Yes, I remembered most all of it, but I hoped I'd never have to do it. The statistics on ejection injuries and survival were miserable.

Then we were at 25,000 feet. The windmilling engine blades were spinning fast enough for a restart. Hoot pushed the engine start button. Ahhhh, the welcome sound of engine whine. The power rolled up to a hundred percent, and we were once again in control of a flyable aircraft. The second engine started as well. Back at the base, Hoot used the old fighter pilot phrase I'd heard before but which had extra meaning for me that day: "Well, we cheated death one more time." The beer at the Officer's Club tasted especially good that evening.

All the ASCANs had work to do for the first flight. At last, I had a job

I felt competent doing. Among their other duties, the MDs in the 1978 and 1980 astronaut classes were assigned to be doctors on the rescue helicopters at the launch and landing sites. There was some chance that the initial flight of this new flying machine would bring unexpected surprises. With ejection seats installed on the flight deck, the pilot and commander could blast themselves clear of a malfunctioning vehicle. Search and Rescue (SAR) teams were stationed at the three possible landing sites: Cape Canaveral, Edwards, and at the Northrup landing strip at White Sands, New Mexico, a backup landing site. Ordinarily, regular United States Air Force flight surgeons with experience in this field would have been aboard the choppers. But our boss, Mr. Abbey, was working hard to make each of us feel a part of the momentous first flight and to have "his people" involved in every aspect of what was going on. Trouble was, none of us young astronauts had any experience in this type of search and rescue, and some had little experience in trauma work. True, we did have more knowledge of the shuttle operations, design, and equipment than other physicians. However, I felt that it would be a big commitment of time and effort to get five astronauts (Norm Thagard, Anna Fisher, and me from the 1978 group; Bill Fisher and Jim Bagian from the 1980 class) and Johnson Space Center's head flight surgeon, Craig Fischer, ready for this operation, and so I put together a plan for Mr. Abbey to evaluate. We'd need to take a couple of week-long courses in trauma life support and to participate in the organization and practice of the rescue operations. In his usual sanguine manner, Mr. Abbey approved the plan and put me in charge.

From my training in surgery and my extra emergency room work, I knew a fair amount about in-hospital trauma, but I had a tremendous amount to learn about in-the-field helicopter rescues. Luckily, I found some excellent teachers.

As head of the astronaut doctors, I got to choose which site I'd cover for the first flight. Who could have chosen anything but the Cape for the first space shuttle launch? Craig Fischer was to be at the Cape, too. So the two of us headed to Florida to define our responsibilities. There, the helicopter crews introduced themselves. Some were from Patrick Air Force Base at the Cape; others were borrowed from SAR forces up and down the East Coast. What a fascinating bunch! This was 1980—not long after the Vietnam War, and many of these guys had combat experience. I'd never thought much about it, but rescuing downed pilots or injured soldiers in the jungles of Vietnam must have been a risky job. While I was at Berkeley protesting the war, these men were fighting it. It was humbling to hear their stories.

If an airplane was hit by enemy fire over the jungle, the pilot ejected and parachuted to the ground. Often injured, he had a beacon and a radio that would let friendly forces know where he was. His beacon, his radio, or the sight of his parachute coming down would alert enemy forces to his presence, also. The North Vietnamese couldn't understand the great effort expended on attempting to get a lone individual out of danger, but they knew more Americans would soon converge on the downed pilot.

The SAR forces would go out in a rescue helicopter, and trained personnel (parajumpers, also known as PJs) would look for the airman. An elite group of men, the PJs would parachute or be lowered into the jungle, find the injured airman, and pro-

The HH3 Jolly Green Giant helicopter used by Search and Rescue forces in Florida had served in the same capacity in Vietnam.

vide whatever medical care was needed or available. From what I've been told, the airmen that the PJs were rescuing were sometimes terribly wounded, and the best the rescuers could do was less than what was needed. This meant that there was great pressure on the choppers to get back to pick up the PJs and the patient and to get out of there and back to a field hospital.

Often, enemy soldiers would be waiting for the chopper to come in low. This was the time

For STS-1, John Smith, or Smitty, was my PJ on the Search and Rescue forces at Cape Canaveral.

they could kill the most people and perhaps blow up the entire helicopter. I heard incredible stories about the door gunners trying to tell the pilot where to put his craft down while dodging fire from the Vietcong. PJs had their hands full lugging a mangled fly-boy and all his gear out of the tangled underbrush with bullets whizzing all around. Many helo crews didn't make it out, and the ones who did were either lucky or skilled, or both. And here I was working with these men who knew their stuff. Not only did the PJs have to be able to parachute onto land, but they had to jump into the water and fish downed aircrews out of the ocean, and this was what most of the East Coast and Florida crews continued to do on a regular basis.

The HH3 Jolly Green Giant helicopter crew I was assigned to was an Air Force Reserve unit from Homestead Air Force Base south of Miami. They were highly skilled with lots of experience working together as pilot, copilot, and door operator rescuing ship and air crews. The lead PJ on the flight would be John Smith, from Patrick Air Force Base. When I first saw him, I thought he looked like a real bruiser: young, big in the shoulders and arms, bull neck, and absolutely no hair, a beefed-up Kojak. But when we were introduced, his infectious grin hinted that he wasn't some sort of brute.

"Hi, ma'am. I'm Smitty, your PJ," he said.

I came to find that a gentler, more considerate person didn't exist. We ended up having a great time, with his teaching me everything I needed to know about out-in-the-boonies medicine and providing medical care in the back of a rockin' and rollin' chopper. I taught him what I knew about the space shuttle and its operations.

One of the things we had to figure out was where to take injured astronauts once we'd rescued them. The Cape itself had a basic clinic, and while there were smaller hospitals in the area, the nearest major trauma facility was in Jacksonville at Shands Memorial Hospital, which was the teaching hospital for the University of Florida. There, they could handle the worst of injuries. They gave us the royal tour when we visited to check them out. Everyone was happy to be part of the space program, especially since nothing had flown in space in over five years.

At one of our organizational meetings with all the rescue forces, I realized that my lack of military experience did have some drawbacks. We were sitting around a large table planning staging areas, evacuation routes, and so on. The officers in charge of all these operations were leading the discussion. The officer sitting across the table from me had been introduced to me somewhere along the line as the guy in charge of the whole shebang. He was doing his thing, giving orders, and getting everyone organized. He looked at me and started dictating which medical facility we'd take the patients to depending on where we found them.

"Whoa," I said as politely as I could. "We won't know which medical facility would be best until we've had a chance to evaluate the patient. The only person who could call where the chopper would go is the doctor on the helicopter."

There was this strange silence in the room. I noticed the PJs seated around the periphery of the room were staring at their shoes. The officer gave me a studied look as if pondering at length what to say. Then, after a long pause, he agreed with me, and we went on to another topic.

After the meeting, Smitty complimented me on holding my ground about the doctor's responsibility for making the transport decision. He said I had a lot of guts to stand up to a "bird colonel." I found this strangely amusing. I didn't know the difference between a major's and a colonel's shoulder decorations. I wasn't military anyway, so rank had little meaning for me. I wasn't even sure where I fit in that peculiar pecking order. The M.D. and astronaut titles meant something, but I was never sure what. When I looked back on the exchange, I didn't think I could have done things much differently. From my background and training, a doctor with the responsibility of a patient's life is the supreme boss, the commander-in-chief. But I vowed next time to try to be a little more tactful and observant of rank.

When evaluating what could happen to a crippled shuttle, there were many scenarios to be considered. Perhaps easiest from a rescue standpoint was an ejection, probably over the water. The two crewmen pulled the handle on the dashboard and out their seats went, like in a jet. They'd separate from their seats and drift down into the Atlantic where their life preservers and life raft would keep them afloat. The helicopter would be vectored to their area by a SAR aircraft flying offshore, and the PJs would be dropped by parachute, along with some rescue gear nearby. Then the astronauts would be hoisted aboard the choppers if they were okay, or sent up in a litter if they weren't. Not much different from an ordinary sea rescue for the team.

But what if the orbiter had crash-landed off the runway, out in a swamp somewhere? That's when it got tougher. The rescue team would all land nearby if possible and set up a safe triage area. The PJs would then go in and extract the crewmembers from the downed shuttle. This might be as simple as opening the side hatch and helping them out, or it might mean cutting through the side of the fuselage or pulling them out the overhead windows above the flight deck. All of these scenarios were practiced with dummies and sometimes live *victims*. The PJs had their work cut out for them. Putting a man, who fully outfitted might weigh 200 pounds or more, onto a backboard and hauling him out with a rope was heavy-duty work. Compounding the difficulty of this task with the fact that the PJs had to wear protective gear and breathing packs because of possible noxious fumes from the shuttle's fuel, all done in Florida's torrid temperatures and withering humidity. It became a particularly difficult task. There were times I thought I'd probably have to treat Smitty and his buddies along with the astronauts if we had to do it for real.

When we started practicing, it was obvious that the PJs knew more about caring for the injured in the field than I did. At first they deferred to me because I was "the doctor." I'd try to remember to tell them to splint the injuries, apply pressure dressing to bleeding areas, start IVs, and so on. But these were things that in my past experience had often been done to patients by the ambulance paramedics before they arrived in my clean Emergency Room, so I often forgot to give the order for them. Gradually, Smitty and I worked out a plan where he'd start doing all the stuff he'd been trained to do, and I'd start assessing the patient like I'd been trained to do: checking airway, beginning rescue breathing if required, assessing circulatory function, the ABCs that all trauma doctors check.

The pressure suit worn for the early shuttle flights added great complexity to doing the things one would ordinarily do. In an Emergency Room, one of the first things that happened to a badly injured patient was that all his clothes were cut off, so he could be fully assessed and various

procedures begun. A thick pressure suit with its metal neck, wrist rings, attached helmet, and gloves was something else. There were things we could do—opening the helmet visor, putting an oxygen mask on, feeling for a pulse at the neck, putting a tube in the airway. But other things would be difficult or impossible—taking a blood pressure, inserting a chest tube to expand a collapsed lung, checking the abdomen for internal bleeding. I had about as much confidence in our ability to save a severely injured crewman as I did in the orbiter's ability to withstand a crash landing. But we had to do our best and plan as well as we could. I would learn in time that NASA took its worst criticism when it failed to consider the possibility of failure or accepted risk without giving the crew a way out.

All the planning and practice by hundreds, maybe thousands, of people leading up to the first shuttle flight added to the excitement. Unlike earlier space shots, there was no way to test this one before people were put aboard. It was a manned vehicle that had no automated landing capability, so it had to have someone to land it. It was an ungainly-looking machine, unlike the slick streamlined rockets of the past. We had lectures from gray-haired engineers about how the early shuttle design went from a plane hooked onto the nose of a big booster to a plane stuck on the side of a big fuel tank, to the final configuration of a space plane with fuel tank and boosters. Wind tunnel tests could be done up to certain speeds to test this configuration, but beyond that we had to trust in the pure analysis that said it would all work. Would there be big surprises on the first flight? Would there be some strange airflow between the components that could cause it to fly out of control or rip it apart? During this time, I came to understand the duties of a group called the Range Safety Officers.

The Range Safety Officer was an Air Force officer who sat in a little room and waited to see if he needed to blow rockets up. Needless to say, we

Space Shuttle Columbia sits gleaming in the floodlights the night before launch.

all hoped he was somebody intelligent and trustworthy. His real responsibility was to keep inhabited areas safe from errant spacecraft that veered off course. He had little lines on a radar map, and if a space vehicle crossed any of them, he had the responsibility of pushing a couple of buttons. For *Columbia*, this activated explosive charges located on the boosters and the external tank that would blow the whole thing up. In theory, this seemed like a good idea, but when astronauts were riding on the rocket, it was frightening to consider.

We ended up having plenty of time to practice for the first launch: there were months and months of delays. The tile problems, the main engine uncertainties, and all the other knowable what-ifs were assessed and in the spring of 1981, all seemed ready. April 10th was set as the launch date, and final preparations began. Teams were sent to the launch site and to all possible landing sites around the United States and across the Atlantic. The astronauts had many responsibilities in Houston and Florida—in Mission Control, in the simulators to work out emergency procedures, babysitting the orbiter on the pad before the real crew got on board, escorting the crew's wives (Susie Young and Ginny Crippen) around. A new era was about to begin.

In the pre-dawn hours of April 10, I drove to Patrick Air Force Base and teamed up with the Jolly Green Giant helicopter crew. As we flew over the Cape to the old Cape Canaveral runway where we would await the launch, I could see the headlights of thousands of cars headed to the various viewing areas. Families, friends, co-workers, and die-hard space fans were gathering from all over the world to see this new beginning. It gave me goosebumps.

As we waited in the dawning light, I set up a small portable TV near our helicopter so we could watch the national news that was covering all the activities of the countdown. Veteran news commentators and astronauts assigned to the television channels were explaining this new space transportation system and touting its great potential. It was a heady time.

Unfortunately, a computer problem scrubbed the launch for that morning, but that somehow added to the excitement. We all came back two days later and tried again. On April 12, 1981, the twentieth anniversary of Yuri Gagarin's flight, the old familiar countdown of *5 - 4 -3 - 2 - 1 – 0 We have liftoff,* was heard in the manned space business for the first time in six years. We were back in space again! And I was part of it now.

Those big burly PJs and the battle-hardened helicopter drivers and their crews stood with me out there in the steamy dawn of springtime in Florida and watched as the newest of space vehicles rose heavenward into view over the treetops. We whooped and yelled and jumped up and down at the beauty and success of this moment. *Columbia* streaked upward and then

Space Shuttle Columbia lifts off the pad on April 12, 1981, exactly twenty years after the first manned spaceflight by Yuri Gagarin.

PHOTO COURTESY OF NASA

surprised us when the sound waves reached us long, long after the sight of it did, and we could feel the rumble down in our bones. I had tears running down my cheeks and looked around to see that all the guys did, too.

After two minutes our attention went to the TV set where a view from the Cape's long-range tracking camera was going to show the SRB separation. There were still questions about how well separation would occur, so we were riveted to the screen. As far as we could see, it all worked beautifully, and the shuttle kept right on heading for space. For the next six minutes we had to count on the main engines to do their jobs. MECO! Main Engine Cut Off occurred right on time. Next, the orbital engines had to work, as well, to get the vehicle to its proper orbit, and they did. Space was our domain again.

We all followed the mission as best we could during the next two days. There were so many new things to learn. The shuttle was bigger than a capsule, but not as big as Skylab, so living on board was different. John and Crip were having a good time checking out all the systems and looking out the window. We hung on their every word.

Then attention began to focus on the landing. Returning into the atmosphere was another one of those big question marks for this new bird. Would the tiles hold up? Would they even stay on in the big fireball that enveloped the orbiter as it hits the air molecules of the atmosphere at such a high speed that it heated up to white hot temperatures? Would the reaction control jets be able to move the shuttle about until the control surfaces could take over in the denser air closer to the ground? Would the computers be able to plot the flight path to dissipate all the energy properly so the shuttle would arrive overhead at Edwards Air Force Base at the precise speed and altitude? My SAR equivalents were ready in the landing area. I had my fingers crossed that the Chase Team would be successful. Hoot in Chase 2 was serving as backup on the alternate runway at Edwards, but I knew his adrenaline would be flowing.

There was some chance that the backup landing sites in New Mexico or the Cape would be used so other helicopter teams were standing by. In a ready room at Patrick Air Force Base, my team and I gathered to see if this first chapter of the new adventure would end in a perfect touchdown. We also knew that the time in our lives in which we worked closely as a team to do our part would soon end, and that was a little sad.

All the re-configuration of the shuttle systems was completed on time, and the orbiter turned around so it was flying tail forward across the Indian Ocean. The de-orbit burn for a landing in California was done west of Australia. Telemetry showed that the orbital engines burned on time and slowed the vehicle down to allow it to fall into the atmosphere somewhere west of Hawaii. In the meantime, the orbiter flipped over to nose forward and tilted slightly upward to let the heat shield tiles face the intense heat of re-entry.

At the start of the shuttle program, communication was still via ground stations, the way it had been since the Mercury days. With the shuttle's communication antennas pointed upward in the heating region of re-entry with hot plasma flowing around the vehicle, there would be a communications black out for a major part of this risky region of flight. We all sat on the edges of our chairs waiting for the shuttle to make it through this trial by fire. But there came the voices just as predicted, halfway back to California. The trajectory looked perfect; the machine was flying solidly.

Then they came over the West Coast of California, and the folks in "LA LA Land" got their comeuppance. As the orbiter passed through Mach 1, not one, but two sonic booms occurred as first the nose, then the tail broke the sound barrier slowing down. What a surprise, but what a joy as first the cameras and then the on-lookers on the desert floor at Edwards caught sight of *Columbia* coming home. The Chase Team, too, saw her in the morning sky and rushed to their rendezvous point. As John Young flew

The view of Columbia from the chase plane as it turns to align with the runway at Edwards Air Force Base./A perfect landing of the first Space Shuttle flight on April 14, 1981.

down the well-practiced path of final approach, Jon McBride managed to do all the pilot stuff it took to join up on *Columbia* and look her over. Pinky Nelson in the T-38's back seat started clicking away with his camera, catching some classic, historic pictures that would portray that day forever.

As soon as Hoot's team was sure the backup runway would not be used, they scooted over to watch the action. As *Columbia* touched down, they were 30,000 feet overhead checking out the scene.

The touchdown on the dry lakebed and the rollout to a stop were perfect. It was a glorious day, and we were all proud and excited to be part of such an historic event.

I left the Cape knowing those times would be forever etched in my memory. I knew, however, that it would be a busy next few months for me. I had a wedding to plan.

CHAPTER 4

★ ★ ★ ★ ★ ★

A SPACE FAMILY

Hoot Gibson and I had gotten to be friends since our class came to NASA, mostly by flying in the T-38 jets. Going so high and so fast was new for me, and I was uncomfortable at first. I flew with many of the pilots, both from my ASCAN class and from the older groups, and I learned that the person in the front seat had a lot to do with my level of discomfort.

There were many different styles of flying among the pilots, based on their own personalities and backgrounds. In general, the Air Force flyers seemed to go by the book. Flights were planned, briefed, and executed according to the detailed plan. The Navy pilots were more apt to go "strap on an airplane" and fly, figuring things out as they went. It wasn't that they

Hoot and I do a walk-around of a T-38 before we go for a flight

didn't follow all the rules and regulations and plan the flight carefully–they just seemed more relaxed. I found myself flying with the Navy pilots more and more. They seemed to be able to handle whatever came along with ease and never seemed stressed.

Over time, I developed a mental list of the people I enjoyed flying with, another list of pilots I felt safe with, and a third list of those who made me feel anxious. This last group either had trouble making conversation during the boring parts of the flight, yelled at me, or ranted at the air traffic controllers when things went awry or, worst of all, got us into unsafe conditions. On one memorable occasion I thought I might die. We were a flight of three T-38s headed to a Navy base on the east coast. My pilot had planned the flight and was in the lead. He had checked the weather at the destination and assured me and the others that the weather was good.

When we got to our destination late that night, the tower told us that the cloud layer was low, almost too low for us to land. Looking at our options, it was clear that we didn't have enough gas to make it to another airport. Our plane started the approach with the two other planes following close behind. We knew that if we didn't see the runway at 200 feet, we weren't supposed to try to land. I called out the altitudes as the pilot flew the jet, watching for the runway lights.

"Four hundred, three fifty, three hundred, two fifty, two hundred, at minimums," I said. Yet the plane kept descending.

The pilot keyed the microphone that transmitted to the planes in trail of us: "You'll break out at about 170."

We all landed safely, but I realized that this particular pilot had pushed the limits. He had gotten us into a dangerous situation with poor weather and insufficient gas to get to another landing spot. The three pilots stepped aside and debriefed the situation, but based on this pilot's behavior after that, I don't think he changed his dangerous ways. I vowed not to fly with him again if at all possible.

Hoot was at the top of my *Fun to Fly With* list. We had a good time and talked about our training and the interesting people we worked with. He always seemed calm. One thing I appreciated was that he'd flown into many airports (like the huge Los Angeles airport, LAX) often enough to remember the traffic flow. He knew it so well that he could tell me ahead of time what Air Traffic Control would be asking us to do and what my response over the radios should be. For a rookie, flying with someone who made me look good (and feel good) in this new environment was fun. I came to find that he'd been fascinated by airplanes all his life, and he seemed to know everything about all of them.

He had flown F4 Phantom and F14 Tomcat fighter jets off aircraft carriers with the Navy in Vietnam. He'd also been one of the select few pilots

sent to the Navy Fighter Weapons School, TopGun, later to be made famous by the movie. Like all astronaut pilots, he'd been to test pilot school. For the Navy, that was at Patuxent River, Maryland, known as Pax River.

We both had been assigned to the half of the ASCAN class known as the Red Group, so we'd made many trips and done much of the training together. While flying in the T-38 he had talked about how difficult the transition to Houston had been for his marriage and about his little girl, Julie, who was two at the time. At some point he and his wife separated, and he moved out of their house as they tried to work things out. As time went by it became obvious that his marriage was ending, and about a year into our training his wife moved back to San Diego. Hoot was devastated. He had no warning she was going to leave, and she took his precious daughter and everything he owned. I had never seen anyone so down.

Watching him cope with all this and still handle all his job responsibilities made me admire him even more. We soon began dating. I had had a number of boyfriends, even making plans to marry once, but there hadn't been many men I could picture spending the rest of

Young fighter pilot, Robert "Hoot" Gibson stands beside his F-4 Phantom jet *(left)*. A Phantom is catapulted off the carrier deck during the Vietnam war *(above)*.

my life with, but Hoot was different. It became obvious after dating for a couple of years that we were having a great time together, and that we could see making it permanent. I wanted to be sure he had plenty of time to think about remarrying because of his recent difficult experience. He told me he'd learned a lot in his first marriage about what to do and not do, and he felt ready to tie the knot again. In February, 1981, he asked me to marry him.

Because of our hectic schedules in support of STS-1 we didn't feel we could set a definite date until the shuttle was back on the ground. When *Columbia* landed on April 14 we looked at our calendars. I had always wanted a spring wedding, but here it was mid-April. How about late May? Could we do it that soon? Would my old family church, the First Methodist near

Later Hoot would fly in the first operational squadron of the F-14 Tomcat.

the antebellum court-house in Murfreesboro, Tennessee, be available for the wedding and the Stones River Country Club able to handle a reception?

Even with the short time, at 33 I was mature enough to focus more on having a happy day and sharing it with friends and less on whether exact etiquette rules were followed. We

Hoot and I are married in the First Methodist Church in Murfreesboro, Tennessee under a stained glass window from my great grandmother's house.

married on May 30 at the church my mother's family had attended for generations. The stained glass window over the altar had come from my great grandmother's house. I wanted to do something special, so I consulted my cousin, Margaret Wright, who would provide the music for the ceremony. Knowing the music world well, she found a young man, Brian Lampkin, from Louisville to play trumpet fanfares for the service. (When I told Hoot we were going to have a herald trumpet, he asked, "Harold, who?" which became a longstanding joke at our house.) Only family and a few family friends were invited to the service because the church was small. It was as though the spirits of all my long gone relatives were present that day. Practically the entire town of Murfreesboro was invited to the reception at the Country Club. We ate a fantastic dinner, complete with a wedding cake with the astronaut symbol on top and danced to the strains of "Fly Me to the Moon" and "Up, Up and Away."

We were the first couple to marry while in the Astronaut Corps.

Rather than asking all our Houston friends to trek to Tennessee for the wedding, we held a reception for all them when we returned home. Besides the NASA troops, we had other friends and neighbors. I invited one of my Emergency Room physician partners, Diana Fite, and while chatting I asked her what she thought about the astronauts. "They're all skinny," was her astute observation.

After a wonderful, relaxing two week honeymoon in Hawaii, we settled back into our crazy lives at NASA. Hoot was Prime Chase for STS-2 which was to fly in November, so he jumped right into that training. I resumed my role as head of helicopter rescue physicians and was also working in the Shuttle Avionics Integration Lab, or SAIL, where the software for the shuttle was tested.

Commander Joe Henry Engle, our next door neighbor, and Co-pilot Dick Truly launched on STS-2 on Nov. 12, 1981. While Joe had flown high enough in the X-15 program to qualify for astronaut status, neither of them had been in orbit before. It was the first time a spaceship had been refurbished and reflown. The flight began to have problems shortly after it launched. One of the three fuel cells which generated electrical power wouldn't work properly. Although there was plenty of electricity with two of the three, a significant power down would be required if a second should fail. NASA never liked to be down to one system or "single string." Also, one never knew at the outset of the shuttle program whether the first failure of a certain component was a random failure or indicative of a common problem that was about to affect similar equipment.

Then there was the "brain tumor" that wasn't. Dick Truly reported he was experiencing some blurry vision. The flight surgeon asked him a few questions to try to figure out what was wrong. Did he have a headache or nausea, which could be a sign of increased pressure inside the skull? Well, not really, maybe a slight headache but that wasn't unusual early in a flight. Joe Engle was asked to check Dick's pupils. Ominously one of them was larger than the other, which could be an indicator of a mass in one side of his brain. There was a flurry of concern in Mission Control. Did he have a tumor? Could he have had bleeding from a stroke? None of those things seemed plausible. Then, a fine medical mind thought to ask if he had used one of the scopolamine patches from the medical kit to protect against nausea that sometimes affected astronauts. Yes, he had. In sticking it behind his ear, he had apparently rubbed his eye and deposited a small amount of the medication there, and it was a potent pupil dilator which can blur vision. After a couple hours, his symptoms resolved and the flight surgeons were heroes.

Upper management decided that the STS-2 mission had to be shortened because of the fuel cell failure. The crew stayed up during their last sleep period to test out the Canadian-made mechanical arm for the first time and get some of their other mission objectives done. They hadn't gotten used to being in space before they had to head home. Joe flew much of the re-entry manually to test out the flying qualities of the orbiter, so it was a long stressful day for them.

I knew it would be a big moment for Hoot who, in the primary chase plane, would rendezvous a NASA T-38 with the shuttle as it blazed over the field at Edwards Air Force Base in the California desert. I was stationed at the backup landing site in New Mexico and had to watch all the activities on TV. Hoot made the close rendezvous look easy, and Joe landed the orbiter safely despite the fact that he was tired and dehydrated after a short, tense flight.

Ominously, STS-2 was the first time there was some erosion of a primary O-ring on one of the solid rocket boosters. After some testing, NASA decided that the secondary O-rings were there as protection, so the design was not changed. This would happen several more times in the shuttle program...until we saw that it could be catastrophic.

We went home to Tennessee for Thanksgiving, and one of my first stops was at the Cotton Patch, my favorite clothing store. Run by a good friend, Susan Loyd, I was always pampered there, unlike at the huge, impersonal department stores in Houston. I noticed I had trouble getting into my usual pants size and wrote it off to the few extra pounds everyone gains after getting married. The next week had me running off to a medical conference in New Orleans, but I was unable to enjoy the good food because I felt like I had come down with what I thought was a stomach flu.

NASA required that we have physical exams each year during our birthday month, so I had mine between STS-2 and Christmas. Because there were no gynecologists among the flight surgeons, when I first got to NASA I'd asked the head of the Flight Medicine Clinic, Dr. Mike Berry, if I could go to an off-site gynecologist. Mike's wife saw Dr. Bill Powell, so I'd been seeing him. I booked an appointment with him in December to complete my physical exam requirements.

Dr. Powell was his usual cheerful self and asked the routine questions: "Have you been in good health?"

"Yes, excellent," I said. Then we chatted about my getting married and what the wedding had been like. When he started his exam, he got a concerned look on his face which caught my attention.

"Your uterus is enlarged," he said with hesitation. As a physician I thought of the most awful thing it could be, advanced uterine cancer. I thought this couldn't be happening to me; I was too young, too healthy.

"Could you be pregnant?" he asked. Surprisingly, that was an odd thought for me. I was 33 years old, and Hoot and his first wife had taken a long time to get pregnant. I was resigned to having some difficulty. And we had only been married a few months.

"I don't think so."

"Any signs of pregnancy: skipped periods, morning sickness, weight gain, fatigue?"

Well, there had been a light period in November which I had attributed to all the travel. I was always fatigued; it was part of the job. There was that tiny bit of weight gain, four or five pounds. No morning sickness, but that nausea in New Orleans—did that count?

"We'd better do a pregnancy test," he said.

"Positive!" he cried, laughing when he came back with the test results. "You're a physician, and you couldn't figure this out?"

Because of the spotting in November, he wanted to double check with an ultrasound.

"Yes," he said, "There it is. Looks in good shape, about eight week's size." Little head, little heart, little baby.

How in the world was I going to tell Hoot? The technician gave me copies of the ultrasound image. I knew Hoot was working a shift at the avionics lab, and I found him there on a break.

"Do you have time to look at some mystery pictures, dear?" I asked.

"Sure – what are these?"

"Guess."

"Let's see, someone sat on a copy machine and Xeroxed his bottom?"

"No, silly. Look here. There's a little skull, a little body, a bump where the heart is."

"Okay, it's a baby. Whose?"

"Ours."

His eyes widened, and he looked at my face to see if I was kidding.

"So soon?!" he said. I could tell he was as surprised and overwhelmed as I.

So we added another wrinkle to our lives. We decided not to tell anyone except our family until we were sure everything was okay. We left a few days later for Christmas in California with Hoot's family. Julie, Hoot's—and now my—daughter had come up from San Diego. She and her six cousins who were about her age wanted to bake gingerbread men. We decorated one to look like each of the seven of them. On an eighth we put a diaper of frosting and big number 8. We asked Hoot's mom and dad if they could figure out who this one was. After some thought, Grandma Rita got a knowing look on her face. "An eighth grandchild!" There was much excitement in the Gibson household.

We called my father that night. I told him I had a present for him, but I'd have to deliver it about a month or six weeks later than his mid-June birthday. He said that would be fine but asked why it would have to be late. I told him because it would be his first grandbaby, expected in the first part of August. There was silence—and I suspected tears—on the other end of the line. There would be a special Christmas for the Seddon family.

We went right on with our jobs, knowing NASA might impose some restrictions on my activities once they knew I was pregnant. Dr. Powell gathered what data he could on flying high performance jets with ejection seats while pregnant. There wasn't much information since the military services skirted the issue by making female pilots quit flying once they knew they were pregnant. Dr. Powell and I giggled over the little evidence there was from animal studies, imagining little rats sitting in tiny simulated airplanes. There was some evidence from studies on monkeys that ejection might cause miscarriage, but it had been many years since a NASA pilot had had to eject, considering the safety-conscious type of flying we did.

So we incubated until we got the results of the amniocentesis back in March. We found out we had a healthy baby boy just waiting to get a little bigger before being born in late July or early August. At this point it was getting difficult to hide my growing belly, and we tried to figure out what we needed to do about letting people know. This was the first time an astronaut had become pregnant, and we wanted everyone to know I intended to have the baby and come right back to my career. I wanted to continue to be a helo doc and work in the avionics lab, like I had been. I didn't want to be held back on jobs or flight assignments. We went to tell the chief of the Astronaut Office, John Young, and he didn't seem to know what to say except congratulations. We talked to Mr. Abbey, the head of Flight Operations and got his usual taciturn response. We decided there might be outside questions about it, so we also talked to our friend and Center Director, Dr. Chris Kraft. He seemed pleased and comfortable with my continuing my current career path.

We left their offices feeling like "No sweat, they aren't worried." Almost before I could get back to my office, my phone started ringing. The Flight Medicine Clinic called to tell me no more T-38 flying if I was pregnant.

"Look, I've checked with my OB, and there doesn't seem to be any reason…" I began.

"Sorry, no more T-38 time. It would look bad for the Agency if something were to happen."

"But how do I do my job as helo doc at Edwards for STS 3?"

"Just take a commercial flight to California." That was the end-of-discussion answer from the flight surgeon.

I had a blue spell. If they thought I was too "disabled" to fly the jets, what other things were in store? NASA was being run at that time by men a generation older than we were. Few of them had working wives, and even fewer had wives with high pressure careers. What did these men think pregnancy was like? I thought of the screened-in porch on my grandparents' house. I was told my grandfather had it built when my grandmother was pregnant with my mother because back then, ladies didn't go out in public when they were *expecting*. Was being grounded from flying a more modern form of confinement? Would NASA managers think I couldn't handle my job and my pregnancy? Would they write me off when it came to flight assignments because I had a young baby at home? Would they think I'd take a long maternity leave after my delivery or perhaps never return to work?

I bent Hoot's ear for a long and tearful time on these subjects but he was his usual calm self. There wasn't much we could do about these older men's perceptions based on previous experience in their own lives. We could only press on with our lives and show them that this new generation of women was different. I was right on the cusp between the Baby Boomers and the '50s Beaver Cleaver generation and part of a growing number of women who knew we could do it all.

In April of 1982, Sally Ride was assigned to STS 7. She would be the first U.S. female astronaut to fly in space. It was a bit of a disappointment for my enlarging self, but I had made the decision that I would rather have a child than an early flight assignment. In my thirties and figuring on some difficulty getting pregnant, and with the uncertainties of the early flight schedules, I didn't want to wait. I tried to envision what my life would be like at 60 with either many flights and no children, or children and perhaps no flights. It was an easy decision for me. Anyway, Sally would have to go through the rest of her life as the FAWIS, the

In April, 1982, Sally Ride is the first American woman assigned to a spaceflight

First American Woman in Space. Maybe that wouldn't be such a great deal. Maybe it would be easier to be just **one** of the first.

The PJs and helo crews at Edwards were surprised to see me show up for our STS 3 exercises in maternity clothes that spring, having taken an airline flight to Los Angeles and driven many miles out to the desert. The shuttle crew members were Jack Lousma who had flown a Skylab flight in 1973, and Gordon Fullerton who had flown some of the landing tests of the Space Shuttle Enterprise when it was dropped from the back of the 747. (After a long and successful NASA flying career, Gordo became a test pilot at Edwards, and in his later years, achieved fame as the first F16 jet pilot on Medicare.) For my helicopter operations I borrowed a flight suit from one of my male compatriots that was big enough to cover my growing midsection. The helo pilot promised to make no rough landings, and we waited for STS-3 to launch in late March and land on the Edwards desert landing strip.

Come landing day, however, the Edwards lakebed was flooded because of torrential rains. For the first (and only) time, Jack and Gordo guided the orbiter to the backup landing site at White Sands, New Mexico. Watching it on TV from California, I could see that the landing was a little difficult, and the approach was made at the upper limits of the speed envelope. Dick Covey was Prime Chase for that flight, and he found out how fast our T-38s could go with their gear and speed brakes hanging out trying to stay abeam the shuttle. We all

The fourth Shuttle flight landed on the 4th of July, 1982. President and Mrs. Reagan welcomed home the crew, T.K. Mattingly and Hank Hartsfield. This was declared the last test flight of the Space Shuttle.

held our breath when it looked like the orbiter's landing gear was going to be late coming down, but it all worked out fine. Then a sand storm hit, and we learned all the places on *Columbia* into which gritty sand could be driven.

STS-4 was next with TK Mattingly and Hank Hartsfield. TK had been both unlucky and lucky in the Apollo program. He had been taken off the Apollo 13 crew three days before launch because he had been exposed to German measles which he hadn't had as a youngster. Then Apollo 13 had a major failure on the way to the moon and had to swing by without landing. TK was later assigned as command module pilot on Apollo 16, a very successful mission. Hank had been unlucky then lucky, too. He had been assigned to the Air Force Manned Orbiting Laboratory (MOL) program in 1966, but it was canceled. Then, he was selected to be in the next astronaut class. Not all MOL pilots were invited to make that transition.

Since their flight was scheduled to land on the 4th of July, a big celebration was planned at Edwards. It would be the first shuttle landing on a concrete runway. Considerable effort was expended making sure the launch occurred on time, so the crew would make it to the party. I had the option of being stationed at Edwards since I'd missed seeing a landing on STS-3, but I decided I didn't want to take the chance of delivering my child a month early on the desert floor in California in the back of a helicopter attended by PJs, so I did beg off that task—one of the few things I declined to do during my pregnancy.

There was great hoopla on the fourth. President Reagan and an entourage were in attendance. The landing was picture perfect, and it was the end of the Orbital Flight Test program. The shuttle was declared "operational," a term that rankled those in the know. (That term would be questioned three and a half years later after an accident when we admitted there were still many things we didn't know about this vehicle.) It would be several flights before the ejection seats were removed. They were deactivated, however, since the next crews would have four crewmembers, and it wouldn't do to have only two of the four with the capability to get out.

There was no way to equip the third and fourth seats for ejection. The fact that thereafter there would be no ejection capability brought an end to my job as a helicopter doctor.

My pregnancy marched along well, and I decided to work until I went into labor. We'd bought a new house and were to move in at the end of July – perfect since the baby was due the first week of August. As luck would have it, labor twinges began on Sunday morning, July 25, 1982, a week earlier than we'd expected. As I hurried about packing dishes, the cramping I had been feeling intermittently for a few weeks became more regular and insistent. When Hoot came home from a flight in his small racing plane, he found me lounging on the floor in the den, pen in hand, keeping track of contraction frequency. We waited a while until things became intense then called Dr. Powell and headed for Labor and Delivery at the Clear Lake Hospital.

Things moved slowly and despite hard labor until the early morning hours on Monday, it didn't look like our Lamaze training was going to work. Finally, about 3:00 a.m., I was getting exhausted, and the baby was showing signs of distress. So we pressed on with a C-section. Paul Seddon Gibson, weighing in at 7 pounds 2 ounces was born at 4:10 a.m. on Monday morning the 26th of July, 1982…*and promptly tried to die.*

Monday's children are supposed to be fair of face, but little Paul looked pretty bad. He had inhaled meconium, a thick gooey substance that resides inside the baby's intestine before birth. When stressed, a baby can expel the stuff into the amniotic fluid during the birth process. If inhaled, it can be disastrous. When pulled from my belly, he was blue and limp. I waited anxiously for a cry. A strangled squeak was all he could manage. Despite excellent care at our community hospital, our pediatrician, Dr. Winnette Wimberly, advised us to send him to the Neonatal Intensive Care Unit at Hermann Hospital in the Houston Medical Center.

He was in such bad shape those first few hours that I hadn't been given a chance to hold him. Before they whisked him away to an awaiting Life Flight helicopter, they rolled his incubator into my room for a brief visit.

He almost looked like a tiny astronaut inside his protective bubble, isolated from the dangers outside. As a physician, I could see he didn't look good: slightly gray, his chest puffed up because he had trouble exhaling through his clogged airways, limp from the sedatives he needed because of the tube in his windpipe connected to the ventilator that was breathing for him. As I held his tiny fingers and marveled at how all his other pieces and parts looked so perfect, I wondered if I'd ever see him alive again. My room, my body, felt empty as I heard the helicopter take off outside the hospital a little before noon.

All that week, Hoot held vigil in Houston and kept from me the seriousness of the baby's condition. I talked several times each day to Paul's wonderful neonatologist, Dr. Gene Adcock. Sometimes I knew that I didn't make much sense because I was taking pain medications after the long labor and C-section. Because Paul was a healthy infant to start with and due to of all the terrific care at Hermann, he pulled through his ordeal.

On Friday morning, Dr. Powell gave me the thumbs up to go to be with Paul. The Life Flight helicopter crew invited

TIME, AUGUST 9 1982

Milestones

BORN. To **Rhea Seddon**, 34, one of eight women astronauts and an M.D. trained to conduct experiments in orbit, and Navy Lieut. Commander **Robert L. Gibson**, 35, also an astronaut and a jet pilot: a son, her first child, his second; in Houston. Within twelve hours of his birth, the first U.S. astrotot logged a helicopter flight after he developed breathing problems and had to be transferred to a second hospital. At week's end his pneumonia-like condition seemed to be under control.

Paul's birth was announced under Milestones in *Time* magazine and the term "Astrotot" is used.

me to ride downtown with them. In the NICU came the moment I'd been waiting for. Despite Paul's rocky launch, he landed safely in my arms. Tears rolled down my face and splashed on his blanket. He had made it. Dr. Adcock's wife Carole Ann, a nurse, had the sense to snap some photos of the first time I got to cuddle my first born. These special shots, me looking wan and droopy, went into Paul's baby album to remind us how precious that moment was and how close we came to not having it.

Our baby, Paul, survived a harrowing birth on July 26, 1982 and spent several days in an incubator in the Newborn Intensive Care Unit. This is the first time we were allowed to hold him and is our first family picture. Our neonatologist, Dr. Gene Adcock looks proud, too.

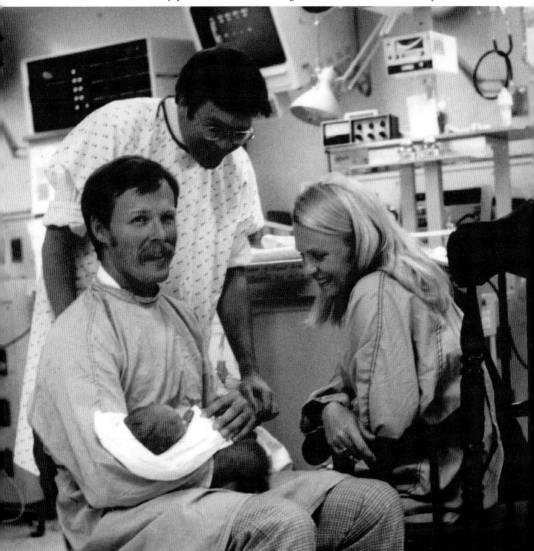

Our family has its first press conference to thank the people who made the day possible.

There had been more press coverage of Paul's arrival than we had expected. One of the news services had coined the term "Astrotot" for the first child born to two astronauts. Life Flight and the neonatal unit asked if we would consider a news conference to show off our baby and let people know what important services these two organizations provided. So there we were with Paul less than two weeks old having his picture snapped.

We could tell Paul some interesting facts about his young life when he was older. He got about 50 hours of jet time before he was born, riding along comfortably inside me in a T-38. He had his first helicopter ride before he was eight hours old. And he had his first press conference, blissfully sleeping, at 10 days of age. The Milestones section of *Time* magazine, which chronicled almost exclusively the deaths of famous people, mentioned his arrival and dubbed him the world's first "Astrotot".

Those early days of motherhood were a blur. I had a new technical assignment. Not knowing much about babies and postpartum recovery, I decided I couldn't stay home longer than six weeks. I'd managed to locate a wonderful young woman, Shirley Baruth, who would come to our house every day. After Labor Day, still exhausted from surgery and getting the new baby settled in, I went back to work. I felt I had a lot to prove. I was anxious to do a decent job, so I'd have a good chance at a flight assignment. I also felt it was important to show that pregnancy and childbirth needn't be debilitating for future female astronauts.

I learned a lot from that experience, mostly that young moms need more than six weeks to bond with their babies. Other stuff, even the important things like the space program, can wait a while. Early baby days can't be recaptured.

In the first part of the shuttle program, each crew had a few junior members of the office assigned as its "Support Crew," and I had been assigned to support the sixth shuttle flight, scheduled for January 1983, when I returned from maternity leave after Labor Day. I thought it was a great way to see what flight training was like in addition to being an overqualified "go-fer." Mike Mullane, one of my 1978 classmates, was already with the STS 6 crew helping them with the main payload of the flight, the first Tracking and Data Relay Satellite which they would launch. It was huge. It filled the cargo bay and had many possible failure modes that had to be anticipated. Most of the other items on the flight were taking a backseat to it.

I offered to work on the other things on the manifest, primarily a science payload called the Continuous Flow Electrophoresis System with a young McDonnell Douglas Company engineer named Charlie Walker. I learned a lot about how a science or technology experiment goes from concept to hardware design, then to flight assignment, to writing down the specifics of how it is to be operated, and to training of the space operator. Since the engineers who built the equipment and the scientists who knew how to best operate it would be back on the ground, everyone had to figure out how the thing could fail, so the crew could salvage it in flight, if necessary. The procedures to correct the problems were chronicled in the Malfunction Procedures Checklist. Understanding how best to document normal and contingency operations in our on-board library, the Flight Data File, was an ongoing process. The smarter one got, the more efficiently and succinctly one could write down what the crew should do. The problem was, everyone had to be working from the same timelines and checklists, therefore, all proposed changes and their rationale had to be documented, and permission sought from Procedures Change Board. If approved, a newer version of the procedure was published, and everyone had to update their books. Later, I was to learn with my own flights that the longer the time to work on these tasks, the better the product would be. However, as the launch date approached the crew had to decide to fly with what it had...*at that point.* Better was the enemy of good enough. (In the coming years, I'd learn that this continuous updating and improvement with its inherent risks was not a trait of the Russian space program. In their system, if it worked you kept doing it the same way. In the old Communist system, failure was punished, and the rewards for success were not great. No one was willing to take a risk. Capitalism has its upside.)

Because of several delays, STS-6 didn't fly until April of 1983. It was a huge success with the first flight of the new orbiter, *Challenger,* and the deployment of the first Tracking and Data Relay Satellite which, along with others that would be launched later, would vastly improve the communications of the space shuttle. Because the spacewalk on STS-5 hadn't been done because of problems with the spacesuits, Mission Specialists Story Musgrave and Don Peterson got to do the first space shuttle EVAs.

Along with the engineers from McDonnell Douglas and the scientists who proposed it, Charlie Walker and I watched the electrophoresis experiment from the ground. It was able to purify interesting chemicals and Charlie also grew some large crystals that could be x-rayed to determine their structure. They were breakthroughs for space science, and I was glad I had the opportunity to make a contribution.

Then, there was the flight that the women of the world had waited for: STS-7 with Sally Ride. It was the first time five people were on the crew, and the first flight of members of our ASCAN class. Physician Norm Thagard was put on board to begin studies of space motion sickness, which seemed to be more prevalent among crewmembers on the shuttle.

Sally had to endure silly questions from the press and crazy articles in the tabloids. She managed to handle the media insanity with

Sally's STS-7 crew launched in April, 1983.

PHOTO COURTESY OF NASA

grace, but she was pretty miffed by it because she was (at heart) a private person and a feminist. She had married fellow ASCAN, astronomer Steve Hawley in 1982, and he was great support, as was Dr. Carolyn Huntoon, who had been the early women astronauts' "den mother" since we'd been selected. Many women dignitaries were invited to

PHOTO COURTESY OF NASA

The payload bay with the arm shaped like a seven.

her launch plus all of the women astronauts – the other five of us female 1978 ASCANS, along with Bonnie Dunbar and Mary Cleave, members of the 1980 astronaut class. An added attraction was a pre-launch appearance by singer John Denver, who had always been a supporter of human space flight and hoped to make a spaceflight someday. He sang for us the night before the launch, and Bonnie and I got a chance to visit with him over dinner.

STS-7 was the first shuttle launch I got to watch from the roof of the Launch Control Center. When the rocket soared into space on June 18, 1983, the sound waves rattled my bones, and they vibrated the massive doors of the Vehicle Assembly Building. I knew I'd be onboard someday soon.

Sally made us all proud with her performance on the flight. She and John Fabian operated the mechanical arm to deploy and retrieve a satellite. Sally had no trouble with the space toilet. And Dr. Thagard had no chance to observe any problems with female physiology.

Life was insane for Sally after the flight, and no one blamed her for getting to the point when she wanted to go into hiding. I was happy to be at home with my toddler.

Sally at the aft cockpit window in sunlight. She made all women proud.

CHAPTER 5

★ ★ ★ ★ ★ ★

SPACE SPOUSE

In early 1983, Hoot received an assignment to fly. At first, his mission was labeled STS-11, the eleventh shuttle flight. The launch date was set for January of 1984. Sometime after STS-9, the numbering system was changed. Some said it was to avoid labeling a flight with the "unlucky" number 13, with memories of Apollo 13 lingering. Under the new system, a flight's first number would be the last number of the fiscal year, so for Hoot's 1984 launch, 4. The second number would identify the launch site: 1 for the Cape or 2 for Vandenberg AFB in California. The letter would be the alphabetical order of the flight in the fiscal year. So STS 11 became STS 41B. It was a confusing and bizarre way to do things, and it didn't last too long.

Hoot was ecstatic. This was an early assignment for someone in our 1978 class. I was thrilled for him and also pleased that he had been assigned before I was. There had been so much hoopla about the women astronauts that it had been ego-deflating for the men. Besides, it would be great to see how the training went before I had to do it myself. I had hoped NASA would wait a while to put me on a flight since having both of us going through that stress at once could have been a problem. And I would have more time to spend with our baby.

STS-41B would be commanded by Vance Brand. A tall, fair haired, All-American type, Vance had first flown on the Apollo-Soyuz mission in 1975 and had commanded STS-5 in 1982. Recently remarried, he had a son, Eric, about my son Paul's age. The other "older" (or "superannuated" as he later called himself) astronaut on the flight would be Bruce McCandless. With terrific flying and academic credits, Bruce had come into the program in1966. He had worked for years on the Manned Maneuvering Unit or MMU, a jet pack to be used for space walkers. It would be tested on this flight. Rounding out the crew would be two other members of our 1978 class: Ron McNair and Bob Stewart. Ron would be the second black astronaut in space since Guy Bluford had been assigned to STS-8, scheduled to fly in a few months. Ron's son, Reggie, was also about Paul's age, so we'd have a gang of three little toddlers to keep up with. Bob Stewart was the only Army officer in our class. He took unrelenting kidding from the jet jockeys in our office because he was a helicopter pilot, but maybe that made him well qualified to be the second MMU flyer. He got the last laugh. Their wives Bev Brand, Bernice McCandless, Cheryl McNair, and Mary Stewart were already my friends and destined to become lifelong ones.

As a *spouse,* I got to know all the traditions that went along with having a husband flying in space – and the modicum of support spouses were given by NASA. When the 1978 class first arrived at NASA, the new astronaut spouses and the women astronauts were invited to attend a get-together hosted by the wives of the older and former astronauts. The invitation was a wonderful thought, but it demonstrated the generation gap that had

Hoot's crew on STS-41B: (front row) Vance Brand and Hoot, (back row) Bob Stewart, Ron McNair, and Bruce McCandless

occurred in the decade since astronauts had last been selected. The party was held in the morning on a weekday in downtown Houston. This would have been a perfect time for stay-at-home mothers with young children in

PHOTO COURTESY OF NASA

school, but many of the wives in our group were in the workforce. But we appreciated the welcoming thoughtfulness and enjoyed getting to know the wives we'd seen featured in *Life* magazine articles and relished hearing their stories—both the delights and the tribulations—of what it was like in the early days of the space program. In the coming years the parties for the wives of our generation were almost exclusively after-work happy hours or after-supper desserts. Times had changed.

One nice tradition that had continued was the *wives' party* given just before the prime crew families left for the Cape for launch. When our group came on board, the wives' party became the spouses' party because the husbands of the women astronauts also hosted. The spouses of the subsequent crew were the hosts and hostesses. The party gave everyone a chance to share the excitement, to give tips to the wives of the first-time flyers, and to send the families off with last minute prayers and good wishes. I had the good fortune to attend lots of these parties as both a spouse and a spouse hostess, and I was able to give pointers to Hoot when it came time for him to play those roles.

In the early shuttle days, there wasn't much support for the families of astronauts about to fly when it came time to head for Florida. Wives could count on a flight to and from the launch and landing on a NASA airplane. Period. We were responsible for getting our children there (and the schools weren't too cooperative about letting the kids make up their school work), for reserving and paying for hotel rooms, for all meals and rental cars. It was bad enough if the flight went on time. When it was delayed, as many were, the costs ran into the thousands of dollars. For those families living off one meager military salary, it was a major expense. There were some families who couldn't afford to send all the children to the Cape, especially if a second trip was warranted because of a launch scrub, and I know it broke some little hearts. There was also the worry that something would go wrong and the kids would be home in front of the television set with the neighbors. I couldn't imagine that kind of stress.

Another tradition was that two members of the Astronaut Office were tapped as family escorts for each flight. Each crew would select these two people from among friends or classmates for this duty. It was sometimes an arduous task but something much appreciated by the families. The escorts were in charge of helping to coordinate travel plans and getting wives, husbands, and kids where they needed to be during this hectic time. Most spouses were real troopers, but a few were high maintenance. I vowed not to be one of the difficult people.

Hoot's training was long and grueling. If he wasn't in meetings or in the simulator, he was flying to the landing sites to practice in the Shuttle Training Aircraft or traveling to contractor facilities to look at the flight's payload. With a toddler in tow, there were times I felt abandoned. The military wives seemed more accustomed to these sorts of deployments, but the loneliness was new to me. I learned that I could count on our group of ASCAN wives and my neighbors to be sympathetic and to back me up.

As Hoot proceeded with his preparations I found that there were a mil-

lion details for me to handle. Wives had a reception at the Cape for all the guests who had been invited to the launch. Location, menus, invitations, flowers, the typical but time consuming to-do list. The STS 41-B moms of small sons decided it would be great to have our three little boys in flight suits that matched their dads', so those had to be planned. Then there were invitations for the launch, advice on hotel reservations and rental cars, maps and directions, details, details, details. I chose to forgo the NASA plane for launch travel and take Paul, my active 18-month-old, on a commercial flight. We decided that Hoot's parents would bring our seven year old daughter, Julie, with them from California for the launch.

Hoot's father, Paul, after whom our son Paul was named, was born in 1907 and learned to fly at an early age. He was one of the United States Army pilots who first flew the mail from the West Coast to the East Coast in 1934, landing in a snow storm. A picture commemorating the event hung on Hoot's wall ever since I had known him: his father in a leather helmet, old-fashioned parachute on his back, standing beside a B7 Keystone bomber squinting into the blizzard at the landing site. After being an airport manager at various small fields and marrying Rita Perrault (Hoot's mother), Paul worked for many years for the Federal Aviation Administration. He went back to college in his late 40s and got his aeronautical engineering degree from the University of Southern California when Hoot was almost 10. Rita, who had worked as a school teacher putting him through college, and their six children attended his graduation.

Rita along with some girlfriends had bought an airplane, a J2 Taylor Cub, in the early 1940s and took flying lessons from Paul who was working for the United States Navy in Rhode Island. As an accomplished pilot

Hoot's father, Paul Gibson, lands his Keystone bomber in a snow storm. He was one of the first U.S. Army pilots to fly the mail from the West Coast to the East Coast in 1934. He was 27 *(top)*. Older brother Jon and Hoot hanging out at the airport with their parents *(below)*.

Paul taught a young Rita Perrault and her friends to fly.
They later married.

and member of the 99s, the International Women Pilots Association, she went on to fly their coast-to-coast Powder Puff Derbies over the years. Several of their children inherited their love of flying, but it was Hoot who focused his whole life on it. He always said that he could remember flying with his parents as far back as his memory went. Given the steering yoke at an early age, he thinks he remembers being coached through a landing at age eight or nine. He began his formal lessons as soon as he could and soloed on his 16th birthday, the earliest student pilots are allowed to fly the plane alone. He earned his private pilot's license on the first day possible, his 17th birthday.

Hoot was a mediocre student going through school because all he was interested in were airplanes. He read about them, and he built and flew radio-controlled models; he flew real planes when he could. It was hard for him to see how Shakespeare or the Crimean War related to what he was sure he wanted to do with his future. Even with math, he chafed at busy work. It was not until he made a stellar score on the math SAT exam that his mother and teachers realized that he knew the material, even if he was unwilling to do the homework. He was a real star once he got into aeronautical engineering in college, but I'm sure his parents worried when he was a youngster that he might not amount to much. It goes to show that some children are late bloomers.

About a week before the early February launch, the flight crew went into what was called Health Stabilization (a euphemism for quarantine). The number of people who came in contact with them was limited to a short list. Wives were on the list, but children weren't. Hoot had to say goodbye to our baby son before we left Houston. At a year and a half old, I wasn't sure Paul was even aware of the gravity of the moment, but I know it tugged at

Hoot's mind was on flying from an early age when he began building model airplanes.

Hoot's heartstrings—and mine—as they hugged each other.

"Bye, bye, little guy," Hoot said, tears welling up in his eyes. I couldn't manage to say a thing. What if something happened and all my son had to remember his father by were pictures?

Quarantine continued when Hoot and his crew left for the Cape three days before launch. The wives arrived at the Cape that day, too, and were chauffeured from our hotels out to have meals with our spouses at the crew quarters at the Kennedy Space Center. Thank goodness Grandma Rita and Grandpa Paul could babysit Paul and Julie. The quarters, in the Operations and Control Building, were abuzz with activity at launch time. The housekeeping staff wanted to make sure everyone was comfortable and well fed. Last minute briefings with the rest of the flight team were held by telecom in a small conference room. The crew checked last minute changes to their timelines and procedures. They also became focused on weather forecasts, not only for the Cape but also for the abort sites across the Atlantic and the landing sites in the western United States. Launch depended on all potential landing sites having acceptable weather.

Another memorable venue used for last-minute visits with husbands and wives was the beach house. It was an old house out on the ocean's edge south of the shuttle launch pads. Located on the Space Center grounds and protected by security, it was very private. Not luxurious, it nevertheless had a large living room with fireplace and a dining area and kitchen. The small bedrooms in the back of the house had been converted into comfortable sitting rooms. It was a place filled with the ghosts of those who had flown before. I was struck by the poignancy of trying to figure out how to spend those last hours before my husband took a major life risk. It was a happy time: a fulfillment of dreams, a culmination of hard work and of years of preparation. But was a scary time, too. We spent a lot of time walking up and down the beach, watching the waves on the sand.

The beach house at the Kennedy Space Center where Astronauts and their spouses could relax together before launch. From the back porch, the launch pad could be seen in the distance.

What do people talk about during times like these? These private talks were not shared with others, and I'm sure the conversations were as unique as the individuals and their relationships. Hoot, the eternal optimist, didn't dwell on many of the what-ifs. He knew I could take care of myself and Paul. He knew I regarded Julie as one of my own, and he could count on me to help her. There were a few details—where the will was, where he'd parked his car, life insurance information—but we enjoyed being able to spend quiet time together. That in itself was somewhat odd. It had been a year since we'd had a vacation and long stretches of uninterrupted time together. The years would provide me with many more memories of the beach and beach house. I tried to find one perfect shell to add to our shell collection each time we went through this experience. I spent a lot of time trying to figure out what our lives meant, trying to see where they would go. It was like an interesting novel unfolding before us. But of course I could never know whether the excitement of it all would be shattered by some horrible unexpected tragedy or if as old codgers we'd be able to recount our story.

The vastness and timelessness of the ocean was a perfect backdrop for such musings. We couldn't see over the horizon just as we couldn't see across time. We knew that the expanse of water could swallow up our rocket ships without a trace or we could soar across it in a triumphant white bird on our way to space to see in wondrous detail what lay out there.

The water and sand also served as a reminder of what a small part we were in time and the universe. Like the grains of sand that washed to and fro, we pressed on with our lives, at times feeling important, at times insignificant. Seeing the double set of footprints we left on the beach always made me grateful that we had found each other in this crazy world and that we had each other to share these times in this special way. It also reminded me of a story I heard in church of the man who arrived in heaven, and God showed him the path he had walked in life leaving footprints on the beach. God pointed out to the man that he had always been there beside him. The man could see the double set of footprints in the sand through the years. But then he noticed something. In the most trying times of his life there was only one set of prints:

"Lord, why in those difficult times weren't you with me?"

"I was with you, my son," said God. "In those times I carried you."

And so, in those difficult times for us, we felt we helped to carry the other – and that God was really carrying both of us.

The peacefulness of the beach and the remoteness of that place were such a stark contrast to the high tech hustle and bustle of our lives up to that point. We'd crammed days full of rocket ships, simulators, engineering drawings, complex communication, computerese – then suddenly this quiet solitude. Yet if we stood on the corner of the front deck of the beach house and looked, not out to sea but northward along the land, across the scrub and low lying brush, we could make out the ominous structure of Launch Complex 39...where fate awaited. Beautiful, wondrous, massive, and terrifying, the shuttle stood on its launch structure. Were all the pieces fitted together properly? Had someone overlooked some small defect? Was there an imperceptible flaw that would take my husband's life and change our family forever? Or was it the magnificent white machine that would race him toward the heavens, make him a hero, write his name in the history books? There was no way to know.

There were also multiple other responsibilities for spouses in the midst of all this reverie. Crew members, especially for first flights, invited all their family and friends to the Cape to share the experience. NASA provided a bus ride out to the viewing site for the launch, but guests were responsible for all their other travel plans. Relatives and close friends always wanted to stay near the spouse and children, and in those early days there was always much planning and replanning. We'd make reservations at one motel only to have the launch slip and the motel tell us they didn't have anything available for the new date. When dates changed we had to let all our guests know (and this was before e-mail!), so they could rearrange their plans.

I always regarded it as an extreme compliment when people would go to all that trouble to watch Hoot or me launch. Yes, they were historic events and exciting if you could say you knew a crew member. But what a hassle! In any event, all the spouses wanted to see and thank their invited guests before the launch. Since spouses and children would watch the launch from the roof of the Launch Control Center, not from the guests' viewing area, a get-together the day before the flight was the only opportunity they'd have to visit with friends. And so the *spouses' reception* had to be planned.

I teamed up with a couple of the other wives and had reserved the Officers' Club at Patrick Air Force Base. My father and sister came. Hoot's mom and dad had paid for tickets for his three brothers and two sisters and had brought Julie from San Diego. Guests of each crewmember wore a particular name tag color at the party. Our friends and family were mingling with Ron McNair's, most of whose guests were African American. I remember someone introducing themselves to our good friends from San Diego, Chuck and Diane McNary. The guest asked if they were related to Ron,

Daughter Julie, at age seven mature and quite a little lady, attends the pre-launch reception.

despite wearing the wrong name tag color. Diane, the blondest of blondes, must have worked hard to stifle a giggle as she replied, "No, no relation. We're McNary, not McNair."

Our huge buffet adorned a long table in the middle of the reception room overlooking the ocean. It was burgeoning with platters full of finger foods. As I circulated through the room trying to visit for a little while with each of our friends, the grandparents were to keep an eye on little Paul. But they got busy visiting, too, so he had to find his own entertainment. I noticed what he was up to. At a year and a half of age, he was just tall enough to reach the food at the edges of the buffet table. So there he went: cruise, reach, grab, gobble, move down, reach, grab, gobble, all around the table. Our dear friend John Kiker, a former NASA employee and the engineer who came up with the idea to transport the space shuttle on the back of a 747, took it upon himself to be Paul's "body guard" and chased him away from the table and around the reception room. When we got back to the hotel,

Paul's little belly was stretched as full as a ripe watermelon. I was sure he was going to be sick, but he fooled me and did fine.

The night before a launch also brought one of the most magnificent occasions for guests: night viewing. Until about 12 hours before lift-off, the orbiter was encased in a large metal cocoon called the Rotating Service Structure. It allowed technicians to work on any level of the shuttle (if needed) and protected the vehicle. As preparations for launch came to a close, the structure was rotated out of the way, and the orbiter in all its glistening glory could be seen, a magnificent butterfly that had shaken off its chrysalis. Launch minus 12 hours usually occurred at night, so huge xenon flood lights were used to light up the pad areas for the workers who were still making last minute preparations or babysitting their systems. The immense white ship, lit up by lights that sent bright streaks into the night sky, and the hissing and venting of gasses all made for an amazing sight. A few special guests were permitted to ride a bus out to the bottom of the hill leading up to the pad, nearer than the public was ever permitted, and what an experience! To

Our friend, "Mr. John" Kiker became little Paul's body guard.

me it was almost as awesome an experience as the launch itself. The launch we'd all see from three or four miles away; this we were seeing firsthand, up close and personal.

For early morning launches, the crews were in bed at the time of night viewing which occurs at about 8:00 or 9:00 p.m.

Space Shuttle Challenger is ready for the launch of STS-41B the next day. It was a chance for all the guests to get a spectacular view of the vehicle at night. This was only time Hoot and I got to go to a night viewing together. Usually the crew is in bed when this event occurs.

But Hoot's commander decided his crew could stay up late enough to join their wives at the viewing site. Since they were still in quarantine, however, they had to remain at some distance from the crowd. We thought it would be great for Hoot to at least be able to wave to a small number of family and close friends who had been able to come out that night. We forgot to tell Julie about the quarantine rules.

At seven, Julie was a mature but sensitive child. Coming from California with Grandma and Grandpa Gibson, she had been enjoying all the excitement and festivities and the chance to visit with her stepbrother, Paul.

She had talked to her daddy by phone and seemed to have it all together. But all that collapsed when she saw him at the launch pad that night. Etched in my memory will always be a picture of this beautiful blonde princess, her arms out stretched to a daddy who couldn't come near her. The fifty feet of space between them would grow to the enormity of space itself the next day, but tonight it was more than she could handle. Crocodile tears rolled down her cheeks. Blowing kisses wasn't enough. It looked to me that her tears came close to breaking Hoot's heart. We realized after that time that seeing at a distance and talking on the phone can never replace hugs in times of stress for kids. Not that we always avoided instances like this in our combined eight launches, but we were at least more prepared for them.

How is it that little kids seem to absorb the adrenalin from the grownups around them? Paul seemed to know somehow that something exciting was going on, or maybe it was all the food he consumed at the party. After night viewing was over, we all hurried back to the hotel to get a few hours of sleep before we had to be ready for a pre-dawn bus ride out to the launch. Julie and I were sharing a room in which they'd placed a crib for Paul, but Paul would have no part of sleeping in his crib. Finally I hauled Paul and a couple of pillows into the walk-in closet and tried to get him to wind down for a little rest. As the night rolled on and I got more and more exhausted, I wondered how I was going to make it through the next day. I think I managed to get about two hours of sleep before I had to get myself, then Julie, then a groggy and cranky Paul, up and dressed for the bus.

I knew Hoot had been up for some hours listening to last minute vehicle and weather briefings and suiting up for the trip out to the pad. He knew what my schedule would be, so he called when he knew we'd be up. He told us that everything looked good for the launch and that the crew was in good shape: he was excited. He wanted to hear that we were excited (no mention of a sleepless baby to worry him) and to have a last minute chat with Julie about what she thought of everything. Then, a quick "I love you – gotta go," and he was off to launch. All thoughts of what might go wrong were pushed somewhere deep out of my consciousness.

Before dawn the spouses and children were escorted by bus to the Launch Control Center which is nestled right next to the huge Vehicle Assembly Building on the road out to the launch pad. At places along the route we could see the bright streaks from the xenon lights slanting across the sky and knew we were seeing the launch pad in the distance. The Launch Director, whose job took him to the Launch Control Center upstairs that morning, donated his office for the families to await the launch.

There wasn't much for young children to do there but get in trouble. There was lots of food to be ground into the carpet. There were sugary doughnuts to rev up the hyperactive. There was a desk to be climbed on and cups of coffee to be overturned. There were stressed out, under-rested mothers to drive crazy, and there was a wonderful woman from Public Affairs who saw my predicament. She took Paul out and let him run up and down the halls of the building. This pleased both him and me. She promised she'd have him back in time for the launch.

Three little boys—Eric Brand, Reggie McNair and Paul Gibson—have flightsuits to match their fathers as they await launch in the Launch Control Center. Cheryl McNair, a very patient mother, watches over them.

Out the large windows looking eastward, we watched the dawn brighten the sky, silhouetting the shuttle on the pad. Somehow the sight always seemed to signal the beginning of a change, a dawning, a newness. Birds flew by, going about their morning chores. The vehicle in the distance that had been lit up by the huge lights earlier, now began to glow gold in the sun.

As we watched the NASA channel, they showed the crew breakfast that had taken place earlier. As all crews before them had, they looked calm, relaxed, and elated. The breakfast itself was a tradition, to show the crew in good health, and ready to fly. Decorating their table was a cake with the crew patch on it. Then Hoot and crew were off to trade jeans and polo shirts for flight suits.

For launch and landing the only thing each crewmember would have to wear for safety was a clamshell helmet with air and communication lines piped into it. They had to be fit checked and adjusted before leaving for the pad, but that was pretty simple. The shuttle was designed to be so safe that it could be flown in "shirtsleeves"—that is, without a pressure suit—by mere mortals like the non-pilot scientists.

When it came time to leave for the pad, there was another photo opportunity for the press. Their lights and cameras were set up at the back door of the O&C Building downstairs from the crew quarters. The families delighted in watching this on television since it meant all was going well, and the launch might indeed go off on time. Here was another chance to see Daddy's smiling face.

A modified passenger van known as the Astrovan waited to whisk the crew to their destiny. Along with them rode the Director of Flight Crew Operations, the chief of the Astronaut Office, and various other helpers. Everyone except the crew would disembark near the Launch Control Center, but the crew was driven right out to the pad and boarded the elevator that would take them up to the crew hatch.

Cameras were mounted in and around the *White Room*. This was the small chamber at the end of the access arm that reached from the launch tower out to the entry hatch on the side of the orbiter. We could watch as, one by one, crew members entered, underwent last minute equipment checks, and then climbed into the vehicle for strap-in. Like race horses before the big race, they were pacing, shaking themselves out, preparing for the confines of the starting gate.

We watched as Hoot appeared in the narrow passageway that led to the orbiter and to space. We knew as the last of the crew climbed aboard and got snugged into position by trusted technicians that everything was clicking along as it should. And then we watched from the White Room cameras as the technicians closed and locked the hatch. This took some time while they verified there was a good seal and placed heat shield tiles around the latch mechanism to protect it during reentry. Then everyone left the White Room, left the pad, left the crew alone looking skyward watching the dawn.

The countdown continued. Each system was powered up, checked and double-checked. Communication links between the crew, the Cape Launch Director, and the CAPCOM in Houston Mission Control were verified. The pressure integrity of the crew cabin was checked. The rescue forces at the Cape, in the Atlantic, and at the emergency landing sites were polled. The weather was watched and measured and forecasted. The Range Safety demon with his DESTRUCT button set to blow up the vehicle and its crew should they stray off course made sure he had his maximum capability. Would there be that one split second in time when it all came together and everything was right for a launch? It almost seemed unbelievable.

One of the most exciting moments was when the Flight Director in the Mission Control Center, or MCC, in Houston *goes around the room*. At each console in the MCC sat a Flight Controller responsible for a particular flight phase or system. He or she had consultants and information in their back rooms to help, but the front room person was the spokesperson. Every part of the orbiter and everything it planned to do was represented. Each of these people must be happy with what they see in their data before the launch is authorized to proceed. Each has an acronym and a nickname – FIDO for Flight Dynamics Officer, GNC for Guidance, Navigation and Control, and so on. The Flight Director cycled through each asking if they were ready. In the efficiency of language expected in this sacred room, it went rapid fire.

"FIDO?"

"Go!"

"GNC?"

"Go!"

"INCO?"

"Go!"

"Surgeon?"

"Go!"

"CAPCOM?"

"Go!"

It sounds like a cheering chant: *GO, GO, GO!* No one wanted to have to say, "Stand by, Flight."

And then the last call, "Launch Director, Houston Flight Director: we are GO for launch."

It never failed to raise my heart rate, to make me proud to have been a part of it.

There were various "holds" in the countdown, designed to give everyone a chance to do last minute checks, to catch up (if necessary), and to get ready to proceed to the next critical step. The last planned hold was when the countdown clock reached Launch minus 9 minutes. After a few minutes of holding to recheck everything possible, if all was ready, the count would resume and march down to lift-off.

As the countdown resumed at L-9 minutes, the families were taken up to the roof of the Launch Control Center. From there we could see the launch complexes to the east, a little over three miles away. Overhead, the

Cape's soaring birds were catching updrafts coming from the huge Vehicle Assembly Building, oblivious to the great drama unfolding below them. In the Cape parking lots, workers were coming outside to catch a glimpse of the vehicle they had so painstakingly crafted. On our rooftop perch, we families clung together to listen as the final minutes ticked off the clock, and the final preparations were announced over the roof's loudspeakers.

There wasn't much time to ponder and worry as the countdown proceeded. There was only time to get our bearings, to make sure the children were close by, and to fix our eyes on the pad in the distance. The call outs from public affairs came more quickly, keeping all the viewers informed of what would be happening onboard.

"Launch minus 5 minutes, and the Auxiliary Power Units will be started."

"Launch minus 1 minute. All systems look good."

"Launch minus 31 seconds, and the Launch Sequencer has taken control of the orbiter."

The onboard systems were now in charge, and the next hurdle would be a final check of all systems at L-15 seconds. Everything had to happen without a single error or a halt would be called.

"Launch minus 10, 9, 8:" the water deluge beneath the orbiter started dumping massive amounts of water into a huge trench below the vehicle to prevent vibrations from the booster

The picture perfect launch of STS-41B on February 3, 1984

ignition being reflected back onto the orbiter's tail.

"7, 6, Main Engine Start," which we saw as huge clouds of smoke billowing out from the launch structure.

"5, 4, 3," and the low rumble of the engines reached us at the LCC.

"2, 1:" *Please, God, keep them safe!*

"0 SRB ignition and we have lift-off, lift-off of *Challenger*!"

PHOTO COURTESY OF NASA

My heart and breathing stopped, it seemed. It was a few seconds before the massive noise and vibration of the booster ignition reached us. Julie stuck her fingers in her ears, and she and Paul clung to me. Tears of joy and fear were streaming down my face as the crackle of the engines carried them off on a plume of smoke into the morning sun. We could hear their calls.

Vance's calm voice said, "Houston, *Challenger*, roll program."

And the CAPCOM's, "Roger, roll *Challenger*," - words they had been practicing in the simulators for over the past year. I listened for words that might indicate some problem but heard none. I visualized Hoot, rattling along in the forward right seat on the flight deck, watching his computer displays the way he had rehearsed. He was responsible for the main engines, the electrical system, the hydraulics, and the small control and maneuvering engines. He had to make sure they were all running properly. I knew he was performing his practiced scan pattern, checking, double checking, lest he miss some small trend that would become a problem. And he'd be backing Vance up on everything

I heard the call, "SRB sep," right on time at about two minutes into the flight and was glad they had separated successfully from the massive boosters. They streaked faster and faster toward the heavens, the three main engines glowing in the distance as we strained to see them. Soon the engines would be commanded to stop at a precise speed.

"MECO," I heard: Main Engine Cut Off. And as the call, "ET sep," came down to us announcing the external tank had come off cleanly, I knew they had made it through the most perilous part of the flight. But they weren't in a good orbit yet. In a few minutes, the Orbital Maneuvering System (OMS) engines had to ignite to give them a further boost, or they'd fall back to Earth like the fuel tank they had just jettisoned.

The families went back downstairs to listen to the Mission Control loop, and Paul finally released his grip on me. Julie kept watching my face to make sure everything was okay. I heaved a sigh of relief to hear that the OMS burn went off without a hitch. Now we could think about heading back to Houston to follow the flight there. But first we had to be a part of an *ancient* tradition at the Kennedy Space Center. After each successful launch, everyone had to eat beans. As we emerged into the hallway of the LCC, we were surprised by warming trays, crock pots, and casserole dishes full of baked beans. Everyone's special cornbread was also in abundance. Here it was, just hours after dawn and everyone was eating big bowls of beans! It wasn't so incongruous considering that most of these people had been up since the middle of the night worrying about the launch. Now there were flushed, smiling faces, and all were feeling they were part of this great success. Many times the beans had to be saved for a later launch date, but only once in our tenure at NASA was the food thrown out.

Back in Houston, we followed the progress of the flight. There were four major goals. They were to launch the Westar satellite on Day 1 and the Palapa satellite on Day 2. Then, Bob Stewart and Bruce McCandless would do spacewalks and test the Manned Maneuvering Unit, a Buck Rogers-type backpack that would allow them to fly free of the shuttle. For the first time in history, two people would do untethered walks in space! And finally, this was to be the first spaceflight ever to land in Florida at the Kennedy Space Center.

The two satellite deployments were expected to be rather routine. Several of this type of satellite with the Payload Assist Module (PAM) upper stage booster had been popped out of the cargo bay before. The launch of Westar from the bay on Day 1 went without a hitch. But by the time I got back to Houston, I discovered that the PAM had failed to fire properly to boost the satellite into its final, higher orbit.

There was much scurrying around at Mission Control to try to figure out what went wrong. There had been no obvious problems during the checkout before the shuttle launch or before it was ejected from the pay-load bay. There were few single point failures in the system, where a single malfunction had no back up and would cause the whole thing to fail. The question was, was this a fluke? Was something wrong with this one booster, or was it a generic failure? Was something wrong with the booster design or with this batch of boosters? It was important to know quickly since the Palapa satellite with the same type upper stage was to be launched on Day 2.

Try as they might, the NASA and contractor engineers couldn't figure out why the booster hadn't worked and wrote it off as a one-time bad deal, something that had damaged that one booster. They gave the go to launch Palapa on Day 4. As was usual, after satellite deployment the shut-tle would position itself so that its belly was pointed at the booster rocket. Even though it would be several miles away, this would make sure there was no damage to the orbiter's window if there was debris from the firing or an explosion. This time to try to catch a glimpse of the booster rocket ignition, MCC gave orders for the Remote Manipulator System (RMS), or mechanical arm, to position its end camera to watch the heavens for the motor firing when it occurred.

There were many rituals in the Astronaut Office around watching friends launch and fly in space. One of the large conference rooms on the third floor of Building 4, which housed the Astronaut Office, was set aside for flight following. In the early days of shuttle flights, when many people worked on each launch and it was all new, most of the office would gather to watch launches. The Flight Director's communication loop from MCC was piped in also, so everyone could follow any behind-the-scenes problems that were developing. As launch time approached, the chatter in the room gave way to a hushed silence so that everyone could hear the last minute calls, could listen for anything...*not right*. All eyes were on the tele-vision screen that showed various camera views of the orbiter. As the final seconds were ticked off, the tension in the room intensified. As the main engines started belching fire, white knuckles gripped the arms of the chairs.

Boom! SRB ignition, liftoff.

"Yes!" everyone shouted.

People would note certain things: the flame pattern off the back of the external tank, the condensation that flew past the forward windows, the fact that some of the performance calls were a bit late. All this to relieve the tension, to claim to be a part of what was taking place, to display some bit of knowledge that said you were qualified to fly on one soon.

After friends had made it into orbit, people would drift out of the room, back to their desks, or off to other areas. For those with flight assignments down the line, they knew they could "move up one" and be closer to space themselves. For those who hadn't been assigned yet, there was the affirmation that the program was progressing, and there would be a ride for them someday.

As long as the shuttle was in space, the conference room continued to be the place where astronauts could monitor the flight. The television focused on Mission Control when pictures from space were not being sent down. The Flight Director and Air-To-Ground (CAPCOM to crew or vice versa) loops were plumbed in. All the packages of paper that documented failures and their fixes or work-arounds that decreed changes to the time-line, that showed what messages were sent to the crew were available there.

As the deployment of Palapa drew near, many of us collected in the conference room to make sure everything went right on this one. The march down to the deployment was normal, no problems whatsoever. Pop! Out it went, and the shuttle did its pirouette as the satellite drifted away. The RMS was lifted up and bent around over the payload bay to look in the direction of the booster rocket plume.

The clock ticked down to ignition time, when a plume of the booster ignition began and then quickly vanished. Another failed upper stage.

What a terrible blow! Although NASA had fulfilled its contract and delivered the satellites to low Earth orbit, the two satellites were useless at this altitude, and someone had lost millions of dollars.

A gray cloud hung over the Center that day as engineers went back to assess why these boosters differed from the previous, functional boosters. It was funny, but the public thought that every time something went wrong in space that it was NASA's fault. In this case, NASA did all its testing, installing in the shuttle, launch into space, and deployment perfectly. Contractors had provided faulty pieces of hardware. However, NASA felt an obligation to help make things right if they could. Not too many days later, clever people began planning how to retrieve these satellites on a future shuttle mission, so they could be repaired and reflown. It was a tribute to the NASA can-do spirit. Their adrenalin flowed strongest when the task seemed least possible.

The most visually spectacular part of Hoot's mission was yet to come. Bruce and Bob began the preparation for their spacewalk. All the pieces of their suits, as well as all their tools and equipment, had to be pulled out of the airlock and into the middeck, so they could be checked and assembled. The checklists for the walk or Extravehicular Activity (EVA) had to be reviewed one more time. Contingencies, or how things might go awry, had to be considered. The biggest fear was, "What if one of the guys flies away from the shuttle and the backpack quits, stranding him off in some corner of space?" The crew had practiced rendezvousing with a lost crewmember, but no one knew for sure what the problems might be or if a rescue would work.

On the day of the big event, once again we all gathered to watch. This time the spouses had special seating in the VIP viewing area at Mission Control. With Bob and Bruce snug within them, the suits hung on the wall of the tubular airlock in the middeck. The pre-breathe for the space walkers to flush the nitrogen from their bodies so they didn't get the bends went well. When exit time approached, the inner door between the middeck living quarters and the airlock was closed. Then the airlock itself was depressurized, or the air let out, so that it was at zero pressure, the same as the vacuum outside in space.

Even breathing pure oxygen, astronauts must have some pressure within their suits, or enough oxygen won't get into their blood. The problem with suit pressure is that the more pressure inside the suit, the more inflated it feels and the harder it is to move the joints of the suit, especially the ones in the hand. Also, the lower the pressure, the longer the pre-breathe to denitrogenate the blood prior to dropping the pressure. The United States compromised on the side of a lower pressure (4.3 psi), more agile suit but more prebreathing. On the other hand, for spacewalks, the Russians chose a higher pressure suit, which required less denitrogenation but was harder to work in. They called it their Orlan suit. Orlan in Russian means sea eagle. When asked why they name their suits after animals, one Russian pointed out that Americans do that, too. Puzzled, the American asked which of our suits carried an animal name and had it pointed out that we called our suit the emu. Oh, yes, our Extravehicular Mobility Unit! We had never considered that.

When the new shuttle suits were in the design phase, they were different than the suits of the Gemini and Apollo programs. The idea was not to have custom-sized suits as they had in the past but to go to a more "modularized" design. The chest part of the suit was a hard shell, called the Hard Upper Torso (HUT). The HUT contained all the connections and routing for the electronics, the communication lines and radios, and the environmental control system. It had hinged connectors at the shoulder joints to which arms of the proper length could be connected. The helmet attached to the neck ring, and correctly sized pants would slip onto the waist ring.

Bruce McCandless had spent years in the spacesuit working on the development of the maneuvering unit. Everyone was delighted that he was getting the chance to test it. Bob Stewart was one of our 1978 group, and all of the TFNG class were proud that he'd be a part of this, too. Bernice McCandless and Mary Stewart were sitting on the edges of their seats in the Viewing Room the day of the EVA as their husbands floated gracefully out the hatch into the grandeur of open space. As was true with most spouses, they were never sure they approved of all this risk-taking but were always supportive of the crazy things their husbands thought important. Heaven knows, Bruce and Bernice had waited many years for this moment.

The early maneuvers with the MMU backpack began with simple checkouts in the cargo bay to make sure all the systems worked, and the flying capabilities in zero G were close to what had been predicted by analysis and by what was practiced in the water tank and on the air-bearing floor. It was a mini-test flight of sorts. Then Bruce went through an orchestrated set of maneuvers that sent him further and further away from the safety of the mother ship. The onboard cameras gave those of us on Earth the breathtaking view of him silhouetted against the blackness of space and the blue glow of the sunlit Earth. It became a little scary when he got smaller and smaller until he was over 300 feet

Bruce McCandless performs the first untethered spacewalk using the Manned Maneuvering Unit backpack. He eventually flew over 300 feet from the mother ship. Hoot took this picture.

away and not much more than a speck in the distance. He could communicate with *Challenger* and the ground through all this, and all his systems seemed to be working well. The backpack was performing as predicted and practiced, so there were never any frightening moments.

Then it was Bob's turn to take a spin around the payload bay. From their voices we could hear what a great time they were having. Once they were back in the cabin I sat back in my seat in MCC and looked over to congratulate Bernice and Mary. They were quietly crying on each other's shoulders, probably with a mixture of joy and relief. I came to realize through all these experiences that the supporting role as a spouse could often be more difficult in some ways than being the one in space.

During the spacewalk I had been focused on Bruce and Bob, assuming that Hoot was watching the show and making sure the orbiter was performing as it should. What surprised me postflight were the magnificent pictures he was taking of the whole ballet. He had a lot of time to think about f-stops and framing and zooming or distant shots. He had a couple of good cameras with many lens selections, and, unbeknownst to me, he had been planning this day for a long time. Because there were no orbiter maneuvers to perform or malfunctions to chase and because Hoot was an excellent photographer to begin with and there was lots of time, he managed to get many spectacular pictures. The memorable one, the finest, of Bruce against the Earth's horizon took a little creativity. He had taken a bunch of pictures with Bruce upright, the way you would take a portrait of your friend standing in the distance. But Bruce was at an angle to the horizon in the background. He then had the idea, why not make the horizon horizontal as we are used to viewing it on the ground and let Bruce be at an angle? That simple move made such a difference! It gave the feeling that the subject was free of gravity and was flying across the heavens. The picture has appeared many times in NASA material and in many other places, always with the attribution "NASA photo" on the side. But we both know who took it, and Hoot is always proud to see it. For this and other wonderful pictures he took on the flight, he was nominated for a Pulitzer Prize in photography. What an honor!

The awesome EVAs seemed to lift the spirits of everyone who felt down after the satellite problems. Then planning began of the last major goal of the flight: the first landing at the brand-new Shuttle Landing Facility (SLF) at the Kennedy Space Center complex in Florida. At 15,000 feet long and 300 feet wide, the runway could be seen from space. Until the handling qualities and the landing capabilities of the shuttle had been explored, landings had been done at Edwards, first on the vast, dry lake bed where deviations a few thousand feet one way or the other wouldn't matter. Then beginning with STS 4, landings were made on the Edwards concrete runway. Even then, running off the sides or end wouldn't matter much since the runway itself was in the middle of the flat, hard lakebed.

Landing at the Cape was trickier. Despite the fact that the runway was plenty long and plenty wide, it was surrounded by a moat. Should there be a problem, such as a skid, a blown tire, or (heaven forbid) bad flying by the Commander (who always landed the shuttle manually), there was a distinct possibility that the orbiter would skitter off the concrete and into the alligator-infested, brackish green slime and be heavily damaged.

The pre-dawn weather on landing day was questionable. As often happens in the early morning hours at the Cape, a low lying fog obliterated most of the landmarks along the coastline. The fog was forecast to dissipate as the sun rose and warmed the land. But would it? The deorbit burn must be executed about an hour before landing, on the other side of the world, so everyone must give a "GO" based on what they predict will happen an hour in the future. Later orbits might place the orbital track too far west to make a Florida landing.

As the families left the hotels in the darkness before dawn to meet family and friends at the landing strip, we still weren't sure whether a landing was possible that morning. As the busses arrived at the landing site at daybreak, we saw the problem. Patchy fog was still hanging around the area. Not only did Vance have to see the runway, but he also had to see the various alignment aids directing his flight path to give him cues for aiming properly. Would they be visible?

Usually, weather forecasters—or weather "guessers" as we sometimes irreverently called them—preferred to take a conservative position. But the one at the Cape that day was brave enough to say he was sure the fog would clear in time, so the crew could go ahead and do their burn and start heading for the ground.

As we found our seats in the viewing stands we were told the deorbit engine burn had occurred and our men were on their way home. Knowing that there was still the danger of burning up in the heating region of reentry, I couldn't relax yet. The viewing area seemed so close to the runway compared to the miles across the desert at Edwards. There were the bleachers, a fence, a narrow grass strip, the moat, and then—right there—the concrete.

The sun began to rise above the horizon, and the chill of the morning air began to fade. Less and less fog obscured the landscape. Then we heard that the orbiter was out of blackout, talking to MCC again after coming out of the fireball of the heating region when communication directly to the ground wasn't possible. As they streaked across the Gulf of Mexico, we began to get reports of their ever decreasing speed and altitude.

Soon we heard they had crossed the west coast of Florida, still at the amazing altitude of 110,000 feet and over four times the speed of sound. They'd have to drop like a rock to land at the Cape in that distance. But that's just what a space shuttle did. Word came that they'd be in sight momentarily.

"There!" someone shouted, pointing skyward.

All eyes followed the line of the upstretched finger to see the tiny black dot overhead. We caught a quick glimpse and heard the double sonic booms as the orbiter crossed above us and headed eastward out over the Atlantic to begin the slow descending circle that would align it with the north-south direction of the runway.

Miraculously, though there were still patches of fog lying low in the brush of the Cape, the weatherman had predicted correctly: clear enough for a good view of all the landing aides and the airstrip. Then another finger pointed in the distance to the northwest. There they were! The tiny dot that had passed overhead at almost 50,000 feet was now a full-sized space vehicle diving at the runway.

The Hoot Gibson contingent—Grandma, Grandpa, Julie, and I—all began the chant, unnecessary, but helping to dissipate our excitement: "Don't forget the gear! Don't forget the gear!" Pilots are kidded that they are along for the ride except for two important tasks: getting the Auxiliary Power Units started five minutes before launch and putting the gear down seconds before landing.

We could see the nose of the orbiter pulling up to slow the rapid descent, "pre-flare" it's called. And then when it seemed almost agonizingly late, we saw the landing gear start down.

"Yay for Daddy!" we all shouted.

And then the final flare, that last tweak of the nose to put the orbiter down at the right spot at the right speed. And they were down! The nose fell gently to the runway as the orbiter rolled to a stop so close in front of us. It was a perfect landing and the first time in history that a space vehicle had landed at its launch site.

There were hugs all around for the family, and all the guests who had returned to the Cape for landing were sending congratulations to the crew. Such a proud moment, such a wondrous relief to have them home safely!

The Gibson, McNair and Brand toddlers with their proud fathers at Ellington Field in Houston after our return from the Cape *(above)*. The landing of STS-41B at dawn with fog in the low-lying areas. This was the first landing of the Space Shuttle at the Kennedy Space Center and the first time a space craft had launched and landed at the same site.

The spouses and children were escorted back to crew quarters to await the returning heroes. Paul had stayed back home, so all I had to contend with was seven-year-old Julie. After waiting while the crew powered down the orbiter and handed it over to the ground crew, we heard they were arriving downstairs. Applause filtered up from the floor below, and at last they were there in the hallway. Julie, unaware of the muscle deconditioning that takes place after a week in space, ran and jumped into her daddy's arms. He had to be steadied by a flight surgeon as he staggered backward under the load. Then it was my turn, and I buried my face against his neck and was amazed that after a week of no showers he didn't smell bad.

Since this was the first KSC landing, a big ceremony was planned. Julie and I were hurried over to the visitor's center for the presentation. There, Hoot's mom and dad sat waiting for us on that sunny day at Cape Canaveral, probably somewhat dazed that this was all coming to pass. This was the son they weren't sure would amount to anything. They hadn't had a chance to see him at crew quarters after the landing but were front and center at the return ceremony, the cameras popping.

Afterward, we had a chance to visit with them for a few minutes before we all had to depart for Houston. Hoot's father had tears in his eyes as he hugged this son who had achieved one of aviation's highest accomplishments.

PHOTO COURTESY OF NASA

Our family at the post-landing ceremony so happy to all be safely home.

CHAPTER 6

★ ★ ★ ★ ★ ★

GOING UP

ife was a challenge during the time Hoot was preparing for his first mission. In 1983 and 1984 Paul became a toddler...with all the expected activity. His learning to crawl, to pull himself up, and to walk—his version of defying gravity—each demanded separate rounds of baby-proofing the house. Dirty clothes required cleaning, and Sesame Street was on a continuous loop. One minute I was sitting on the side of the tub trying to potty train Paul, and the next I was learning how to read the space shuttle's electrical wiring schematics.

In August of 1983, Hoot was focusing on training for his first mission a few months away, and I was figuring out how to be a supportive wife, a perfect mother, and an astronaut-in-training. Out of the blue I got a call from Mr. Abbey's secretary.

"Mr. Abbey would like you to come over to talk to him," she said. "Would it be convenient for you to come now?"

Could it mean a flight assignment?

Sally had already flown and

Judy was assigned to fly in early 1984. It was unusual for George to assign flights from his office. It was traditionally done off in a corner at some party or during happy hour. Since the baby, I hadn't been partying much, and my *happy hours* consisted of collapsing in a heap on the floor to play with Paul on a Friday evening. Still, the call to his office caused a nagging fear that I had not measured up or had committed some unpardonable sin, and he was going

Originally our flight was STS-41E but renamed STS-41F. Our five crewmembers were Bo Bobko, Dave Griggs, Don Williams and Jeff Hoffman and me

to tell me I wasn't suited for this job.

George in his laconic way welcomed me into the inner sanctum of his corner office on the 8th floor of the JSC Administration Building.

"How are things going?" he asked.

"Great, thank you," I said, unsure of where the conversation was headed. George always had a dead pan expression, and it was hard to read his thoughts. Was this good news or bad news? I couldn't tell.

A man of few words, George said, "Okay. I was wondering if you'd like to fly on STS 41E next year."

"Yes, sir!" My heart was pounding. I had no idea what was on that flight, but no one ever turned a flight assignment down. "Who else would be on the flight?"

Bo Bobko was to be the Commander. He was the pilot from STS 6, and I knew him well from having served as his support crew. The rest of the crew was from my 1978 class: Don Williams as the pilot; Dave Griggs as MS2 or the flight engineer; and Jeff Hoffman as the other mission specialist. We would launch two communications satellites, one on a Payload Assist Module (PAM), a fancy name for the booster on the bottom of the satellite, and the other on a Syncom, which was popped out of the cargo bay like a Frisbee. Neither would be new, as several had already been launched from a shuttle.

Later in 1983 we were redesignated STS 41F for launch in August of 1984. One interesting addition to our flight was SPARTAN, a small, self-contained instrument package, which rode to orbit on a pallet in the cargo bay. We would lift it with the Remote Manipulator System (RMS) robot arm and drop it off to free fly for a few days in space. Then we would rendezvous with it, pick it up with the RMS, and put it back on its pallet. During its free flight away from the gasses released by the shuttle and above the Earth's atmosphere, it would use a small telescope to observe our sun. The precise arm operations and the space rendezvous (which was more challenging than most people recognized), would be the most challenging and unique part of our flight.

It wasn't a major flight, but it would make me the third of the six women to fly in space. In fact, Sally and Judy had gotten flight assignments but the press raised the issue that there were few women on the flight schedule. General James Abrahamson was the NASA Associate Administrator in charge of the shuttle program, and he made a faux pas when asked about this. It gave a little insight into the minds of the men running NASA. When someone in the media pointed out that few women had been assigned to the early flights, he said it was because the women kept getting pregnant. He was referring to me and Anna Fisher. My son Paul was a year old and Anna was a month from having her daughter Kristin. This comment was not well-received by the women astronauts, or many other American women seeking to combine work and motherhood. He later made a trip to Houston to meet with the women astronauts and apologize.

Many members of my class hadn't received flight assignments yet, so I felt honored. None of my crewmates were my best friends, but I liked all of them. I thought it would be a good, solid first mission, and it would prepare me for one of the major science payloads downstream that I wanted to do.

The launch date was mid-1984, so we were already late getting started on our one year training plan. After our newly-formed crew gathered for hugs, handshakes, and high fives, we knew that we had a lot of work ahead of us and that we were going to work closely together for many months. Everyone had children, and I liked all the spouses – and so did Hoot. This was going to be fun!

Dividing up the duties on the flight was the first task. Bo was the commander, and Don was the pilot. Dave would serve as the flight engineer. They would be in charge of all the flying and related systems. Who would be assigned to train for possible spacewalks, one of the most difficult and exciting part of any mission? I wasn't even in the running for that assignment. I couldn't fit into the spacesuits. When the spacesuits with their hard upper torso shells were designed, no one considered petite women. To get into the upper suit, I had to put my arms up through the waist ring and out through the armholes, allowing my head to pop up through the neck ring. The problem was that the hard body of the suit had to allow my arms and head through and then fit snugly under my arms. For me, it didn't. The chest portion was too large, so my arms stuck out to the side and were useless. I tried a smaller chest segment and try as I might, suffering terrible bruises in the bargain, I couldn't get my arms and head up through it. The same problem befell some of the other smaller females.

Spacewalks on our mission were not scheduled, but two crewmembers were trained on each flight for contingencies, such as closing and latching the payload bay doors if the automatic system failed. An unplanned space-walk had never happened on a shuttle flight, but almost all the mission specialists wanted to do suit training because it put them in line for an exciting, planned spacewalk on a future mission. This plum went to Dave and Jeff.

I had completed initial training on the mechanical arm or Remote Manipulator System (RMS), so I was named the prime RMS operator for deploying and retrieving the SPARTAN telescope with Jeff as my backup. As for launching the two expensive satellites, Jeff and Dave would do the first deployment and I'd do the second with Dave's help. We were behind in our training. We would stay behind for over 20 months, and we'd still launch not a hundred percent trained for the mission we performed.

It was a busy and stressful time. For a first flight, there was a lot to learn.

Astronauts, pilots or not, were expected to know a huge amount about all of the systems aboard the shuttle: electrical, computer, communications, hydraulics, propulsion, and so on. I'd had some training on those systems as an ASCAN and had delved into others in my technical assignment in the avionics lab. But now I had to learn them in detail especially how they were linked to the payloads I was responsible for and how failures in those systems would affect the work I'd be doing.

One secondary payload that caught my interest was a medical experiment called the American Flight Echocardiograph. It was a small, off-the-shelf ultrasound machine that used sound waves to generate pictures of the heart. Scientists knew from the Skylab flights in the 1970s that an astronaut's blood redistributed in weightlessness. On Earth, if someone holds up a water-filled balloon, gravity pulls on the water so the balloon is pear-shaped. Take away gravity, and the balloon would take on a round shape as the water became more evenly distributed. That's what medical scientists thought was going on with fluids inside the body. Astronauts' faces became puffy and the veins of their neck stood out as their legs got skinnier when they first reached space. The theory was that there would be more blood in the central part of the body, and the heart would swell up. The heart might also shift and be pointed more to the left side rather than hanging downward; however, no one had been able to look at the heart in space, and this would be the first opportunity.

We were planning to fly with the American Flight Echocardiograph which would take pictures of the human heart in space for the first time.

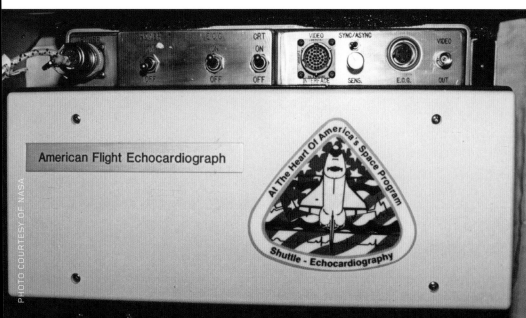

SPARTAN, a small telescope, would fly in our cargo bay. It would be deployed and retrieved using the large mechanical arm, the Remote Manipulator System or RMS.

A young MD biomedical engineer named Dave Wolf had been assigned to "fly-bidize" the echo machine – that is, hybridize it, so it could fly in space. The off-the-shelf unit would have to be modified to meet NASA standards, to pass the testing necessary to fly on the shuttle and to interface with the craft's electrical and data recording systems. Dave was confident those things wouldn't be a problem. From my space scientist's perspective, gathering important medical data was more interesting than launching satellites or retrieving telescopes.

During the extensive testing, I came to respect Dave Wolf's can-do spirit. After making all the required engineering changes, he sent his precious, highly modified piece of hardware to White Sands Missile Range in New Mexico for what was known as "Shake and Bake." Here machines scheduled for flight were shaken like crazy to make sure they wouldn't fly apart or cease to work from the strain and vibration of launch. They were also heated to ensure they wouldn't melt or "off-gas," releasing any noxious fumes if the shuttle's temperature rose on the pad while awaiting lift off.

Unfortunately someone set the oven temperature too high, baked the gear too long, and melted the darn thing. I couldn't believe how calm Dave was when he told me about it. He said he already had the parts to build a new one and assured me it would be ready in time for flight. Dave's path and mine would cross many times in the years to come, and it became a mutually beneficial relationship.

In January of 1984 as if the scramble to get Hoot off on his first flight the next month and training for my own first flight weren't enough, Mr. Abbey (at a beer party, of course) asked if I'd also like to fly on the Spacelab

4 mission. It was to launch in January of 1986 aboard *Columbia*. It was the flight I had been hoping for all along, having followed my mentor Dr. Joe Kerwin across the country talking to the scientists who hoped to have experiments on board.

Could I fly in mid-1984 then be ready to go on an ambitious science mission, one that needed two years of training in a mere 18 months? Was it going to be too much with being a wife and mother, working in the ER, and learning to be both subject and operator for about two dozen science experiments from all over the world...all while working on my first flight? Adopting the can-do spirit of my astronaut friends, I didn't express those concerns to George as I accepted the assignment.

Fate ensured there would be plenty of time.

All of this brought home to me that I would have to work out my priorities. With my 24 hour day, I

The large simulator facility where RMS training took place.

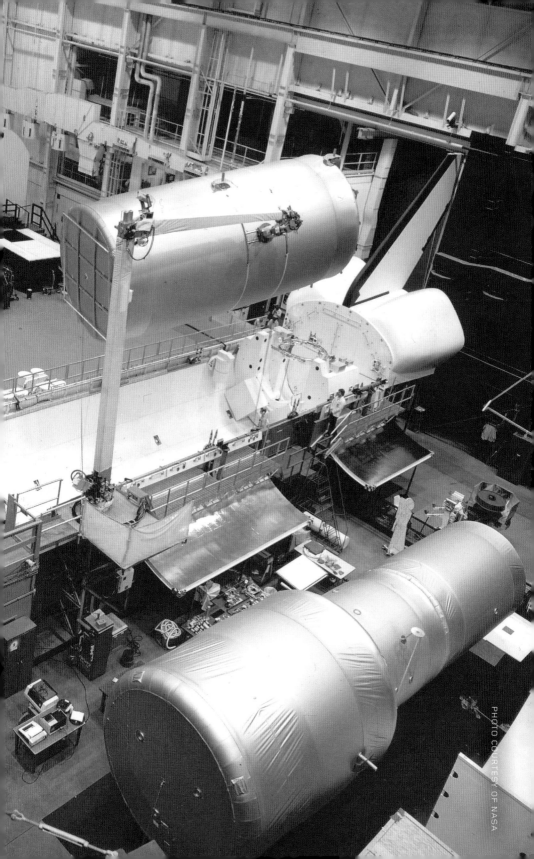

had to perform two full-time (mom and astronaut) and at least three part time (physician, wife, and home) jobs. Each day, each week, I had to parcel out the hours. Training for my two flights occupied the hours from about 8:00 a.m. to 6:00 p.m. Hoot, Paul, the house, my friends and family members, my ER practice, and--oh yes--my needs, had to fit into the hours between 6:00 p.m. and 8:00 a.m. as well as the weekends.

It was insane.

Most days I didn't feel like I was doing a good job at anything: never enough sleep, no time to eat right, not able to get all the studying and paperwork done, let alone make it to the gym. Hoot was busy with his flight and post-flight work, Shirley Baruth, my babysitter, had her two children to worry about after work hours, and grandparents were far away. It was a difficult time, and it wouldn't get a lot better for many years.

One of the first things Bo decided when our crew was assigned was that we should have a crew meeting every Monday at 7:30 a.m., before the 8:00 a.m. all-astronaut meeting. That made sense for everyone except for the working mother on the crew. Since this was my first flight and I was the first of the women astronauts to have had a baby, I didn't want to ask for favors. Hoot had his own Monday morning meetings, and Shirley couldn't get her children on the bus and arrive at my house until a little before 8:00 a.m. It wasn't possible to get a babysitter for half an hour on Monday mornings. At first I felt like I was looking at another brick on the bottom of the swimming pool. Thank goodness for wonderful neighbors. Luanne Fagan who lived next door had four grown children. She found out about the problem, and (bless her heart) volunteered to come over every Monday morning about 7:15 and look after Paul until Shirley got there. She kept saying it was such a little thing to do, but I appreciated it beyond measure.

Then, in June of 1984, when our flight had slipped to August, everything went haywire. Hank Hartsfield's flight was before ours. As they sat on the launch pad awaiting launch, a frightening thing happened. The countdown proceeded past 10-9-8-7-6, and the main engines started right on cue – 5 -4 -3. Then there was an ominous silence. I'm sure there were some expletives and some increased heart rates in the cockpit. The main engines had shut down just before liftoff for the first time in the shuttle's history. Crewmember Steve Hawley, sitting atop that swaying stack of explosives, always a quick wit, said "Gee, I thought we'd be a lot higher at Main Engine Cut-off."

Things were not so humorous in the Launch Control Center (LCC). For a few tense moments no one was sure what was going on. Were the boosters safe, or was there some chance they would fire unexpectedly? Via the launch pad cameras, everyone could see heat shimmering below the engines. Was there an invisible hydrogen fire? Should the crew evacuate the orbiter quickly, run across the cat walk, and escape from this massive bomb by scooting Earthward in the none-too-safe slide wire baskets? Told to sit tight on top of over four million pounds of explosives with a possible fire going on underneath, they put their faith – and lives – in the hands of the calm and competent people in the Launch Control Center. All astronauts understood through folklore, history, and extensive training with the control centers in Houston and the Cape that at times in their missions they'd have to put their trust in others. Ground controllers had more data and more people with more extensive systems knowledge. During the Apollo 11 moon landing, a young Steven Bales in Houston Mission Control avoided a close-to-the-moon abort of the landing by understanding that a malfunction warning light was not a critical failure, and he passed the word to the Flight Director Gene Kranz to continue. Trust – we knew that our lives could depend on the decisions made by others.

Back in Houston, those of us who had taken a break from our work to watch the launch in our conference room rocketed from sitting calmly in our chairs to standing and shouting our opinions:

"Get them out of there!"

"The thing is going to blow up! Put out the fire!"

"They're safer in the cockpit, you guys!"

Eventually, amidst a deluge pouring water from the fire suppression system that had been activated, the launch pad team was given the go-ahead to swing the access arm back to the shuttle, open the hatch, and evacuate the crew down the elevator.

It was a close call.

Oh, the ripple effect it had on my crew!

NASA management decided to combine the payload from Hank's aborted flight and most of ours and to use our launch date for this re-configured mission in August. When announced, no one had told our crew what this meant for us. We were seven weeks from launch, and a press release came out announcing that our mission had vanished from the schedule. Most of our training had been completed. All of the guest invitations had been mailed. All but the final preparations had been completed. We were ready to go, so close to flying. We all felt like we had been erased from the history of the world. We had no idea what our boss, George Abbey's, plans were for us. Never had I been so shocked, angered, and disappointed in my life.

I called my father and ranted. I raged to Hoot until he got tired of listening. I thought about getting in my car and abandoning the whole place. I envisioned myself confronting George, telling him he was both unfair for bumping us and cruel for not talking to us about it. How much longer would we have to wait to fly – or were we even a crew anymore? What would it do to my assignment to the Spacelab flight?

Our bad luck continued. The next flight was Bob Crippen's, and he was of such stature that no one messed with his flight. It also featured Sally on her second flight and Kathy Sullivan, who was slated to be the first woman to do a spacewalk. After that was Rick Hauck's flight to retrieve the two satellites that had failed on Hoot's flight the previous February. Joe Allen and Dale Gardner had spent endless hours in the spacesuits working out the procedures to grab the lifeless satellites and stow them in the payload bay. For a brief time we had the faint hope we might bump them and get that exciting flight. It turned out that mission wouldn't be ours.

So where did we fit in? The end of the line? It wasn't that bad, but almost. A Tracking and Data Relay satellite (TDRS) was to be launched in March of 1985, about nine months away. That satellite was so massive and heavy that there would be no mechanical arm, no echocardiograph experiment, no other interesting payloads, but it became ours, and we were three months late getting started on the year-long training.

Bo gave us all two weeks off until the dust settled. We sent hundreds of letters to the guests who we'd invited to attend our launch during their summer vacations and suggested they replan for March next year. It seemed so unfair. I went from being the third woman in our ASCAN group to fly to the fifth. I would also not be the first mother in space because Anna Fisher's daughter Kristin had been born in 1983, a year after Paul, and she would be on Rick Hauck's flight in the fall. In the grand scheme of life perhaps these weren't major losses, but they were important to me. Everyone wanted to be near the front of the line with their flights and to be the first at something. Having two weeks off to regroup, to remember that I was going to fly in space, and to know that no one would remember in what order we flew gave me a little bit better perspective.

In the ensuing months there were many other surprises. French Payload Specialist Patrick Baudry was assigned to our flight. Payload specialists were non-astronauts assigned to certain shuttle missions, either as technical or scientific experts or to represent foreign governments. Patrick was bringing along several medical experiments, one of them a French

Patrick Baudry from France was added to our crew when we were reassigned to STS-51E *(above)*. Baudry's name was added to our patch and the orbiter was switched to Challenger. There was nothing we could do about the now incorrect sixteen stars on the flag *(below)*.

ultrasound machine that could take images of the heart much like the one I had trained on. Since he was a pilot, not a scientist, I was asked to serve as his back-up for the studies. I had the opportunity to go to France to meet the investigators and to learn more about the machine. While I looked forward to the data that would be collected, I was sad that this important work wouldn't be done by our AFE, the echo machine I'd trained on, the first letter of which stood for American. Meanwhile, we had to change the orbiter

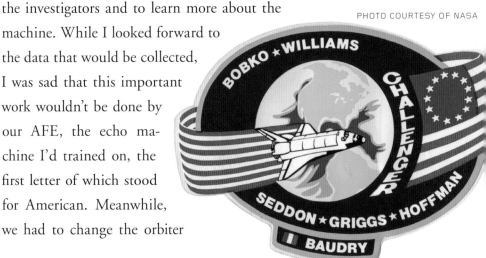

name on our patch from *Discovery* to *Challenger* and to change our crew patch to include Patrick's name. We also had our crew picture retaken to include him.

A few months later, for unknown reasons, NASA decided to fly a politician in space. Utah Republican Jake Garn was a member of the Senate Appropriations Committee and served as chairman of the HUD-Independent Agencies Subcommittee, which determined NASA's funding. He had been agitating for a flight for some time. He would later tell me that he never thought NASA would consider it, but he gave it a try and was amazed when the administrator offered him a seat. It wasn't that Jake didn't have good qualifications. He was a former Navy pilot and had thousands of hours flying tanker aircraft for the Utah National Guard. He knew how to be a part of a flight crew. Though he was in his 50s, he was in great physical shape, running several miles a day. Unlike many politicians, he was straight talking and willing to be a junior person on the crew, asking no special favors. He had made a trip to JSC, and we'd met him, but no one knew then which flight he'd be assigned to.

We were training in the simulator one day in November when Bo was called to Mr. Abbey's office. We wondered if it was to put this guy Garn, on our flight. Most of the crew felt at the time that it was an unnecessary annoyance we'd prefer to do without. Sure enough, Bo came back 20 minutes later and wrote us a note so our instructors who monitored conversations in the simulator cockpit wouldn't hear the news which wasn't public yet. It said, "Garn has been assigned to our flight." I remember remarking at the time, "Well, you just never know. This might be a good thing in the end."

Again, new patches had to be ordered with an additional name on them, another crew picture to be taken. New job assignments were passed out, one of which was to help get Jake ready for the flight. Mike Smith, one of the younger astronauts in our office, was assigned to escort Jake through training. Jake got to know Mike and his family well and never forgot their kindness. One day, he would return that favor.

Jake asked to have something useful to do on the flight. The medical scientists came up with a number of experiments for him to do to see how he adapted to weightlessness. Gary Trudeau spoofed him in his Doonesbury cartoon series as "Barfin' Jake Garn" because a number of the studies were looking at space motion sickness. Jake had never been sick in the many airplanes he'd flown, so he wasn't sure he'd be a good subject for the experiment but he signed up. It told us something about Jake that he laughed at the comic strips right along with the rest of us.

PHOTO COURTESY OF NASA

We were introduced to Jake's legislative aide, Jeff Bingham.

Jake Garn suddenly became part of our crew and a new crew picture was made *(below)*. Garn's name was added to the patch *(right)*.

PHOTO COURTESY OF NASA

We were fascinated in those days before personal cell phones to have a guy tagging around with us who had a briefcase with a huge cellular phone in it. It kept them in touch with all the goings-on in our nation's capital.

Jake, being the good Mormon that he was, had married early and had a family of four children. Then tragically his first wife Hazel was killed in a car accident. The children had been in the car with her and when Jake received the call from the police, he thought for a while all of the children had died, too. He wrote about this in his book *Why I Believe*. I couldn't imagine him thinking all of his family had been killed, and then finding the children alive and uninjured at the hospital when he arrived. He later remarried and he and Kathleen (who had a son from a previous marriage,) had two more children of their own. Their Christmas card each year showed the ever increasing size of their extended, blended, and wonderful family.

Time marched down to our March 7, 1985 launch date. In the meantime, Hank Hartsfield's crew flew on our original launch date. Kathy Sullivan became the first United States female spacewalker, and Sally made her second flight. Then STS-51A's satellite retrieval mission was a success with two spectacular spacewalks and Anna operating the arm and becoming the first mother in space. Our crew plugged away at learning how to launch the huge TDRS satellite attached to the Inertial Upper Stage, a massive booster that would propel it to the proper geosynchronous orbit of about 22.000 miles above Earth. The behemoth filled almost the entire payload bay and looked like a missile with a pointy satellite on top and a rocket stage with one large solitary nozzle on the back. Its aft end was locked into a tilt table that would elevate it about 60 degrees, so it cleared the crew compartment when it propelled out of its holder into space over the top of our heads. We practiced how to deploy it under normal conditions, then how to send it out despite multiple possible failures requiring the activation of back-up systems.

We went down to the Cape for a practice run for the launch. We strapped into the orbiter, went through a simulated countdown then practiced how we would escape from the vehicle in an emergency. The craziest part of the day was learning to drive an armored personnel carrier away from the launch pad. There I was, my head poked out the top of a tank, driving through the scrub brush pretending to get away from an exploding spacecraft. Being an astronaut brought some interesting and unusual experiences.

Then, when we were least expecting it and without warning, a week before our launch date, when we were about to go into quarantine, some sort of defect was identified in the booster. The shuttle would have to be rolled back from the pad, the satellite and booster taken out and returned to the factory. We felt like the most snake-bit crew that had ever existed. Would we ever fly? This time, Mr. Abbey told us face to face, and he had a plan ready for our future.

We would take over the next mission, flying soon, a few weeks hence in late March, with PAM and Syncom satellites like the ones on the earlier mission for which we had trained. Some of the secondary payloads would be switched around. No one was sure which of the payload specialists (our Baudry and Garn or the ones from the flight we were taking over, Charlie Walker and Greg Jarvis) would be with us. And we'd again switch orbiters, from *Challenger* back to *Discovery*.

Charlie Walker had a good reason to fly with us. A McDonnell Douglas engineer, his large piece of scientific equipment, the Continuous Flow Electrophoresis System, was already bolted to the middeck floor of *Discovery*. For a while it looked like we would have Greg Jarvis. As for Jake, he was taking time from his senatorial duties, and at the beginning of our training had told George Abbey that he didn't care when he flew…as long as it was with the crew he'd trained with. Patrick's experiments were stowed in small, movable lockers in the middeck, allowing him to move to a later flight. Poor

Greg got bumped downstream…until he launched on a vehicle that would be his doom. It was decided. Garn and Walker would be with us, and we went back to the patch designer and the photo lab once again. In the end, we would have four different crew pictures, four different crew patches, three different payloads, and two different orbiters. After that, the payload specialists names were put on a separate tab that could be sewn on then taken off and replaced by another if the crew changed. No longer would the orbiter name go on the patch.

For the third time, we were behind in our training. George, NASA management, and the payload world trusted that we could be ready to fly. The launch slipped a few weeks into April, but we had barely enough time to go back and brush up on the satellite training we'd stopped working on the previous July. Fortunately there was room for the American echocardiograph, so I set about relearning it. The RMS, the mechanical arm, was back. The one thing required was to drape the arm across the payload bay and look past the belly of the orbiter to make sure the booster on the PAM ignited. This procedure was an easy, programmed maneuver, so I was limited to three or four simulator sessions. I didn't know then that RMS operations would be my most important and exciting task on this flight, and the whole world would be watching.

We didn't feel entirely prepared to fly when we entered our pre-flight quarantine, but we weren't too worried since it was going to be a pretty dull five-day mission with nothing new except the echocardiograph and Jake. Much of the press focus was on the senator, which he deflected with grace, but it was still a letdown not doing anything different or newsworthy. The world had even gotten used to having a woman onboard. But getting ready for spaceflight was exciting to us, and we were more than anxious to get underway.

Quarantine wasn't fun, but it served several purposes. Since most illnesses in healthy young people are due to viruses or bacteria, exposure to others was restricted. Beginning seven days before launch, we couldn't be around children under 18 or anyone who didn't have a *primary contact* badge. A primary contact needed a reason to be near the crew, like our trainers, the food preparation people, upper management, and—of course—our spouses. Each had to pass a brief physical exam. Passing these two hurdles entitled people to

PHOTO COURTESY OF NASA

When our second mission was canceled our crew was reassigned to STS-51D. Charlie Walker and Jake Garn now became the crew *(below)*. Our fourth crew patch with the final crew complement and our orbiter, *Discovery (right)*.

PHOTO COURTESY OF NASA

a large yellow PC badge that said they were special and important. If the badge's owner became sick, he or she had to report to the clinic and give up this special status.

The Flight Medicine Clinic would post notices around the JSC when quarantine went into effect. The crew went few places, but the rules said that personnel who weren't PCs had to clear the way if they saw them coming. The crazy government rulebook even said if a crew member was outside, the person had to remain at least 10 meters downwind of them. We thought about wearing caps with windsocks on top, so people could tell where downwind was.

To attract attention and stress the necessity of keeping the crew healthy, the Health Stabilization Plan (as it was called) displayed humorous posters when quarantine went into effect. Cartoonish green fungi asking "Is there a fungus among us?" and "Don't blow our launch!" showing someone sneezing appeared across the Center.

In the early 1980s, the crew quarters for quarantine at JSC were awful. For several days until we left for the Cape, we were required to live in ancient trailers in an empty warehouse, and upper management wasn't in any particular hurry to improve conditions. The crews slept on sagging mattresses in musty surroundings with noisy, underpowered air conditioners. We'd go to a separate trailer outside for meals, where the food prep ladies weren't pleased about their cramped quarters. In the warehouse was a lounge area with a pool table and TV: if anyone was awake, everyone was awake. Shifting our sleep schedules to coincide with what our sleep times on orbit would be was difficult because the trailer's window blinds did a poor job of filtering light. Despite the miserable quarters, we figured they got us away from home responsibilities, allowing us to relax and cram for the final exam—our flight.

It also was a bonding experience for this *camping trip* in space we were about to begin. Our crew had gotten to know one another well through all our training, trials, and tribulations. Bo Bobko, our Commander, was even-tempered and often made fun of himself and his ancestors from Poland. We had gotten together to review our checklists, and put personal reminders in them a few days earlier. While the rest of us were working with our yellow highlighters, Bo picked up a fat black marker.

"Bo, what are you about to do with that?" someone asked.

Bo looked a little sheepish then said, "Oh, this is a Polish highlighter."

Bo's relaxed demeanor was counterbalanced by the serious one of our pilot, Don Williams, who watched us all to make sure everything was done per the checklists. Dave Griggs was the Flight Engineer, also known as the Mission Specialist 2. A man's man, Dave didn't lay much store by small talk but was focused on doing his job well. I sometimes felt that he wasn't sure women ought to be astronauts. Jeff was Mission Specialist 3 and my intellectual soul mate. A graduate of Amherst College, Rice University, and Harvard, he was well read and from a family of doctors. He had even volunteered to train with me as one of the two Crew Medical Officers for the flight. I told him I'd give him an honorary medical degree to show his family. Charlie Walker was Payload Specialist 1, and he had made his first flight the previous year. I had gotten to know him when I helped get his electrophoresis experiment ready for the crew of STS 6 to operate, and we were old friends. Jake Garn, Payload Specialist 2, still couldn't believe he was going with us, and he was doing his darnedest to be a valuable member of the crew.

My guest list for launch had dwindled considerably with all the delays. When I was to launch the previous summer, an army of friends had wanted to come as part of their summer vacations. When the flight slipped to March, some of them couldn't take children out of school. Then when we slipped to mid-April at the last minute, many of the rest gave up. Rebooking plane reservations, changing hotel dates, rearranging work and school schedules: it was a wonder anyone came but, as it turned out many did.

I had started out with so many guests that I couldn't be assured of having room at the Officers' Club for the prelaunch reception, so I located another venue for the get-together and worked out a menu with a caterer, all this completed in my *spare time*. Then I turned the details over to Hoot and my father.

In April of 1985, Paul was less than three years old. Shirley Baruth, the lady who'd stayed with him as a baby, had left to have a baby of her own the previous August. Paul had started into a pre-school program, but we knew Hoot would have his hands full if we didn't get some help. Through a local family, we found out about a young French girl, Claire Dehaye, who wanted to come to the United States to improve her English. We paid her way over, and she stayed with us to make sure someone was around the house in the mornings and at night when Paul was home.

Being in quarantine was difficult for me and for Paul. He wasn't old enough to talk on the phone well, and he didn't understand why I couldn't be with him if I was living so close by. Hoot, Claire, his preschool teachers, and I all worked hard to make things easier for him, but I felt a mother's guilt.

As the time to leave for the Cape approached, I began to get the usual willies that I supposed some people got (but most of the men wouldn't admit to), thinking of all the single point failures in the shuttle that could end in disaster. As I worried more and telephone conversations became less and less satisfactory, I had this tremendous urge to see Paul one more time. He was well, and I knew I'd only spend a few minutes saying goodbye. Making an excuse that I had to run over to the office after work hours, I slipped out of the front gate and toward home, a short two miles. As I sat in the playroom and Paul played with my car keys (his favorite thing to do), I told him one more time that I loved him. I held his little face in my hands and made him look at me. I told him to remember my face until I got home from space. His little blue-green eyes peered into mine, and I prayed it wouldn't be the last time he saw me. Sometimes kids pick up on the fact that a moment is of some higher importance, and he gave me one of his best little hugs and a big kiss. I wondered if I was doing the right thing to be risking my life going on this flight but then I was out the door off to a launch, tears streaming down my face.

The flight to the Cape from Houston was exciting. NASA crew members would go in the T-38 jets. The Payload Specialists Charlie and Jake would go on another NASA plane and meet us there. Bo, Don, and Dave all wanted to pilot a plane and Jeff would fly in one of their back seats. A couple of the flight surgeons needed rides, so we decided to enlist Hoot's help. As the *Florida Today* newspaper reported on its front page along with a picture of us, Hoot flew me to work that day. Our sleek jets pulled alongside each other west of Cape Canaveral for the traditional fly-by of the launch pad where our orbiter waited. Our four-plane formation pulled into a snug diamond pattern as we passed over the landing strip and made a low pass around the pad. Employees at the Cape would hear the unusual roar of jets flying low overhead and know that the crew was arriving. Some would stand outside, shade their eyes from the sun, and be excited along with us that this day had arrived. It was their launch, too: all of those fine people who worked every day to make launches happen.

Discovery was cocooned like a butterfly in a massive metallic carapace called the Rotating Service Structure, and the spacecraft stood in silence on the mobile launch platform. Workers like army ants dashed around below and around her. Suddenly, it all became real, and I peered at the vehicle as long as I could, hoping to sense that she was strong and perfect and ready to carry us safely on our journey.

We landed our jets with military precision at the Shuttle Landing Facility, and the other spouses walked out to greet us, along with Jake and Charlie. The crew then said a few words and answered a few questions for the waiting reporters before we were whisked off to the crew quarters for dinner.

The next two days were filled with a busy schedule of events: final systems briefs, weather forecasts, helmet fits, and equipment checks—all of which would culminate with a ride out to the launch pad on the appointed day. If all went well, that would occur on April 12, the 24th anniversary of Yuri Gagarin's flight, the first human spaceflight. It would also be the fourth anniversary of the first space shuttle launch. I took this to be a good omen.

Hoot had flown the year before and understood that there was a lot of last minute stress before flying, and he took over all the family and guest responsibilities in Florida. Julie had flown in from California with

When a crew flies to the Kennedy Space Center for launch they are allowed to fly at a low altitude around the launch pad. It makes an exciting arrival.

PHOTO COURTESY OF NASA

Grandma Rita and Grandpa Paul and she would get to see this launch holding her daddy's hand. My father had come from Tennessee to be close by in case of problems and, as we called his rather formal social behavior, *hold court* at the prelaunch reception. He was a proud parent, not quite sure how his little girl came to this.

The forecast for launch morning was rotten. Clouds and rain were predicted with little chance of acceptable weather, but there was nothing much to do but hope and warn our guests there might be yet another delay.

Once again, Hoot and I walked the beach at the beach house in the warming spring weather. Again, the ocean lapped around our feet, and I looked for one perfect shell for our collection. I was more melancholy than he was and more worried about what would happen to Paul if I wasn't around in the future. I had learned about Hoot that he didn't deal with my emotions well. He wanted to be able to fix everything, and if he couldn't, he pretended there was nothing to worry about. So, we talked less about the bad things that could happen and more about the flight, the guest reception, and the plans for when I got back home. My second flight had slipped later into 1986, but we knew I'd come back to a hectic schedule. Hoot's second flight was planned for late in 1985, about seven months away, so we had much to anticipate and a busy year ahead.

Bo had decreed that brunch the day before launch would be the last time spouses could visit. That way, we would have a quiet afternoon for a last minute review, supper at our leisure, and time for a full night's sleep before our long-before-dawn wake-up call for an early morning launch. At that last get-together, Hoot and I had time to visit and go over the details for the afternoon's pre-launch reception. I was sorry that I wouldn't get to see my guests because of our quarantine. They were all good friends and interesting people from many different phases of my life, and it would have been fun to introduce them to one another.

We had a last hug at the third floor elevator outside crew quarters and a last long look into each other's eyes. How many good-byes had taken place there before and would in years to come? Up until that time, they had been brief good-byes and not final farewells, so there were only vague twinges of fear that something bad would happen.

Our crew spent the afternoon outside the crew quarters catching a few last rays of sun, reading through our timelines, and reviewing procedures one last time. Despite the fact that this was the third payload we'd trained for and it had been ours for a mere six weeks, we felt confident we knew it all well enough. It was all straight forward and little could go wrong, we told ourselves.

No one sleeps well the night before launch, especially a rooky like me. Even though I knew all my tasks, I went over them in my mind again and again. I worried about doing something wrong or stupid. All of us by then had adopted the fighter pilot creed: *Better dead than look bad.* About the time I'd worn myself out worrying about everything and had drifted off to sleep, the knock on the door came and a voice announced "Wake up time!"

The head of the Vehicle Integration team at the Cape was Rick Nygren, and he was verifying that everyone was up and moving. He had instructed us on packing up our bags the night before. He'd make sure one bag would go to wherever we landed and would take the other to our homes in Houston. As I had packed them, I decided I needed to write a short note to Hoot in case I didn't come back. I worried that my bags might never be unpacked after a disaster, so on flight morning I entrusted that note to Rick. He assured me he'd give it back to me at landing. He'd done that for many astronauts. Then a quick phone call to Hoot, and it was time to get ready.

Everyone scrambled for the bathrooms and enjoyed what would be our last shower in many days if the launch went off that morning. Everyone was squeaky clean as we sat down for the traditional crew breakfast photo op.

The crew's traditional pre-launch breakfast before dressing for the launch.

What to eat for breakfast? In the days when men were men (and only men were astronauts), steak and eggs were de rigueur. Then, once spacecraft got large enough and those manly men began floating around in zero G soon after launch, motion sickness became a problem. The dictum then became "Don't eat anything you wouldn't want to see in a few hours in its undigested state."

Coffee and toast became more popular.

The traditional cake with our crew patch on it graced the table. It would be frozen after we launched, transported back to Houston, and eaten post-flight. NASA cameras were capturing us smiling and horsing around, broadcasting us on NASA TV to whoever wanted to see. I knew our spouses and children would gather around the television in the Launch Control Center where they were waiting.

"There's Mommy!" Hoot would be telling little Paul, dressed in his blue flightsuit that matched mine.

Dressing for launch mornings for the first twenty five flights of the shuttle were simple. Besides our *Columbia* blue flight suits and underwear there were our helmets...*and* some form of urine collection device. After Alan Shepard had been delayed on the launch pad on America's first human spaceflight and had peed inside his pressure suit, risking electrical short circuits in the electrodes taped to his body, solutions had been found for this problem. The men all wore an external catheter, a roll-on condom connected to tubing with a bag strapped to their body. It was not 100 percent satisfactory, I had been told. It could become uncomfortable, it sometimes leaked, and some men couldn't urinate lying on their backs with their feet in the air the way we sat for launch. Nonetheless, it was all that was available for them at the time.

When the women came along, more gender-specific technology was needed. Something was required for both the occasional interminable holds on the launch pad and for inside the spacesuits women would wear during spacewalks. Several external contraptions were designed and tested, but none was comfortable or reliable. Eventually we all settled on a diaper-like device, called in NASA-ese, the Disposable Absorption Containment Trunk, or DACT. Built like an old-fashioned panty girdle, it had disposable diaper material in the front, back, and crotch areas. Snug around the waist and thighs, it was designed to hold about 1000 cc of urine, the most anyone could imagine we'd ever produce at one wearing. There was a powder between the absorbent layers that turned to gel when exposed to liquid which helped keep the wearer dry. If it was full, however, it felt like sitting in a bowl of Jell-O when you sat down.

Since the DACTs had to fit well, they were custom designed for each of the women. They cost hundreds of dollars each, and we went through a number of them during training exercises and actual flights. We were given a couple to take home for *practice*. I was surprised to find that once potty-trained, it was difficult for an adult to wet her pants. One had to be stowed on the shuttle for landing, as well as a couple more in case the landing was delayed once or twice. They did serve their purpose, and NASA may have helped push the technology for diapers and absorbent adult underwear, even if the DACTs also made the wearer look about 10 pounds heavier in her flightsuit.

The helmet designed for shuttle flights was simple. It opened like a clamshell and had a rubber face seal in front, providing fresh air from the shuttle supply or from an air bottle for breathing when disconnected from the ship. And it filtered out the deafening roar of launch. Outfitted with earphones and a microphone, it also made communication with the ground and each other possible. Other than that, we

The women wore a diaper device under their flightsuit called the DACT, the Disposable Absorption Containment Trunk.

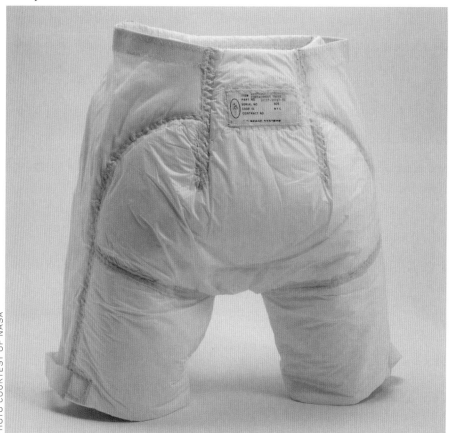

PHOTO COURTESY OF NASA

A small harness was worn over the Columbia blue flight suit.

flew in our special *Columbia* blue flight-suits and flight boots.

Why was there so little safety or survival equipment? None of us then questioned it, although it was different from earlier flights in which crews wore pressure suits and had parachutes. We were led to believe this was an *advanced* era of working in a shirt-sleeved environment, and additional equipment wouldn't be needed. There was no way provided to get out of the orbiter in flight, so we had no need for parachutes. We would later learn that there had been considerable discussion during the shuttle design phase about doing business this way. The Astronaut Office had fought for an escape system to be able to bail out of a disabled craft but was overruled by the people who had to figure out how to design and pay for it.

We had a quick weather briefing. The morning of April 12, 1985 looked like a bad choice for a launch day. There were low clouds and rain at the Cape and the forecast for the entire launch window wasn't supposed to get any better. There were so many weather reports that all had to be good – emergency landing sites in Africa, the runways at the Cape and at Edwards – in case of failures getting to orbit. It was miraculous shuttles ever got off the ground. There was some chance the clouds would part enough over the Cape runway for us to fly through, so off to the pad we headed.

People all over the world see astronauts emerging from the crew quarters to board the Astrovan for the ride to the pad. Many of the pictures come from overhead cameras, so it looks like we come out of some sort of triumphal archway. Spouses and other visitors on tours are often surprised to see the real exit door and how inauspicious it is. It is a plain, unassuming back door to the Operations and Control Building, leading to a back alley housing various empty gas tanks and other pieces of stored equipment.

On launch morning, however, this area takes on all the glow of a pathway for conquering heroes. Many of the people who had been working so hard to get the vehicle and the crew ready, many of them familiar faces to us, lined the path out of the building and to the van. Lights for the video cameras glared into our faces, and flash bulbs blinded us the minute we stepped off the elevator. I was surprised to see my congressman, Bart Gordon, in the contingent. He had come to see the launch. A cheer went up, and we already felt on top of the world.

The Astrovan, a shiny silver converted motor home, stood at the end of the alley waiting for the crew and a few higher ups. (Later we would see a picture of this event in the newspaper. While the crew was properly named, our boss George Abbey was labeled "an unidentified NASA official," which is how we often referred to him after that.) We rolled into the pre-dawn darkness for the short trip out to the launch pad. There were cars parked at the side of the roadway early on launch morning. There were workers coming and going, making all the final preparations. Our security escort had red lights flashing as we sped along, and other vehicles pulled off the road to let us pass. For once, we didn't have to show our NASA identification badges at the security gate that led to the launch complex.

The van stopped at the turn in front of the Vehicle Assembly Building to let the Chief of the Astronaut Office, John Young, disembark, allowing him to fly the weather check flight for us. We begged him to find a hole in the clouds, so we could launch that day. He vowed to try his best. Others on the van who would watch the countdown from the nearby Launch Control Center, the LCC, stepped out there, too, wishing us a good flight. It was down to us and the driver who left us to our reverie.

The LCC's windows faced east toward the pad where the sun had not yet risen. As we passed it, we knew that our families had arrived there and would be watching our van's lights as we streaked out into the darkness to our awaiting vehicle. All along the road from the small buildings and the cars that were pulled out of the way, gathered clumps of people who clapped, cheered, and gave us the thumbs up sign as we passed. Launch mornings for the shuttle were spectacular at the Kennedy Space Center. There was a great feeling of camaraderie, of team spirit. We knew that when the boosters ignited, a little part of each of those people would leap off the pad with us.

Soon, the buildings, cars, and people were left behind, and we entered a dark stretch of road. Suddenly, almost unexpectedly, there—ahead— loomed *Discovery*, our spacecraft. Close, huge, steaming, it waited, lit up like Christmas by huge xenon spot lights shining up on it. No longer shrouded in its preparatory chrysalis, it seemed alone and fragile, like a bride at the altar. There was almost a communal gasp from those of us in the van as we stood up and strained forward to see the awesome sight. She was our ticket to space today. Would all her pieces and parts hold together? Would the weather cooperate?

The van pulled all the way up to the bottom of the launch tower. Always before, it had stopped at a fence down the hill, and we'd had to walk up. Today, we were not tourists or workers; we were "the crew." We had a brief moment to look around the base of the pad, empty of all equipment then and devoid of people except those who would help us strap in. It was ominous and eerie. I had only seconds to savor that moment and to ponder my fate.

We boarded the ancient, rusted metal elevator that had whisked Apollo and shuttle crews before us to the tops of their rockets. Along with the launch pad itself, the elevator had withstood the rocket blasts from blazing spaceships for almost two decades. Up we went, all the way to the 195-foot level (our ascent measured in feet rather than floors like a normal elevator) where a walkway led out to the White Room, a small antechamber at the end of the retractable arm that snuggled up against the crew hatch. It was a cool, damp spring morning with drizzle starting to fall. As I waited for the crew compartment to be readied, I walked out on the gantryway and saw the first faint light of dawn to the east over the vast waters of the Atlantic. The vehicle groaned as various fuels were loaded on-board and hissed as gasses vented. Like a mighty race horse snorting impatiently in the starting gate, *Discovery* had come alive.

There was a feeling of anticipation that the moment had come to begin our spaceflight. Having been through so many delays getting to this point and knowing that the weather was not good, I still couldn't believe it would happen today. Maybe April 12 would be just another realistic practice run.

One by one we crawled through the open hatch and snaked to our seats. With the orbiter tipped with its nose skyward, our seats lay on their backs, and everything looked odd. It was difficult to find my way around, even though we'd practiced it in one of the simulators back in Houston and in the real vehicle on the pad during a launch practice countdown. Like a car upended, the dashboard was above us, and the floor was vertical. I walked on temporary platforms laid across the rear cockpit windows. The

The crew watched the dawn on launch morning from inside their spacecraft.

experienced hands of the suit technicians guided us in the right direction. Lead Tech Al Rochford, who had overseen all the strap-ins since the Apollo days, awaited us. He anchored us to history.

As I eased into my seat on the flight deck, my hands fluttered around, trying to be helpful with my seat harness. Jean Alexander, the tech helping me, tapped me on the shoulder, sighed, and patiently looked me in the eye.

"Go limp," she said.

The voice of experience. I vowed to remember that phrase in the future whenever I was trying to be too helpful or too controlling when something needed to get done. It was best to let the expert locate the seat straps and route them the way they needed to go. The air hose from the helmet to the air supply had to be attached...just so. The communication lines and boxes had to be positioned correctly, and the microphone and earphones had to be checked out. No one launched without being able to hear and talk.

Lying on my back strapped into the seat wasn't particularly uncomfortable – for a while. With all the preparations completed, the last of the techs patted the commander on his helmet, waved, and disappeared out the hatch. There was never a greater sound of finality than the CLUNK of the shuttle hatch closing. Suddenly, it seemed quiet. It was now too late to get out. Even in the practice countdowns they had never closed the door.

The final countdown preparations swirled around us and below us. The Orbiter Test Conductor requested that either our Commander (Bo Bobko) or Don Williams (our Pilot) reposition certain switches, check certain meters. As the clock passed our planned launch time, he let us know what was obvious out our cockpit windows – that the weather was NO GO. The dawn had revealed what the weatherman had predicted – low, gray clouds obscured the sky. Occasional sprinkles of rain passed across our windshield. A typical spring day usually included vultures catching warm updrafts of air to circle the pad. Not today. On April 12, 1985, they stayed home.

The countdown continued until the nine minute hold, a built in stopping point where all the systems were in a good configuration for launch but could wait for several hours. We waited a long hour, getting uncomfortable in our hard seats, our bladders filling, dozing, and going over the procedures we would need to perform in space.

Soon we all began shifting around in our seats, trying to relieve the pressure on the spots we were lying on. My legs began to feel stiff from being bent up for so long. The bladders that we had emptied a couple of hours ago began to refill. I wasn't too worried about having to void into my *diaper,* the Disposable Absorption Containment Trunks. I had tried it both at home in the privacy of my empty bathtub and again on our practice countdown. But Dave Griggs, sitting shoulder to shoulder with me to my left, began to wish he hadn't had so much coffee for breakfast. He either didn't want to or couldn't pee lying down and began saying he hoped he could hold on until the end of our launch window when we'd have to abandon launch attempts for the day.

As we checked our watches, it became clear that if we were to get off the ground before the end of the launch window, the decision would have to be made soon. There had been little conversation with Launch Control for over an hour, and the weather hadn't looked even close to being good enough. We had all resigned ourselves to launching the next day. So sure was Dave that he began to unbuckle his seat straps. He then swung his legs over the left side of his seat and sat upright with respect to the ground. He unzipped his flight suit and with his back to me, he relieved himself into the collection device he had worn onboard. He rezipped then sat perched this way, urine bag in hand, waiting for the call that we were going to scrub the launch for the day and climb out of *Discovery.*

As if on cue, the test conductor came on the line about one minute before we had to pick up the count.

"Commander, what would be the best way to get this thing off the pad today?"

"We could pick up the count," Bo said, almost quizzically.

"Roger, Commander. Launch Team, we will pick up the count on my mark in 30 seconds. *Discovery* crew, good luck! Have a good flight!"

I knew that with that call, our families would cheer as they sat in the Launch Control Center listening and waiting. It was time for them to climb to their rooftop viewing area to hear the final countdown. They'd soon be watching from that outside vantage point three miles away.

I was stunned and thrilled as the clock began counting downward. There sat Dave, though, unstrapped and with a bag full of urine in his hand. Quickly he swung around and tried to hand me the bag, but I wasn't even sure he'd sealed it, nor was I sure I could get it into the trash bag on my right side. He saw my reluctance, fiddled with it to make sure it wasn't going to spill, and stuffed it into the trash bag to the left of his seat. He then began the struggle to strap back in.

All this time, the launch countdown had been proceeding. At the 5 minute point, Don had to complete his task of bringing up the Auxiliary Power Units which would drive our direction control mechanisms. If he didn't get them on in time or if they didn't perform perfectly at start-up, we couldn't launch. There was no time to troubleshoot any problems. We passed that milestone.

The Launch Control Center personnel were checking each system. Our on-board computers were ingesting thousands of bits of information each second. It was as if some giant chain reaction was getting bigger and bigger racing, beyond my control, toward an explosion. All I could do was "go limp."

Bo, Don, and Dave, who in a flurry had secured himself back in his seat, had many little tasks to accomplish and they cross-checked everything. There was no idle chatter during these last minutes. Everything became deadly serious. But we had practiced it just like this so many times in the simulators that it felt routine. Running through my mind the whole time was the question: how in the world could the weather have improved enough over the landing strip to permit us to go? Had someone fudged the weather report a little?

I had no task in all this except to get myself prepared for the ride uphill. I closed my eyes, took a deep breath, and wondered if years from then I'd remember those moments and be able to recount them to others. Or was I about to be blown to smithereens and never see the light of another dawn? All astronauts have to either deny to themselves that there is any unusual risk in spaceflight or somehow come to terms with whatever risk they perceive. I'd always vowed to make the best use of whatever time God allotted me, and I felt content in the fact that I had crammed all the living I could have into my thirty seven years. My only prayer was that whatever happened I'd do a good job of everything expected of me on this flight.

I could see the gaseous oxygen vent arm, the "beanie cap," swing away from the nose of the big, orange external tank. The fuel tanks were now pressurizing. I could feel the far away vibrations of our main engines repositioning themselves. The calls from the test conductor, and Bo's and Don's answers, became more rapid-fire and clipped. Time seemed to compress.

At 31 seconds to go, our on-board launch sequencer took over automatic control. The personnel in the launch center ran through their last second checks. The on-board sensors fired rapid bursts of data at our computers. If at any point something wasn't right, the launch sequence would halt.

Sixteen seconds before lift-off, a huge waterfall at the base of the launch pad activated to dampen the reflected sound vibrations about to belch forth from the boosters and engines. Three hundred thousand gallons of water gushed into the flame trench below.

At launch minus 10 seconds, the ground's launch system sent its final command to *Discovery: GO for main engine start.*

We were on our own now.

Just before the chain reaction reached critical mass, I turned my head to the left to watch the launch tower out the side window. At launch minus 6 seconds we felt the deep, throaty rumble of the first main engine igniting. Then in rapid sequence the second and the third. Boom! Boom! Boom!

As expected the firing of the engines caused the tip of the rocket to sway backward about two feet. The booster hold-down posts would be groaning with the strain of the tilt. Slowly the vehicle swayed back upright. I knew that when it pointed straight up the eight explosive bolts on the hold-down posts which attached the two boosters to the launch pad (and us to the Earth) had to fire at the precise millisecond that the boosters themselves ignited. If there was any hang-up in that choreographed timing, if the bolts didn't separate cleanly, or if one of the boosters hesitated, there would be a horrendous cataclysm in which all of us and the vehicle would be blown to bits.

Six seconds before liftoff the Space Shuttle main engines roar to life.

Lift off!

The split second I felt the bone-jarring blast from the boosters, my gaze shifted from the launch tower, which had vanished from the window, to my hands in my lap. From the noise, vibration, and acceleration, I was sure the shuttle had blown up, and I was about to watch my body disintegrate. That fearsome thought was interrupted by Bo's call as we cleared the tower, going upward now at over a hundred miles an hour.

"Houston, *Discovery,* roll program." said Bo.

We were on our way! I was alive!

"Roger, roll, *Discovery*!" responded our CAPCOM, the astronaut communicator. Mission Control had taken control of our flight from the Launch Control Center at lift off. As we went through the rain, little rivulets of water collected and danced around the edges of our windshield. Bits of the fluffy insulation from the External Tank flew past, several hitting our forward windows leaving whitish streaks. *No harm done*, I thought. We broke through the gray of the clouds and could see blue sky and sunlight above us. I craned my head around to look out the overhead window but was disappointed to see only gray cloud tops below us, so uniform that it was hard to tell if we were one mile or a hundred miles above them.

The early ride on the boosters was teeth-rattling, more intense than I had ever experienced in the simulator. This was for real.

Two minutes after launch at an altitude of 150,000 feet, there was a sudden forward lurch and the flash of an explosion out the forward windows. The boosters blasted themselves away from the tank, having burned up over two million pounds of propellant. After that I wondered if we were still flying it was so smooth and quiet. The main engine instruments signaled everything was working as expected, and the gentle push skyward continued. Almost imperceptibly at about seven minutes after launch, the G-forces began to press down on my chest as the acceleration to orbital

STS-51D lifts off at 8:59 AM on April 12, 1985. We are on our way to space.

velocity continued. Somewhere around eight minutes the crush reached the maximum of 3-Gs—three times the force of gravity—and became uncomfortable. Difficult as it was to breathe, to talk, to move my arms or turn my neck, I was comforted to know this would last only about 30 seconds.

And then it happened. At over 25,500 feet per second, more than 17,000 miles per hour, and at 165 miles above Mother Earth, we reached the point of "Main Engine Cut-Off." The acceleration stopped, and we lurched forward against our harness straps. Gravity disappeared.

An errant bolt drifted up from behind the instrument panel beside me. Pencils, books, our arms, sparkling dust particles – everything – was adrift. Since we had expected and trained for this moment, all of our equipment including books and pencils were tethered. They wouldn't float far away from us, but, oh, the wonder of seeing them unfettered by Earth's pull!

Dave Griggs, sitting in the seat next to mine, turned to face me, and his enormous smile mirrored mine. Bo said the words we had all waited so long for:

"Well, rookies, welcome to space!"

CHAPTER 7

★ ★ ★ ★ ★ ★

DOING THE UNEXPECTED

A few more things had to be accomplished before we were safely in Earth orbit, the most immediate of which was getting off the external tank. With a bang and a thud at the right moment, the automated system shed the now-empty ugly orange container that had supplied the fuel for our journey. "Wow! Look at that!" said Don, looking out the pilots' window to his right as he got his first real look at the sunlit Earth below.

One by one we started getting out of our seats, doffing our helmets, and getting our space legs – but really getting used to doing without our legs and flying wherever we needed to go. The next part of the flight was called post-insertion and consisted of getting the shuttle ready for on-orbit operations. In 1985, our ancient computers had limited software storage capacity, so we had to do several software loads from the mass memory unit during the flight. Once in orbit, we switched from the launch phase programming to the orbit configuration. The life support system had various valves reconfigured, so a balanced environment of nitrogen and oxygen would be automatically supplied, passing the air through the proper filters, removing carbon dioxide and humidity, and then recirculating fresh air back to the cabin. Bo and Don proceeded with those chores and several more. There was an orbital engine burn on the other side of the Earth to put us in our final orbit between 160 and 245 nautical miles above the Earth. My most important duty came next.

The Payload Bay Doors (PLBDs) over the cargo bay had to be opened, a critical step for two reasons. One, it cleared a path for the satellites to be launched into space, and two, because of the radiators on the inside of the doors. If the PLBDs wouldn't open, all the heat from the shuttle's electrical equipment couldn't be radiated into space and we could remain in orbit only for a few revolutions of the Earth. The coolant Freon circulated through the radiators and heat was dissipated to the cold of space, particularly when the orbiter was out of sunlight on the dark side of the Earth. It was beautiful to watch the opening itself. The computers did the sequencing of the door latch releases and the door openings, but the crew monitored this critical function carefully. We had spent a number of hours in the simulator practicing how things could go wrong and what we'd have to do about it.

Looking back through the windows at the aft of the cockpit, the cargo bay looked like the inside of a big aluminum truck. But the view changed incredibly as the doors were opened. Group by group, the latches along the centerline of the doors released, their curved latching mechanisms sliding from around circular rollers. Then the forward and aft bulkhead latches on the starboard door let go. Slowly and majestically the silver door began to swing outward, like a curtain revealing a tantalizing glimpse of what lay beyond. The port side door unlatched and swung out of view. There gleaming in the sunlight was Earth, her blue ocean and white clouds drifting below us. For a space rookie, the moment was stunning. How few people, how few women, had been given the opportunity to see our home planet this way?

Astronauts are often asked if this was a religious moment. An early Russian cosmonaut reportedly said he didn't see God when he viewed the Earth from space. When a Russian church prelate was asked about that, he was reported to have said, "If you don't see God on Earth, you won't see him in space."

When I viewed Earth for the first time from that lofty position over 200 miles up, I tried to identify what I felt. We couldn't see the entire Earth from our vantage point like the Apollo astronauts could from the moon, but we could see large swaths of it. From overhead San Diego, I could make out the Black Hills of North Dakota in the distance. While I am a scientist who believes in the scientific truths of the Big Bang, the evolution of the Earth, and the living creatures on it, I am open to the differing beliefs of

others. I couldn't help but believe that the hand of God or some higher being was responsible for creating the beauty before me. I couldn't pretend to understand the how or why of it, but the greatness and complexity of what appeared touched my soul.

There was little time for watching the scenery

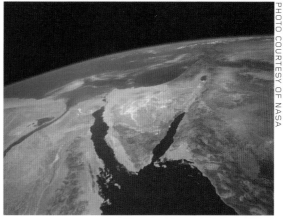

PHOTO COURTESY OF NASA

The first views of Earth from space captivate everyone. Passing over the Middle East the green of the Nile and its delta give way to the desert of the Sinai. Israel appears as a darker area up the coastline.

The cities of Italy lit up at night.

float by. It was on to important, but more mundane things, like activating the toilet. The connections to the electrical and venting systems had to be made. The accessories (urinal funnels, toilet paper, and the rear view mirror) were unstowed and stuck on Velcro around our space bathroom. I unfurled the pleated privacy curtain and removed my soggy diaper. Taking a deep breath, I did a functional checkout of the potty. A cheer went up from my waiting compatriots when they heard the exhaust fan running. It wasn't exactly like I had practiced on the ground, but it was with a great sense of accomplishment that I completed this first of many new experiences in weightlessness.

The next major task for Jeff and me was to check out the large mechanical arm which lay along one side of the bay, known as the Remote Manipulator System (RMS). We began running through the checklist to put the arm through its paces. It needed an early checkout on this flight because it would be used to watch the booster firing with the arm camera on the first satellite we deployed. On Hoot's flight the previous year, two satellite boosters had failed. Rick Hauck's STS-51A crew had retrieved those satellites the previous November, and the manufacturer was sure they had fixed the problem, but they wanted verification that our booster fired properly.

At this point in the flight, Jeff and I were having a great time. A scant couple of hours into the flight and we were making helicopters out of half-peeled bananas and then devouring them for lunch as we worked with the

To operate the remote arm, I had to look out the aft cockpit windows. I wasn't tall enough to see out the window so I had to bungee myself to the switch panel. That worked well in weightlessness and replaced the footstool I had used on Earth.

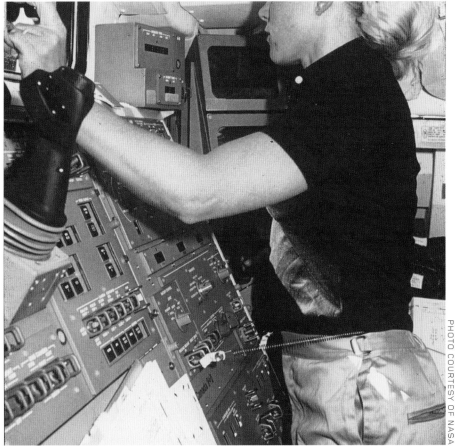

arm. We were not affected by motion sickness. What luck! Some of our other crewmates were not so lucky. Astronauts were secretive about who got motion sick and who didn't, fearing it would somehow limit their career or their later in-flight job assignments. Jake was open about the fact that he was ill the first couple of days, since this would be his sole flight.

Down on the middeck, Jake recalled sitting in his seat after we got to orbit and watching another crewmember having a vomiting spell. He told me he felt so sorry for the guy…until he tried to get up and move about only to find out his "gyros were tumbled" (as pilots call dizziness and disorientation), too. As with most of the astronauts who had the problem, trying to minimize movement was the one way to lessen the symptoms. Jake found a way to hang onto one of the sleeping bags along the starboard wall of the middeck to keep from floating around. Besides infrequent forays to the toilet across the middeck, this is where he stayed planted. We kidded him after he was feeling better, that we had renamed this area of *Discovery*, the *Jake Garn Memorial Bulkhead*. A few days later, he could laugh with us about it, in his good-natured way.

After we were sure the arm was in good shape, we began the steps to deploy our first satellite. In the early shuttle days, taking satellites to orbit as paying customers helped fund the cost of the launch, so the rest of the flight could do the research and development that NASA regarded as its primary missions. On our flight, the first day's job was to launch Telesat, a communication satellite for Canada. It was a PAM-class satellite, meaning the communications portion of the thing sat atop a booster called a Payload Assist Module which would fire 45 minutes after we deployed it. First thing on orbit, an igloo-like sunshield was closed across the top of the satellite to protect it from temperature extremes. This couldn't be done before launch because it had been a late-design add-on, and the closed shade was too tall to close the bay doors over it.

As we got close to the satellite's deployment, we began powering up and checking out the satellite systems. We opened the sun shield and spun up the satellite like a huge gyroscope. One of the advantages of having the shuttle do the deployment rather than sending it up on an expendable rocket was that the crew could turn on the electrical and communications systems, then they and the ground could make sure everything had survived the jarring of launch before sending it off into space. Of course, this didn't guarantee everything was functional, as Hoot's crew had discovered over a year earlier. Failures of the booster itself could prevent the satellite from reaching its planned orbit and render it useless. That's why, after the deployment, we planned to use the camera on the end of the arm to watch the timing and duration of the booster firing.

After the satellite was turned on and checked out, the orbiter was pointed at a precise spot in the sky so that after deployment, the satellite could boost itself into its final destination over 23,000 miles above the Earth. Unlike the orbiter, which was a couple hundred miles above the Earth and goes around the world every ninety minutes, communication satellites are in a much higher orbit, going around the Earth once every 24 hours. Since the Earth also turns at that rate, the satellite stays over one spot on the Earth. That is why a television dish can look for its signal in one place in the sky. The PAM booster's job was to get it up to an orbital altitude of 23,000 miles.

Dave and Jeff did the checkout and power up as they'd practiced many times in the simulators, but this time everything worked as planned. All those practice runs in the simulator where multiple malfunctions had to be analyzed and dealt with were for naught. I had set up all the video cameras to record the deployment. Bo was ready with the still camera, and Jeff did the final countdown to the precise moment when he would hit the launch switch. Bang! With a metallic clank and a shudder of the entire orbiter, Telesat was propelled into the darkness of space and rose out of the bay. I drove the TV cameras in the payload bay to follow its path. It was picture perfect. Bo then maneuvered to get a respectable distance from Telesat and to put it beneath the belly of the shuttle. Even at a distance, should the satellite explode at the time it was to start its booster burn, there could be significant damage to the orbiter's windows. It always surprised me that we weren't concerned about hurting the Styrofoam-like tiles on our undercarriage.

Jeff and I started the maneuver of the arm to bring it over the bay and drape it like a big inverted U to look in the direction of the satellite booster firing. The ground had given us exact positions for each of the arm's joints since Mission Control's computers were needed to pinpoint the dark object too far away for us to see against the black sky. At the planned moment, the end camera on the arm picked up the bright glow in the sky that signaled the ignition had begun. The glow continued for precisely the correct amount of time. Halfway through our first day in space, and we'd accomplished one of our major objectives. We thought we were pretty hot stuff. What could possibly go wrong with such simple payloads?

We took some time at this point to assess what parts of our timeline we'd completed and what we needed to do to catch up. Several of the folks onboard weren't feeling too well, so the rest of us were trying to offload as many tasks as possible from them. We'd purposely planned a light first day since five of the seven of us were rookies (Bo and Charlie had flown before), and we weren't sure whether we'd feel well or not.

NASA had done extensive work over the years to discover the cause and treatment for space motion sickness. They'd even given it a new name, Space Adaptation Syndrome, since they weren't sure it was a form of motion sickness. Many of us performed various nauseating tests preflight to see if the sickness could be predicted depending upon what made someone sick on Earth. It turned out that none of the ground tests could, as

Astronaut Dr. Bill Thornton liked to say, tell "the sheep from the goats." In addition, no matter what kind of training was done to try to *cure* the tendency to get sick (acrobatic jet flight, biofeedback, et cetera.) none of it worked. Astronauts and test subjects just spent more hours being made sick. All of us rookies knew that somewhere around a half to two-thirds of us wouldn't feel well the first couple of days.

One thing I hoped to do on Flight Day 1 was the American Flight Echocardiograph (AFE) experiment. Everyone knew that there was significant fluid redistribution around the body on entering weightlessness. One only had to look at fellow crewmembers' puffy faces to know something was going on. But it was hard to quantify how much fluid was moving upward from the lower extremities, how the heart expanded to handle the extra fluid, and what the time course was before the body excreted some of that fluid through the kidneys. Jake, Jeff, and Charlie had volunteered to be my *victims*, besides my own heart. As soon as the busy deployment activities were over, I dashed around to get the AFE plugged into its power and recording outlets. Poor Jake wasn't happy to have to move across the middeck to my equipment but the echo itself only required that he stand still. He had a tall, thin build that made him a good subject for echoes, so I was able to persuade him to let me get images.

Imagine the elation after following a piece of hardware's development, getting to know the engineers, scientists, and trainers who have put so many hours into the study, and then seeing it work without a single flaw. We'd heard in more than one astronaut's debrief the utter disappointment when the ON switch on an important payload was flipped and nothing happened. Astronauts always put forth heroic efforts to fix hardware in-flight, but some are beyond repair. Not being much of a fix-it person, I had nightmares preflight that the echo wouldn't work, and I wouldn't be smart enough to do anything about it. So when I turned all the switches on and

was greeted by a beautiful image of my heart on its little screen, I could have jumped for joy. Of course, jumping at this point would have crashed me into the ceiling, and I laughed at the thought. Having finished images on myself and Jake, I radioed the ground the AFE had been activated, and I'd recorded good images. I knew that Dave Wolf and friends back on the ground would be doing the jumping for me.

Those of us who felt well enough at the end of the day set about making a reasonable dinner. Because Charlie Walker's large experiment on the middeck took up the space where the galley sat, we had to do without it. The galley wasn't a high-tech piece of equipment. Besides providing hot and cold water through a water gun, it had a small forced air oven with a couple of hot plates inside. Rehydrating with hot water made food preparation easy.

Instead of the galley, on this flight we had a couple of *food warmers*. The size and appearance of small metallic suitcases, inside they had a warming plate and a series of bungees to hold food packages up against it on both sides. We had only an ambient temperature water dispenser to rehydrate our dehydrated foods. Along with other food packages (like the foil wrapped meats), they went into the food warmers for anywhere from 30 to 60 minutes for heating. It required that someone do the preparation in advance of mealtime, so hot food would be ready when everyone was ready to eat. We all shared these duties per Bo's orders, which I appreciated because I didn't want to be considered the cook. (When Jake felt better, he did a lot of our meal preps which was also much appreciated.) On this first night, a few ate real space food, and a few sipped on a little clear soup.

During our training we'd had the chance to sample the food available in the inventory and to suggest other favorite items. Besides dehydrated

The first use of the American Flight Echocardiograph or AFE. I was able to send back the first ultrasound images of the heart—mine—from space.

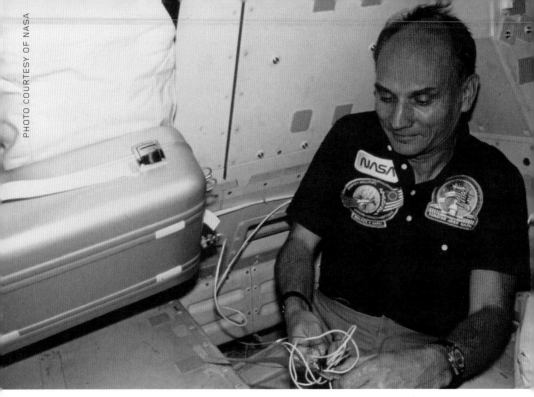

Instead of the larger Space Shuttle galley we carried two small food warmers to heat up our meal packages.

food like soup, vegetables, and casseroles in small square packages with a lid we could cut open, we took foil packages of meat used as *Meals Ready to Eat,* or MREs, by the military. Fresh food like fruit and packaged items like cookies, candy, and peanut butter were in the pantry. Our individual meal choices would fit into a metal tray that we could strap to our leg or Velcro to the wall. If careful, foods that had liquid in them would stay inside the packages and stick to a spoon.

Some of the foods were good on Earth but tasted different in space (like coffee and any food not well rehydrated), so we all made mental notes about what to stow on our subsequent flights. Because all the food had to be shelf-stable for weeks, there were some items that no one liked, like individually wrapped, irradiated slices of bread. Having gotten to know the food systems people, I vowed to request packaged fresh bread in the future – or fresh tortillas if the bread crumbs were a problem.

We each had specific colors assigned to us according to our position on the crew. Being Mission Specialist 1, my color was University of Tennessee orange and everything on board that was mine had an orange dot on it, from my urinal funnel to my food packages. Each day's menu was printed on a card, and my section of the card had an orange dot. Being honorable people, we didn't eat each other's food without asking, but we often engaged in vigorous bargaining.

I had looked forward to my first experience at weightless sleep. At its simplest, space sleeping required nothing more than closed eyes. Most astronauts have drifted off for cat naps this way. Since the head doesn't droop and it doesn't require support, napping was easy. Sometimes, how-

Jake set our food packages and made many of our meals when the rest of us were busy.

ever, those asleep would drift into a wall or someone else's path, and the bump will wake the sleeper up. Also, when asleep, the metabolism slows down, and the astronaut would tend to get chilled, and covering up with a blanket wouldn't work.

Astronauts and the crew equipment people solved these problems in a simple way: sleeping bags that were suspended by clips in any convenient part of the cabin, and the astronauts could zip themselves in. The bags themselves had various straps, so we could sleep with our knees flexed up so our backs wouldn't hyperextend. Also, some of us found it disconcerting not to have the feel of a pillow against our head. So the sleeping bags had a pad at the top with a strap to hold our head on it. We didn't have to sleep horizontally with respect to the floor. It was just as easy to sleep up against the ceiling. I found that sleeping inside the big airlock canister in the middeck was quiet and being wedged between the two spacewalker suits stored there was comfy. I often hooked the foot of my sleeping bag at the top of the airlock, so I could have my face facing out of the airlock hatch which was near the floor in the fresh air. The crew said I looked like a bat sleeping upside down, but it worked for me. Because the sun filtered in during our daylight passes and some of our onboard equipment (like the toilet) was noisy, most of us slept with sleep masks and earplugs. The guys didn't look very macho in sleep masks, but they abandoned vanity in order to get a good night's sleep.

For most, that first night wasn't restful. Like a kid on an exciting vacation or a businessman in a strange hotel room, there were many things to keep us awake. We all managed to zip ourselves up for the night, having gotten through our first day with no major problems. I rehearsed the Syncom satellite deployment I'd be doing the next day as I drifted off to a fitful sleep.

The big event on Flight Day 2 was the launching of our second satellite.

Unlike the PAM-class, it wasn't spun up in the cargo bay but flipped out like a Frisbee which powered on an activation timer inside of it. At the end of a short predetermined time, the Syncom would pop up an antenna on its top, and small jets would fire to increase its spin rate to keep it pointed in the proper attitude, like a top. By comparison with the Telesat from the day before, the pre-deploy activities were pretty simple. Prior crews

PHOTO COURTESY OF NASA

Syncom deploys out of the bay like a Frisbee. Everything went completely as planned. As we watched Syncom drift slowly out of our view, we realized that it had not activated as it should have.

had already launched two of these satellites and they had experienced no problems whatsoever.

At the appointed time, we all gathered on the flight deck. With the ground following our every move, we started all of our pre-deploy steps. As deploy time approached, everything had gone smoothly. Jeff had cross-checked everything I'd done, so I pushed the switch to launch it on its way. Thump! We watched it roll out of the cargo bay. It was a piece of cake.

"Houston, *Discovery*. Syncom's away," I said.

We began congratulating ourselves. As we snapped pictures with various cameras, it was Jeff who first noticed the problem.

"The upper antenna didn't deploy," he said, more quizzically than ominously.

As we all fixed our eyes on the satellite and checked our watches several times, it was clear that the satellite hadn't increased its spin rate, either. It hadn't turned itself on properly.

"Houston, *Discovery*, the Syncom antenna has not deployed nor has it spun up," I radioed Mission Control. There was a brief pause, and I knew the Flight Director's heart rate went up a notch and he would ask the CAP-COM to have us repeat what we had said.

"Houston, we repeat, the antenna on the Syncom has not – repeat, has NOT – deployed. The spin rate has not – repeat, has NOT - increased. We will continue to watch and take pictures as long as it is in view."

It was bad news for Hughes Aircraft who had built the satellite and for the Navy who would be using it. We knew there was nothing we could do to help this cripple we had flung into the void. I remembered that the ground controllers had some commanding capability—but only after the upper antenna deployed.

On the off chance that the booster hadn't been affected by whatever was wrong with the beast, MCC told us to proceed with the planned separation maneuver and asked us to monitor for the booster ignition with the arm camera as we had done for the Telesat the day before. As we drifted away from Syncom after our maneuver, we watched the camera monitor carefully.

Was there any ignition? Was there an explosion? Was there anything?
Nothing.

The fact that the booster didn't ignite was good news, considering what might have happened. Without the increased spin rate, the satellite would have wobbled and wouldn't have been pointed in the correct direction. It would have ended up in the wrong place in the sky anyway. And if it had gotten to any higher an orbit, a shuttle would have no chance to retrieve or repair it during a future mission.

Over lunch, we racked our brains for what we knew about the inner workings of Syncom, but we couldn't remember much. It was a simple deployment system, but we had no insight into its internal systems. But we knew the folks on the ground were busy with their analysis.

When something like this went wrong on a flight (like the booster failures on the two satellites on Hoot's flight) even though the crew had nothing to do with it, there was a sense of disappointment. Since there was nothing we could do, we resigned ourselves to getting on with the rest of our mission. Then a calm request from Mission Control changed all that.

"*Discovery*, Houston. We'd like you to perform a short engine burn to stop your separation from Syncom."

"What?? Why??" we asked each other.

We knew that there must be some sort of assessment on the ground that said there was a possible fix for the malfunction. What that was, we couldn't imagine, but we knew if details were available, we'd have been told. Being the cool pilot-type that he was, Bo didn't ask any questions.

"Roger," he said. "Ready to copy the numbers for the burn."

While we continued with the tasks in our flight plan for the afternoon, over dinner we made wild speculations on what might be afoot.

The next morning, Houston gave us a little more information.

"Do you guys remember the separation switch on the Syncom from your visit to the factory?" CAPCOM asked. Jeff and I looked at each other in bewilderment. Since that tour had been early in our training for the first mission we had been assigned to, it had been over eighteen months since we had seen the hardware up close, and that didn't ring a bell at all.

"Uh, is it that little thing near the nozzle?" I asked.

"No, you're way off," CAPCOM said. "The sep switch is a spring-loaded switch located on the underside of Syncom as it sits in its cradle. On deploy from the shuttle, the little switch pops out and starts all the activation sequences." Neither Jeff nor I had the foggiest.

"Oh, yeah, Houston. *That* switch."

Apparently it was the sole *single-point failure* the Hughes engineers could come up with, the one thing that by itself would cause this problem. Everything else had redundancy, had a backup system that would function in case of a failure of the primary piece of equipment.

Mission Control said people were scrambling around trying to see if there was some way we could verify the switch had flipped all the way to the ON position, and if not, how to get it there. Jeff and Dave were beaming. The one way they could figure this could be done was with an EVA, a spacewalk. And who better to carry one out? These guys had trained for possible failure scenarios for not only this flight, but also for the other two we'd trained on. And they were READY! But, man, what a lot of work, trouble, and risk to flip a simple ON/OFF switch.

Bo and Don looked a little more worried. Getting close enough to the satellite to view it or repair it meant flying a rendezvous and doing what was called "prox ops," or proximity operations. Using the vagaries of orbital mechanics, the shuttle had to be flown over to the satellite and then kept within an appropriate distance without running into the thing. It would have to be close, close enough to reach out and touch.

While our commander and pilot had done most of the training to perform this kind of maneuver as we trained to retrieve the small telescope, SPARTAN, on our first-assigned mission, it had been months since that training. More importantly, they hadn't made it close enough to that flight to do all the simulations to train on what to do if things went wrong. They couldn't do this complex task from memory, and we hadn't brought any of the rendezvous checklists. How in the world were we going to plan and accomplish all these activities in a couple days? We were more than a little incredulous at the entire idea.

We stayed busy with our other experiments to keep our minds off what was happening on the ground. Jake felt better and was doing his medical experiments. He and Jeff and Charlie seemed to enjoy playing subjects for the echocardiograms I was performing on them. It forced them to float peacefully while I scanned their chests and recorded these first-ever images of hearts in space that I'd later downlink to the ground. They often napped during the test. It was so easy to close your eyes and drift in space! Bo and Don completed a number of engineering tests.

Soon the ground came up with what had to be one of the strangest plans in the history of spaceflight. Calmly, as though they had all the confidence in the world in us, they summarized their thoughts. First, we were to fashion some sort of device that could be attached to the end of the RMS arm to use to snag the wayward switch. Second, an EVA was to be done to attach this thing to the arm. Third, a rendezvous would indeed be performed to bring us within the arm's reach of the satellite, and then the crazy thing on the arm would be used to pull the switch into the ON position. It looked like there would be something wild for each of the five

NASA crewmembers to do. Jeff and Dave would do the EVA; then, Bo and Don would pilot the rendezvous. This was getting to be exciting – and also scary. I was to be the arm operator, the official *snagger*.

We didn't have much time to think about all the things that could go wrong. The ability to upload pictures from the ground hadn't been developed yet, so Mission Control had to send us information on the snagging device using words over our voice links and via teleprinter messages. The teleprinter could generate lines of letters or numbers, but not pictures. It was like describing to a friend how to build a new and unique device…over the telephone or by using dots on a page. There was no way to describe its size with your hands or how to shape it using a picture. We had a few laughs trying to figure out what this thing was supposed to look like. Besides a lengthy word description, the communications people came up with a clever way to illustrate it with the letters on the teleprinter page. Since we could download pictures from our onboard cameras, we could show them our interpretation of the instructions.

"You mean I should bend the book cover around the stick like this?" I asked.

"No, lengthwise and with the edge lower down," the CAPCOM replied.

"Like this, then?"

"Yes, that's it, that's it! Now smash it flat so you can stick the other cover on the end," he said.

"And where do you want to add the stitches?" I asked.

"They need to go where the two book covers are joined, to reinforce the connection," the CAPCOM responded. And on it went.

What we built came to be known as the *flyswatter*. Each flight carried what is called the Auxiliary Reach Mechanism or more simply, the *swizzle*

Following instructions from Mission Control, we began fashioning two devices we called the flyswatter and the lacrosse stick from material we had on board.

stick. When seated and strapped into the seat for launch and landing, there were certain switches and circuit breakers crew members couldn't reach. A lightweight aluminum Y-shaped tube was designed with a setter and popper for circuit breakers and, on the other end, a switch flipper. This would serve as the handle for the flyswatter. For the swatting, or snagging part, we would use a couple of plastic book covers from our checklists. We'd stick them together with gray duct tape. How would this tape, used for everything inside the shuttle, perform in the temperature extremes (+250 degrees F in the sunlight, -250 degrees in the dark) and in the vacuum in space? No one was sure, so we were to sew parts of the swatter together to reinforce the tape.

One thing had to be modified on the business end of the swizzle stick before we could begin our assembly. Part of the switch flipper would be in the way, so the ground described how we could saw off this metal appendage with the bone saw in the medical kit. I had always wondered why we carried a bone saw (usually used for amputations) in the kit, but now it had found a use.

Astronauts were not trained in how to saw metal aboard space vehicles. Little specks of aluminum would be ground off and might float around the cabin. To keep these foreign bodies out of our eyes and lungs, the ground suggested we break out the hand-held vacuum cleaner and suck them up as they were generated. I don't think any of us believed this was particularly safe and effective, but I guess the safety guru in Mission Control had somehow been convinced it was okay. Eventually, anything that got loose would be removed by our air filtration system anyway.

Being the prime medical officer on the flight and the only one among us who could claim to have ever used a bone saw, I said I'd do the sawing. Off we went, Jeff and Jake to hold the swizzle stick, Charlie to manage the vacuum cleaner, and me, the pseudo-orthopedic surgeon, to amputate one leg off the end of the stick. We all secured ourselves to the middeck floor or walls with foot loops so we'd be steady, then I pulled out the double-handled sawing wire and went to work with care so Charlie could suck up the shiny shards of metal that were flecked off. I was able to report to our commander that the surgery went well; the surgeon and her assistants all survived, and the patient had no complaints.

Next, the instructions were to take the plastic cover from one of our checklists and roll it into a funnel, taping the small end of the funnel onto the end of the swizzle. Then we would flatten the big end of the funnel and stick another plastic cover on the end of the funnel, so it looked kind of like a flyswatter. By cutting rectangles out of the flat cover, we had a device that could be used to snag the on/off switch on Syncom.

This entire contraption was connected together and wrapped with gray duct tape. In a good example of NASA's belt and suspenders system, we used another piece of onboard hardware for a task that was never intended. A large needle and thread were carried in case a spacesuit needed some quick repair. Directed where to find them and given suggestions on how best to use them, off we went. One of Jake Garn's favorite pictures from the flight is one of him wielding needle-nosed pliers to drive this whale-needle through several layers of tape and plastic to ensure the flyswatter wouldn't disintegrate when the sticky tape was exposed to space vacuum and temperature extremes. We also removed a rectangular metal stiffener from one of the window shades we carried onboard and attached a wire loop on the end to make a second device we called the *lacrosse stick*.

When complete, we downlinked pictures of our proud accomplishments to MCC, hoping of course, we'd understood their written instructions and verbal descriptions. It was a happy moment when they congratulated us. Someone in the control room said I was a good seamstress, and Sally Ride reminded them that I was a good surgeon. I wish I'd been there to thank her for that.

Then we had to figure out how to attach the swatter and stick to the can at the end of the arm. This would involve not only an EVA, tricky in and of itself, but also some real-time fiddling with available equipment to define the best way to secure the two devices to the outside of a can. Each flight carried a general purpose strap called a Payload Retention Strap. The idea was that at some point in time, we might need to tie something down in the payload bay. The ground thought Dave and Jeff could use this thing to do the job, but they'd have to try it out to make sure.

Preparing for an EVA was a complex task. All of the equipment was packed in the middeck, both in the airlock and under the floor. All of it had to be unstowed and inspected the day before the actual spacewalk. Our cramped middeck living area became a fishbowl full of pants, boots, helmets, gloves, and a myriad of other pieces and parts drifting about in our gravity-free environment. I kept asking myself, "Is this going to happen – an unplanned and unpracticed spacewalk?"

That night another activity had to be accomplished. The environment in the spacesuits was about 4.3 pounds per square inch (psi) when out in space. The cabin pressure inside our living area was at Earth's sea level pressure of 14.7 psi. If a human went from 14.7 suddenly to 4.3, the nitrogen in his blood would turn into bubbles causing what is called *the bends*. The gas bubbles clogging blood vessels could cause damage to the lungs, the brain, and many other organs. On shuttle flights, instead of breathing oxygen for three or more hours to flush out the nitrogen, the cabin pressure was lowered to 10.2 psi and kept there for 12 hours or so. This flushed some of the nitrogen out of the blood. The EVA crewmembers then had to get into their spacesuits for a shorter time and breathe pure oxygen to flush more of the nitrogen out, allowing them to go outside without danger.

The procedure to get down to 10.2 was rather lengthy and crew intensive. Air had to be vented out of the orbiter to a certain pressure level and then oxygen added when its content got too low. Yet the oxygen couldn't get too high, which could cause a fire hazard. So it was burp a little pressure, add a little oxygen, burp a little more, add more oxygen for what seems like hours.

Detail-oriented Don Williams took on the responsibility of putting together the rendezvous checklist. When a planned rendezvous was scheduled on a flight, the crew carried a checklist volume on the subject in the Flight Data File, the collection of books that told us everything we needed to know. But we never planned for a rendezvous with a broken satellite on this flight so we didn't bring that particular book.

What we had for receiving written messages was that antiquated teleprinter. It could receive (slowly) instructions from the ground and print them on a continuous roll of yellow paper. So some poor soul (bless him or her) on the ground had to type the major sections of the checklist into the teleprinter format and uplink it to us: reams of weightless paper drifting around all over the place. Though Don could have cut the long sheet into page size segments and put a paper clip on them, he came up with a much more elegant solution. He cut out page-sized sections and taped them onto pages of one of the checklists we'd finished using. When complete, the book looked beautiful, like one of those polished reports the A students in school always turned in. It was a lot easier to use than a bunch of floppy pages. It was ingenious and so like Don.

What was it I, the snagger, was to do with the arm? The ground had been working on that, too. We found out they had considered a variety of options, one being to put a crew member on the end of the arm and let me put him up near the Syncom. He would reach out and flip the switch with his gloved hand. Another was to give the flyswatter to the crewman and let him hold it out to snag the switch.

These ideas were rejected for a number of reasons. For one, I had no training on working with a person on the end of the arm, and in fact, very little RMS training at all. Another was the danger of somehow getting the crewman tangled up with the satellite, injuring him, or tearing his suit. But that didn't stop them from spending a bunch of hours working out how a suited person and the RMS could perform the task. Lots of people suddenly got involved with this flight, something that always happened when it was needed at JSC. I was glad they picked the most conservative option. We didn't need anyone getting injured performing this stunt and certainly not on my account.

Besides the suit folks, all the RMS experts on the ground got involved. A detailed message clattered up on the teleprinter with the plan. The idea was to reach up and wipe the flyswatter along the side of the slowly rotating satellite until the device snagged on the protruding switch. The flyswatter was made of flimsy plastic book covers, so the plastic would tear through. Much analysis had shown the tearing force was sufficient to pull hard

All the instructions for the rendezvous with Syncom were sent up in a long teleprinter message.

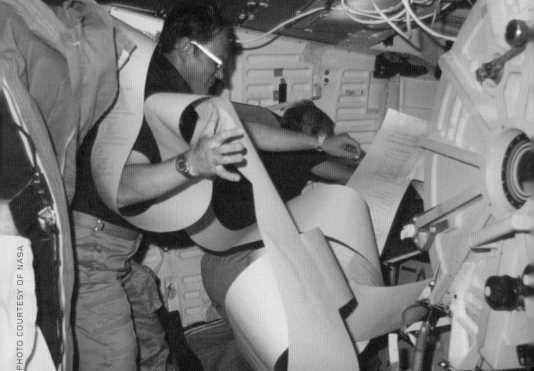

enough on the switch to tug it into the ON position without dragging the arm around on the Syncom…hopefully. They'd done the same analysis on the wire of the second device, the lacrosse stick.

EVA day arrived. Jeff and Dave started suiting up, first struggling into liquid cooling garments which looked like stretchy long johns with tubing snaked through them. Chilled water would circulate through the tubes so their bodies wouldn't overheat. Then the lower portion of the spacesuit was pulled on. Jeff remarked that floating in space, he could put his pants on two legs at a time. Bo had served as the IVA, or intravehicular activity, director on his first mission, so he took that duty upon himself again, helping get both Jeff and Dave outfitted. Then one at a time the EVA-ers entered the airlock and snaked their way up into the hard upper torsos of the suits which were mounted to the wall. Bo was kept busy fetching things then rigging up and checking over all their equipment. The waist rings were sealed, the gloves and helmet snapped on. It was crucial that everything was airtight. All the checkouts were completed while the suits were still attached to umbilicals in the airlock. After successful completion we took some last minute *happy face* photos of our unexpectedly suited crewmates along with the swatter and the lacrosse stick, and the inner hatch from the middeck to the airlock was slammed and locked. The prebreathe of pure oxygen was completed, then the internal volume of the airlock was slowly vented down to space vacuum: they were ready to exit.

Charlie had the foresight to take pictures of Jeff and Dave going out the hatch from the small inside window into the airlock. Bo, Don, Jake, and I were busy watching from the aft flight deck on the payload bay cameras. We could hear the giddiness in their voices as they gave us descriptions of what they were doing.

For safety sake the flyswatters were tethered to the EVA crewmen and the guys were tethered to the orbiter at all times. After retrieving the re-

PHOTO COURTESY OF NASA

tention strap from a tool box in the floor of the payload bay, they worked their way, hand over hand, down the rail on the starboard side of the bay. I had positioned the end of the arm within reach, and they proceeded to strap the devices to the end of the RMS. It took about an hour of trying different configurations before we were all happy that our little inventions were secure.

Next, the ground wanted us to recradle the arm on the port side of the bay where it needed to be for landing to make sure the swatters wouldn't be in the way of the payload bay doors closing. On his way back across the bay to check on this, Dave got a surprise that scared us all. He was tethered to a slide wire on the port side and when he let go of the starboard hand rail, he arced slowly across the cargo bay out of sight in the direction of the port wing. Trying not to sound panicky,

During their spacewalk with the sunlit Earth in the background, Dave and Jeff work at the longeron of the payload bay to attach the flyswatter and lacrosse stick firmly to the end of the arm.

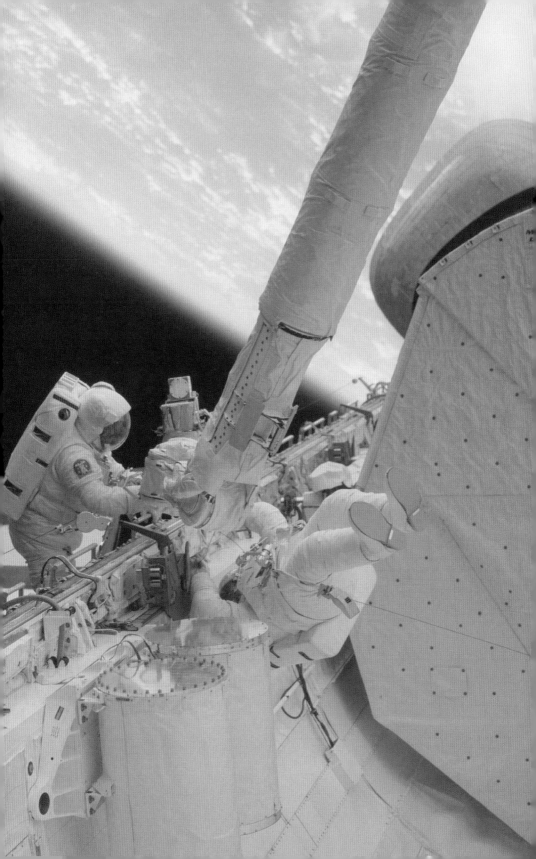

Dave shares a happy moment at the end of his spacewalk at the aft window of the cockpit.

Bo said, "Uh, Dave? Are you OK, Dave?"

Always cool, Dave replied, "Sure - just taking a little ride over here. Be right back," as he bounced on his backside off the wing. Attached to the shuttle, he floated to the handrail where his tether was hooked. We could hear him laughing. Mission Control had been watching on our cameras and called up that they had given his Olympic-style feat a 9.5 for difficulty but only a .5 for form.

We verified there was no arm interference problem, and it was time for our guys to come back in. But they asked Mission Control for a few more minutes outside to *increase their experience base*, but we all knew it was to play around and learn how to work in this bizarre environment. They moved effortlessly around the payload bay, right side up, upside down, and sideways.

Kathy Sullivan, the first female spacewalker had told me the previous year about a strange experience she had had while learning the best way to navigate. At first, she started working her way down the handrail on the side of the bay with her feet pointed down toward the bottom of the orbiter. Then she discovered that *feet up* was easier, kind of like walking on her hands if the orbiter had been on the ground. But since the shuttle was actually bay-to-the-Earth, when she looked *up* past her feet, she saw the blue ball we call home. She suddenly had the feeling she was hanging by her hands, not walking on them. She said she took a deep breath and had to reorient herself to overcome the feeling that she would drop Earthward if she let go.

We often get those odd sensations in zero gravity. One day I came up to the cockpit from the middeck knowing that the floor was *down*. But when I looked out the window, Earth was overhead, and I got disoriented as though I was upside down. I once put my feet in the foot loops on the middeck floor and did some deep knee bends. It felt like I was pushing the shuttle up and down. Sometimes I floated into the middeck upside down and felt lost because everything looked out of whack, like when I stood on my head as a child and looked around.

So there really was benefit to EVA crewmembers puttering around outside, seeing how to stay oriented, to move around, to handle tools, to keep tethers connected. Just in case someone broke free, shuttle commanders were trained to fly over and scoop up anybody who was drifting away. But that never happened, thank goodness.

After a few minutes, Dave and Jeff floated up to the cockpit's aft-facing windows to have their pictures taken by those of us inside. Someone captured a portrait of Dave Griggs, waving and grinning from ear to ear inside his helmet. It would later serve as a snapshot of one of Dave's happiest moments, and it is how I will always remember him. We didn't know that this would be his only EVA, his one flight. On the other hand, Jeff had gotten the experience he would need to be assigned to a spectacular EVA flight later in his career. These were moments captured in time in a story that took years to play out.

Back into the airlock they swam. The outer hatch was closed, the airlock was pressurized, the inside hatch was opened, and the two of them wiggled out of their suits. There was as festive a celebration as we could muster inside our little space house that night. No champagne, but we did the toasting with our plastic drink containers full of juice. They did it! But would the rest of us be able to do our parts? Could Bo and Don get us to the right distance from monster satellite? Would I be able to do what was needed with the arm? It was hard to sleep that night with the excitement, the wondering, and the worrying.

The next day brought another flurry of activity. A rendezvous in space was tricky business. We were miles above and behind Syncom. The ship couldn't speed up and then fly down to it. Because of orbital mechanics, if the shuttle increased its speed, the altitude would increase, then it would take longer to go around the Earth, and we'd be even further behind. So we had to slow down. Computers in Mission Control figured out how this should be done to get us pretty close. The plan was to swoop up from below the satellite until we were out in front of it. Then we'd point the payload bay at the target, and our commander could look out the overhead windows and drive precisely toward a specific point in the dark sky. At some time before we got too close, the orbiter's sensors would be able to *see* the target and help refine the ground's targeting. When we closed in, the target would become visible to our own eyeballs.

When our sensors told us it should be within sight, we all strained to pick Syncom up against the blackness of the sky.

"There it is!" someone shouted.

A faint gold glow appeared, and I was surprised until I realized that we were looking at the gold foil and booster nozzle on the underside of the satellite, the end opposite the one we were looking at when we flung it skyward from the cargo bay. That meant we were looking straight into the *business end* of the rocket. Somehow this was the moment that I started taking this operation seriously. Here we were, facing a rocket nozzle which, should it start firing, could blow us to kingdom come. We hadn't asked the ground if it had made sure in all the assessments that there wasn't any way this thing was going to blast us. We had to trust that we were safe... and trust we did.

Closer and closer we got. Bo took up his station at the aft of the cockpit craning his head back to look out the overhead windows. In his left hand he managed the handle that moved us up and down, fore and aft, side to side. In his right hand he twisted the controller that pitched us nose up or tail down, moved the nose left or right, or rolled one wing or the other up. No one made small talk or joked around. Our entire focus was on the Syncom growing ever larger in the windows.

I had uncradled the arm and was using the joint angles provided by the ground to poise it high above the bay much like a ballerina's upstretched arm, its *wrist* cocked to my left so the satellite would drift down into view in the camera mounted on the end of the *hand*. Don was in the pilot's seat, monitoring all of our systems, ready to take action if anything went wrong and set off an alarm. Jeff was behind me, backing me up, as we peered out the overhead and back windows at the arm. I didn't even realize Dave was there on the flight deck capturing everything on film. In fact, the greatest pictures of the flight were ones he captured over my shoulder.

Like expectant fathers of yesteryear who were banned from the delivery room, Jake and Charlie had been banished from the flight deck. I did glance down once at the interdeck access opening and saw four eyes as big as saucers staring up at all the activity. I couldn't help feeling that we couldn't have dreamed up a finer scenario to demonstrate to our congressional passenger the real-time capabilities of our space program team at its finest.

Then we were at the appointed place. We had to wait—*station keeping* in shuttle language—until the right time. If we managed to turn the satellite on, its internal timer would fire the upper stage exactly 45 minutes later, and it would boost itself to the right place in the sky. We knew that we had a time window of just a few minutes, or the final positioning of the satellite on orbit wouldn't be optimal.

Jeff and I peered at the television screens with the view from the arm's end effector camera, anxious to see the little finger-like projection we had to snag. There it was, inside a bright, 4-by-6-inch orange-colored square. Our hearts sank a bit. It looked like it was pulled over to the ON position already. But maybe it was part way and needed a little tug. I worked hard to align the flyswatter with the switch as the Syncom rotated slowly above us. It was like trying to touch something on

PHOTO COURTESY OF NASA

We could see the Syncom coming into view as we slowly approached. The on/off switch is the small finger-like projection in the lower orange square.

We proved we had snagged the switch and it had torn through the flyswatter plastic and had pulled the wire loose on the lacrosse stick.

a merry-go-round as it swung by. Once we had the swatter aligned, we watched the time tick down. The Swat Team was ready.

Three, two, one: it was time to go for it!

On the next pass we slowly moved the swatter into position. Whoosh— as predicted, the switch caught on the plastic rungs of the device and tore through, tugging with the right amount of force on the switch.

We let the satellite go around again and tried to catch the switch with the wire loop on the lacrosse stick. *Yes!* It caught, and we could tell that it yanked pretty hard on the switch. Surely we had pulled on that thing as much as we could, but we tried several more times by hitting it with the base of the swatter.

What we should have figured on (but didn't) was that we were smacking the side of a giant gyroscope. When you do that, the gyroscope moves. We realized that Syncom had gone from being out over the bay to being up over the cockpit. It was getting hard for me to see the target, so I gave Jeff a shot at it. He swiped at the switch one final time as our window of opportunity ended.

The indication of success was to be a spin up of the satellite. We couldn't see the antenna on the top but knew it should also pop up, making it possible for the ground to communicate with it. Neither happened as Bo once again used the hand controllers to back away from the satellite. We watched as it disappeared into the sunset of our day, then we fired our orbital engines to get a good distance from it in case its booster ignited.

We positioned the arm to watch for booster firing 45 minutes later but saw nothing in the darkness. It hadn't worked. Our friends in Mission Control were trying to make us feel better by telling us what a great job we had done, but we weren't feeling bad at all. We were elated that we'd gotten to do some exciting things—the first unplanned EVA, first unplanned arm operation, first unplanned rendezvous, first in-space use of a bone saw!—and we had done them the way they should have been done. We all wanted to be heroes, but we had a tremendous sense of accomplishment that we hadn't messed anything up and had done our best. We were all safe and sound and had a great story to tell our grandchildren.

CHAPTER 8

★ ★ ★ ★ ★ ★

MORE DAYS
IN SPACE

I t had been an exciting but exhausting few days. Mission Control read our minds. They asked to talk to Bo about some planning options. We could work like crazy to get everything buttoned up to come home tomorrow, or if our commander thought that was pressing us too hard, we could have another day on orbit to get things finished up and come home the day after.

Who in the world would pass up another day in space?

Even though I was beginning to get a little homesick to see my boys again, I was tired, hadn't had a chance to do space gymnastics, or look out the window. Bo took a quick vote and it was unanimous: we'd take that extra day, turning a boring five-day flight into a fascinating seven-day one. We inventoried our food supplies while the ground checked the status of our oxygen, fuel, and other consumables. They assured us we were in good shape. We discovered we'd be eating hot dogs and junk food for breakfast, but we wouldn't starve.

Everyone set about finishing up all the things we hadn't had much time for. I got a few more heart pictures with the echo machine. Charlie puttered with his Continuous Flow Electrophoresis System. Electrophoresis—the separation of materials by their slight differences in electrical charge—can be done on the ground but gravity causes mixing of the solutions so it doesn't work as well as in space. In weightlessness this gravity-induced mixing is absent, so solutions of chemicals can be much better purified.

Charlie also had a little crystal growing device that benefitted from two extra days of space time. Crystal growth on Earth is also impeded by the gravity-induced solution mixing and by the bending effects on the crystals as they get bigger. Larger, more perfectly-formed crystals can be grown in space and later x-rayed to define their three dimensional shape much better.

Both electrophoresis and crystal growing were potential money-making ventures for space industry. It reminded me of the gold that America's explorers sought. Would the outcome of these early ventures into space lead to large factories there, or would we be in for the kinds of surprises that the European explorers discovered:

Charlie at work with the Continuous Flow Electrophoresis System or CFES.

PHOTO COURTESY OF NASA

PHOTO COURTESY OF NASA

Jake was doing brain wave tests for which his hairline was well suited.

El Dorado or a whole and unexpected New World?

Aboard as a passenger observer for Congress turned test subject, Jake had a medley of medical experiments to do. There was a great deal of interest in space motion sickness and what caused it. Although a seasoned pilot with many thousands of hours of flight time, Jake had never experienced motion sickness. Like most pilots, he figured he was immune but signed up to be a guinea pig in case he had some symptoms. We found out at the start of our flight that he was an excellent subject for the studies and was as Doonesbury called him, "Barfin' Jake Garn." We did find what we dubbed *the politician's cure*.

On the third day in orbit, we had scheduled a photo opportunity with Houston. For some reason, NASA Public Affairs always wanted to have astronauts' smiling faces beamed back from space, so the press didn't think there was anything wrong and that we were all hale and hearty. We began to hear rumblings that the media was beginning to ask questions about Jake because he hadn't appeared in any of our video downlinks since launch.

We tried to figure out how he could be seen and heard without his having to move around the cabin and make himself sick again. Someone pointed out that if we showed him as a volunteer for my echo tests, he'd have to be positioned firmly against the locker fronts. So on Flight Day 3 each of us took a few minutes to talk to Earth about what we had done so far. Other members of the crew talked while I got Jake all set up. I wasn't sure this would work since he still wasn't feeling well and looked a little peaked from not eating much for a couple days. We crossed our fingers, and at the appointed time turned on the lights, shifted the camera toward him, and handed him the microphone.

Thereupon, a miracle happened.

We should have known that handing a politician a hot mike would cause him to rally in the face of great adversity.

It did.

His face lit up, and his eyes glowed with fervor as he explained the echo experiment and all the others he was performing, as well as what wonderful things would be learned from them. His voice, which moments earlier had been muffled with mild dehydration, became positively silver-tongued. He was brilliant! We were impressed and knew the worst was over for old Jake.

Later in the mission, when he was having great fun doing somersaults with the rest of us, Bo presented Jake with a set of the Doonesbury cartoons that Gary Trudeau autographed as a present to the senator for being a good sport. They would hang in a long hallway full of space memorabilia in Jake's and Kathleen's beautiful home in Salt Lake City to remind Barfin' Jake that space motion sickness is no laughing matter.

There is perhaps one picture from the flight that I hope never surfaces. Jeff was our onboard astronomer, and he wanted more than anything to get a good view of the stars during some of our night passes. However, he was told by previous flyers that it was difficult to get the flight deck dark enough to prevent the light from reflecting off the windows and ruining the view. We darkened the flight deck lights as much as possible. Jeff had designed

a clever black bag that he could wiggle into and attach around the rim of one of the overhead windows to block out any other extraneous light. He was up there *ooh-ing* and *aah-ing* at one point, and I asked if I could look out with him. The bag wasn't designed for two, but we managed to squeeze into it. Someone at that moment took a picture of us stuffed into this cozy contraption with our stocking feet sticking

Jake is presented with a Gary Trudeau drawing of Barfin' Jake Garn.

PHOTO COURTESY OF NASA

Jeff and I play with the Slinky which would become part of the Toys in Space video for children. Our alma mater insignias are on the locker faces.

out. Someone could get the wrong idea if an explanation wasn't provided (which I'm doing now). But the stars were spectacular. Being a couple hundred miles closer didn't make them any larger, but there were so many more visible. If you've ever been on a mountaintop on a clear night and marveled at the huge number of lights in the sky, then imagine a thousand times more, and you will get an idea of what the stars look like when you're up above the Earth's atmosphere. I hoped that in later years I would be able to conjure up that view in my mind's eye.

Dr. Carolyn Sumners who had taught us star identification at the planetarium during our ASCAN training asked us to do something in space we couldn't resist. If there was time she wanted us to video how some children's toys performed in zero gravity for the Houston Museum of Natural Science. Being our commander, Bo had taken dibs on the gyroscope and spinning top. Don had a little rat that, after it had been wound up, could do a back flip. Dave became a yoyo expert. And Jeff, the physicist, chose a bag of magnetic marbles and a car on a track. I chose a Slinky and a ball and jacks. Jake flew a paper airplane for the Smithsonian Air and Space Museum. The educational film *Toys in Space* would be put together after the flight. It was a great way to demonstrate the physics of gravity and its absence to young kids. Playing with the toys was a fun way to finish up our on-orbit duties.

Jeff, my very erudite crewmate read an excerpt from a novella by René Daumal. The words I remember most were:

> *You cannot stay on the summit forever.*
> *You have to come down again…*
> *There is an art to finding your way in the lower regions*
> *By the memory of what you have seen higher up.*

Jake's paper airplane ready to fly.

PHOTO COURTESY OF NASA

Coming home from space was easy. The evening before deorbit everything had to be stowed so it wouldn't rattle around or hit something as we encountered gravity and did our landing maneuvers. The next morning the only things we had to put on, other than our regular NASA flight suit, were our diapers—or urine bags—and our boots and helmets.

Mission Control gave our onboard computers the landing target, which for STS-51D was Runway 33 at the Kennedy Space Center in Florida. Our computers figured out what to do for our *deorbit burn*. To get into space, the thrust of our boosters and engines had enabled us to get to orbital velocity. To return home, the shuttle needed to slow down, which would lower our orbit and allow the craft to fall back to Earth. Exactly how to do that was easy for our computers and the ones in Mission Control to figure out. Pick a point on the ground to end up on, know the altitude to start from, understand how much atmosphere was between those places and how much energy to dissipate and, voila, plug the solution into shuttle's guidance system and head downhill.

Capsules in earlier space vehicles fired their retrorockets to get out of orbit. The shuttle turned around backwards so that the large Orbital Maneuvering System engines fired enough to slow the vehicle down. Done at the right time (for STS -51D, over the Indian Ocean) for just long enough, *Discovery* would fall back into the Earth's atmosphere at about 400,000 feet altitude, west of Hawaii. At that height, the air molecules hitting any vehicle (or a meteor, for that matter) would begin to decelerate it so that it plummets to Earth.

There is another effect of the air molecules. When an object is going fast, even though there aren't many molecules at high altitudes, those molecules create tremendous friction and heat, which is why it's important to turn back around nose forward at the top of the atmosphere, or Entry Interface, as NASA calls it. The special materials on the nose and the front of the wings and the heat shield tiles bottom of the space shuttle are designed to withstand the tremendous heat of reentry and must be pointed into the airflow.

The view out the orbiter forward windows during reentry into the atmosphere was spectacular. We were in pitch black night when we started down. Slowly, it began to get lighter out those windows. Over the next few minutes it went from dull orange to brighter orange to pinkish to blinding white. It felt like we were flying through a fireball...which we were.

Looking out the overhead windows on the flight deck provided an even eerier sight.

As the hot air molecules wrapped around the shuttle, they hit the tail and were deflected one way or the other. This had the appearance of giant bolts of fire being thrown at the cabin. For some reason it made me think of the Greek god Zeus flinging bolts of lightning at his enemies. Had there been missing tiles on our undercarriage, this immense heat could have burned through the delicate aluminum skin beneath. Again, all we could do was pray and trust. Inside the cabin, we felt none of the heat and were relieved to see the fire dissipate as we slowed down.

Although my seat for landing was on the middeck with Jake and Charlie, Bo allowed me to stand behind him upstairs to watch the light show until we began to feel the onset of "Gs," or gravity. The first thing I noticed was that my hands weren't floating anymore. They went from being somewhere out in front of me to being planted on the back of Bo's seat. At first we were only feeling a fraction of gravity's force, but it was there.

As Bo had ordered, I took one last look out the forward windows at the fading glow of the onrushing Earth and made my way down the ladder: no more zipping to the middeck head first! As I stepped off the last rung, I had this funny sensation of being extra light, as if on the surface of the moon. Jake and Charlie, already strapped into their seats in the middle of the middeck, were entertained by their favorite space physician doing giant ballet leaps across the floor and the types of bouncy kangaroo jumps that moon walkers favored over walking. It was fun but became harder and harder as gravity's pull got stronger and stronger. To a body which hadn't fought to oppose gravity in a week, my muscles had weakened so that somewhere around a half a G it began to feel like I was back on Earth.

My seat for landing was in front of the bathroom door, with a view out the side hatch porthole. The orbiter banked left and right as it flew graceful S-shaped turns to dissipate energy for landing. As we came into daylight and banked to the left, I had a great view of the Gulf of Mexico whizzing by beneath us. We were still many miles up and going about Mach 5, five times the speed of sound. With no man-made objects to give perspective, it felt like we were just above the clouds in an airplane that was going incredibly fast and way too fast to slow down before we were to reach Florida.

Mission Control had warned us about high winds at the Cape. The landing runway runs southeast to northwest, and there was a strong wind from the east. We would be landing with the highest crosswind that the shuttle had seen so far, and there were reasons that that could be dangerous.

The space shuttle had four main landing gear tires, which was pretty dinky for that large a vehicle. We all knew they were a weak spot. In talking to our old NASA engineer friend, John Kiker, about the early days of the orbiter design, Hoot and I discovered how that had happened. The wheel and brake designers in the early 1970s were told to plan on a vehicle that weighed 200,000 pounds. There was considerable incentive to make the landing gear and all its associated paraphernalia as light as possible. Tires, brakes, struts, landing gear doors, and so on had to be hauled into orbit and flown around, only to be used for a few moments at the end of the flight.

Previous space vehicles required no landing gear. At the proper altitude, the Mercury, Gemini, and Apollo capsules popped out parachutes to slow their descent into the ocean. But the shuttle was to be reusable and needed to land like a plane on a runway.

As the orbiter continued to be developed, it got heavier and heavier until it weighed a good deal more than what the wheels were designed for. There was considerable concern before the first flights as to how much safety margin we had in this area. How close were we to breaking something? Early landings were done on the dry lakebed at Edwards Air Force Base to allow the engineers to look at this system's real capability. A primordial lake, in drying up it left a huge flat spot baked hard as concrete by the blistering desert sun. The Air Force merely marked out runways on it and took advantage of its *forgiving* nature.

If the shuttle landed at Edwards on the lakebed and blew a tire, there would be no problem. It might go swerving to one side or the other, barreling off the runway but so what? That would mean that it would end up on an unmarked section of the hard packed lakebed.

Even the formal concrete runway at Edwards offered the same sort of advantage. Although raised a bit above the surrounding desert floor, running off the side (or the end if the brakes failed) meant a little downhill dip, then onto the vast safety of the dry lake.

The brakes and tires were pretty chewed up after each flight, though, and had to be replaced after every landing. Like a number of things, NASA declared them safe for flight, despite understanding that there was a decreased safety margin. Decisions like this were later called "normalization of deviance," meaning the performance deviated from what was expected but was declared okay because nothing bad happened. Unbeknown to the astronauts, leaking of hot gasses past the O-rings in the boosters was also being called normal.

Florida offered none of these safety features. Reclaimed from the alligator-infested swamps of the Kennedy Space Center, the shuttle landing strip was surrounded by a moat. Have a bad day, lose a tire or your brakes, and you could get your feet wet. But the engineers decided the crosswind for our landing would not be a problem.

So Bo was thinking hard all the way through entry about getting blown off the side of the runway by the wind if he wasn't careful or the designer's predictions about how much crosswind this vehicle could handle were wrong. There wasn't much small talk as the shuttle slowed down inexorably. From having attended other landings, I knew Hoot, Paul, and the landing guests seated in the bleachers were about to be surprised by the double sonic booms as the vehicle came back through the sound barrier. That noise preceded seeing a tiny speck in the sky as the shuttle passed over the runway and commenced its slow arc around to land.

After slowing below the sound barrier, after the few seconds of vibrations known as the *transonic buffet*, Bo pushed buttons on a panel in front of him that allowed him to take over from the computers which had flown us to this point. The final approach and landing were always flown manually. This meant he was at last flying the airplane he had spent years training for. I knew it was an exciting moment for him.

The commander had a stick, or controller, in front of his seat (like in a fighter jet) that controlled the ailerons and rudder to make the machine perform like a glider, about the heaviest glider in the world. He also had a throttle at his left side, although there are no engines on the shuttle at this point to throttle up or back. The throttle controlled the speed brake. The rear part of the tail of the shuttle swiveled back and forth like the rudder of an airplane but also split open into the wind to slow it down. Push forward on the *throttle* and the shuttle went faster because the speed brake was closed; pull back on the throttle and the brake opened up, slowing the ship down.

276

Bo intercepted the heading alignment circle and swooped around in a descending arc until aligned with the runway using the stick, the throttle, all the onboard meters, and the three separate computer screens, as well as the airspeed and altitude calls from Don. Guests were amazed as we passed overhead the bleachers, that the shuttle was a tiny dot in the sky, still nine miles up, but yet in a moment or two it would be landing right in front of them.

The shuttle, in pilot-speak, flew like a brick. Its heavy body and stubby little wings gave it just enough lift to come blazing out of the sky and then make a passable landing. As our commander made the turn to line up with the runway, turning onto final approach, we were at 10,000 feet altitude and only seven miles from the place he planned to put in down on the

ground. Looking at the touchdown point from that perspective makes it look like you are going almost straight down.

The wind was blowing from the east, off to our right. To keep the orbiter going straight ahead and not be blown off course, he had to point the nose to the right to compensate for the crosswind. Bo made a great landing at the beginning of the run-

Hoot waiting for me at the landing strip in Florida. way and so smooth we barely felt it. The wind kept trying to push us to the left. All the way down our 10,000-foot rollout Bo had to apply the right brake to keep us going down the centerline. As we were almost to a stop, we heard a shuddering bang beneath us.

To those of us on the middeck it was loud, and to me it sounded like it was right under my seat. It must have been more muffled on the flight deck because Bo said, "What was that?" (Pinky Nelson, a fellow middeck passenger a year earlier, had briefed the flight deck crew never to ask a question that ended in "that" since it tended to scare the people who couldn't see the control panel or out any windows.) Dave said maybe it was the brakes releasing. There were no red lights on the Caution and Warning panel, so they figured it couldn't be anything too bad.

Seconds later we were stopped. Home again – safely! We'd survived. We all cheered for Bo's excellent landing. Mission Control radioed, "Welcome home, *Discovery*! Great job!" and we started unstrapping. It was so

Bo made a perfect landing for the waiting crowd.

comforting to have wheels on the ground and feel the familiar and reassuring hug of gravity again.

Not long thereafter, the white room (a little enclosure on the top of a truck) pulled up to the side hatch of the orbiter and popped open the door. Oh, the muggy, wonderful Florida fresh air! There were bottles of cool water to begin replenishing what we'd lost on orbit. I was out of my seat and ready to disembark in short order.

Then I looked at my fellow middeck passengers. Charlie looked chipper, but Jake had a funny, pale look on his face like something wasn't right. He had the not-too-uncommon reaction after landing of the same *tumbled gyros* dizziness that he'd had when we got to space. After being free of gravity for a week, the vestibular or balance system in the inner ear quits paying attention to the gravity input, and there it was again. It sometimes took a couple days to get used to maneuvering around again. Compound that with being a couple liters low on the body water that people get rid of in space, and a fair number of returning conquerors are pretty unsteady on their feet.

Yet we knew that Jake was the big star on our mission, and all the cameras would be on him as he walked down the stairs outside the white room. The flight surgeon came on board and started plying him with water hoping it would help.

Would a microphone cure him once again, I wondered evilly?

After a few minutes, Jake felt well enough to make his way down the steps and into the waiting arms of George Abbey, who escorted him to the Astrovan.

The biggest surprise of all was the shredded right inboard tire which we were allowed to view from a distance lest the other tires explode from the heat. That explained the post-landing bang. The brake on that tire had overheated and failed, locking up the wheel. The tire was dragged along the runway and came apart. It was a casualty of the design that didn't provide enough safety margin in our tires and brakes. This event would change a lot about landings in the years to come.

More impressive to me, mentioned as an afterthought by one of the support people getting us off the orbiter, was a pie plate-sized area on the left wing where a tile had come off, and the aluminum skin underneath had been melted away. I was glad that spot wasn't underneath my little pink body during the fireball. On my next two flights I remembered that the danger of a flight wasn't over until your own two feet were planted back on terra firma.

The excitement and elation of a mission completed were tremendous, but the thing I wanted most was to see Hoot and Paul. We had decided not to drag Paul down to the Cape for landing. That would give Hoot and me a chance to visit on the plane ride back to Houston. Hoot was waiting for me when I got off the elevator on the third floor of the O&C building, where I had left him before the flight. It was a wonderful feeling to be back in his arms having "cheated death again," as the pilots said.

Hoot was uncharacteristically talkative about the press coverage we'd gotten in our attempt to rescue Syncom. Press coverage? I realized that without newspapers or TV, and with communications with the ground always crisp and business-like, we hadn't been aware that millions of people all over the world had been following our escapades. We'd made the front page several days running. It was a strange realization about how out of touch we had been.

How did it feel to be back on Earth after a week away from gravity?

Heavy, man, heavy! Initially it felt like I had gained a hundred pounds, and my arms and legs felt like dead weights. It was hard to predict where my feet were when I tried to step up because it required so much more effort to get them off the ground. I had to watch my feet with my eyes as I attempted to go upstairs to make sure they made it up each step.

There was also a strange unsteadiness. Before the flight, if I leaned to the side my inner ear responded to gravity's pull, and I could tell how far over I was. As I moved up, down, forward, back, or from side to side, I would sense that because gravity acted on my inner ear. In space the inner ear didn't register leaning, rotation of the body, or movement in any direction since there was no pull from gravity. On return from space the inner ear often confuses the different kind of body movements. So at first I staggered around looking much like a drunk, swerving into corners and walking with my feet wide apart, grinning at the odd sensation.

That first shower after landing felt fantastic. I never felt grimy and stinky in flight where we washed off with wet wipes, but I always seemed to have dirt under my fingernails and never felt clean. As we made our way to the bathrooms, we were warned, "Don't get soap in your eyes!" I knew that if I closed them before I was fully readapted and tilted my head back, I might get confused about where I was in relation to the floor. I decided to take my shower sitting in a chair to keep from falling down.

Jeannie Marks was my secretary at the time. A great friend, she would someday be greeting her own husband returning from space. She had offered to keep three year old Paul while Hoot came to Florida and to bring him to Ellington Field for our return ceremony. As we got closer and closer to Houston, my heartstrings got tauter and tauter. Oh, how I'd missed that little guy! Hoot had been telling me how he'd been prancing around telling everybody that, "Mommy's gone bye-bye on the space shuttle." But would he remember me? Would he be mad and stand-offish that I'd left him? I hadn't seen him since my sneak visit to our house and tearful departure ten days earlier.

Welcome home ceremonies at Ellington Field were another tradition that was special. Everyone who had worked on the flight, friends, neighbors, and the press all turned out to share the joy of a safe homecoming and show the team spirit so typical of NASA's human spaceflight program.

As our crew and families stepped blinking off the NASA plane into the sun, we were greeted by cheers from the crowd. But where was my little man? Did Jeannie get delayed? Was he sick? As I reached the bottom of the plane stairs, a little voice from the midst of the cordoned off crowd yelled:

"Mommy!"

Then bursting out of the gaggle of well-wishers came this little blur all dressed up in his flight suit designed to look like mine. The pictures of him flying across the tarmac into my arms, tears streaming down my face, made *People* magazine the next week. It was so wonderful to have that moment captured on film because it still warms my heart to look at it. It was not until the next day that I noticed Paul had the tell-tale red spots of chicken pox.

So at the end of a long day at the end of long week at the end of a long couple of years we drove home to our snug little house in the suburbs

PHOTO COURTESY OF NASA

Paul was waiting for us at the crew return ceremony at Ellington Field in Houston.

The stuff on my desk at home got out of hand during prelaunch training, the flight and the postflight time period. Hoot captured the chaos of those days.

where I spent a couple hours cuddling my two boys and recounting tales of wonder before crashing for a full twelve hours of sleep in my own bed.

A great surprise awaited me in the coming weeks. I had thought the worst of the long hours was past, and I'd have a little time to relax. But no, postflight was even busier. Crew members got a day off before debriefs began, but then it was off and running again. Hoot presented me with a picture of my desk at home during this period. He was right. It looked like a bomb had gone off in the study there was such a pile of undone work and unanswered mail.

The first people to hear about our flight were the Chief of the Astronaut Office and the Director of Flight Crew Operations; at the time those were John Young and George Abbey. John was a good listener, often asking more detailed questions. George was there to *help* us focus on what the crew wanted the rest of the world to hear from our debriefs. There were certain nuggets of important information from each flight that needed to be stressed, certain recommendations that we didn't want to get lost in the rest of the discussion. It reminded me of our public speaking class where we were advised to always have a message in mind when we were on stage. On our flight it had taken tremendous teamwork between folks on the ground—Mission Control, numerous astronauts in support roles, the Syncom and arm contractors, and many others—as well as our crew in space to pull off all the unplanned activities. That was what we would focus on. We also used these activities to show the reason to have people in space, with their unique abilities to rethink, replan, and rework a situation, things that couldn't be preprogrammed into robots.

Charlie Walker's contraption had worked well and separated his solutions beautifully. He'd also begun some exciting work on growing protein crystals in space. Jake had performed his medical experiments admirably. He'd had a chance to train with us and get to know many aspects of the space program. He'd gained tremendous credibility in Congress for having *been there*. We didn't know then how vital his role would be in the coming years. We completed some engineering tests on the orbiter, and our video on toys was a hit with educators, fulfilling one of NASAs primary roles, that of educating the public about space.

After talking to our own bosses, the debriefings continued with all the other groups who had supported our flight. They could learn from what happened to do better work in the future and we could hear about all the activities that had transpired on the ground to help us. The briefing we most looked forward to was to the Astronaut Office. We could be completely honest about motion sickness and any mistakes we had made. Every crew had the strong desire to use their experience to help others avoid the same errors and to better understand what they'd be up against. For our crew, this debrief was much more a two way conversation. Many in the office had been surrogates for us as the satellite rescue was planned. We were fascinated to know what had been going on back at home. Bo was interested in knowing whether everyone had done due diligence in deciding that working that close to the satellite had been safe. We were reassured by the descriptions of all the work that had been done and the options that had been discussed. There were thousands of decisions during each flight that had to be made in Mission Control on behalf of the crew; we had to depend on them to make the right ones.

The flight controllers in Mission Control were anxious to know how we interpreted their written messages and their radio communications. The arm experts needed to know how the arm performed this strange task and how well the training had prepared me to do a spur-of-the-moment job. The EVA folks wanted to know how the spacewalkers had done their work and how the equipment had operated. The medical folks were interested in the scientific research results – mostly my echo and Jake's studies.

Meetings were scheduled from sun up to sun down with little free time. In addition, we had a press conference about a week after landing. We had to review all our film and photographs to put together a little show for the media. Once we had a movie, we had to decide how to narrate it to tell our story. And of course we had to choose the best of the still pictures to show things we hadn't captured on film and perhaps some especially nice views of the Earth for color. This planning was done after work hours and on the weekend. Astronauts often kidded that if you didn't bring back pictures, people would think you didn't go to space at all. Trying to describe in words what we had seen wasn't the same and even the best of pictures couldn't capture it.

After the debriefings and the press conference, the crew had to write the formal crew report, noting all the things accomplished, summarizing the problems (or surprises) which occurred and how they were remedied or accommodated, and making recommendations given for bettering the system. These went from the ridiculous (increase the airflow on the potty) to the inspired (train EVA crewmembers on more generic tasks). Crew reports became part of the library of little known history of spaceflight.

After talking and writing nonstop for a couple months, crew members were put *in the barrel*. The expression was coined back in the Mercury days and referred to the ease with which fish can be shot in a barrel. For astronauts it meant being trotted about all over the country by NASA Public Affairs people to excite the public about space or to convince congressmen and their constituents of the value of space programs.

One of the most wonderful parts of this whole process was my *hometowner*. NASA footed the bill for a return to Murfreesboro and let me spend several days enjoying the glory of "Local Girl Makes Good." The red carpet was certainly rolled out for me. The highlight of the series of talks I gave and places I visited was the congressional hearing held in the Boro, as locals call Murfreesboro, Tennessee. As it turned out, Congressman Bill Nelson from Florida, Chairman of the Space Science and Technology Subcommittee in the House of Representatives, owed my congressman, Bart Gordon, a favor. Bart had helped him get elected to his chairmanship, and that would play a large role in Chairman Bill Nelson's future…and to our family's, too.

Congressman Nelson decided that rather than having our crew testify about our flight to a committee in Washington, he'd move the hearing to my home town and invite his committee there. This turned out to be a wonderful occasion for my friends to turn out to hear about my space adventures. I'm sure it helped Congressman Gordon prove he was a supporter of these futuristic endeavors, and that probably didn't hurt his re-election chances. And maybe Congressman Nelson, whose home district included the Kennedy Space Center, had a few cards up his sleeve.

Bo accompanied me to my hometown of Murfreesboro, Tennessee for the huge welcome home ceremony.

The hearing was held at Middle Tennessee State University in my hometown, and a huge crowd turned out. I appreciated the opportunity to thank all the people who had played such vital roles in my life: teachers, scout leaders, mentors, medical personnel, friends, and neighbors.

The other big event was presenting a banner I'd flown for my old high school to the kids of the town. Central High School had been changed to Central Middle School but the halls still looked the same when they gave me a tour. I could remember which classroom was Miss Herron's homeroom my freshman year, where Mrs. McFerrin talked us through advanced math, where Mrs. McNabb had algebra classes, and where Mrs. Ogino taught me to appreciate literature. I remember as a cheerleader sitting on the steps during summer practice with Mrs. Jordan, our sponsor

President Ronald Reagan met with us in the Oval Office during our postflight visit to Washington.

and PE teacher, telling us to behave ourselves because if any of us got pregnant (I'm not sure I knew how that happened when I first heard her admonition as a freshman), she'd personally kill us. I remembered Mr. Blair, the principal, and then Mr. Bandy who took his place, talking in a crackly voice over the school intercom, making school announcements and telling us what time we'd take a break in our classes to watch that day's NASA launch. Something wonderful came full circle for me on that day.

As I looked into the faces of those little kids who welcomed me that day, I remembered how it felt to be 11 or 12 years old with my whole future in front of me. I wondered if one of those bright faces would gain some sense of inspiration from my visit and understand that what my father had always told me was true, "You can go anywhere in the world from right here in Murfreesboro, Tennessee" – and maybe beyond.

Next up was the crew's visit to Washington, D.C. Like a school kid on a field trip, I gaped at the agenda that took us around to see the nation's high and mighty. Many crews visit a few congressmen and senators, most from their own states and most NASA supporters. But since Jake had been on our flight and a Republican inhabited the White House, we had some awesome times.

Jake took us to see the Republican minority leader, Bob Michel. We also met Bob Dole, Jake's fellow Utahan Orrin Hatch, and fellow westerner Alan Simpson. I also had a nice visit with Bart Gordon and my Tennessee senator (my former congressman and future Vice President) Al Gore. When I think back on it, I was only the fifth American woman to fly in space and was something of an oddity. I was well received by several other Tennessee leaders, and I felt proud that most of them were NASA supporters. One thing that I learned on that visit was that it is congressional aides who really run Washington. I met many who covered NASA for their bosses and were much more knowledgeable about space issues than the guys with the titles.

The big Washington event for our crew was a visit to the Oval Office to meet President Ronald Reagan. He was as personable and jolly as he seemed on television. He even had a joke for us. Jake had always been a big supporter of his, so it was a cordial visit and we all had our pictures made.

The next exciting event was a postflight trip to Utah. What an unusual place! I had talked often with Jake—and fellow astronaut Don Lind and his wife, Kathleen—about the tenets of the Mormon faith, but it was interesting to see the lives built around this religion and a state built around it. We were welcomed into the home of one of Jake's friends, Jon Huntsman who owned a large chemical company, situated on the hillside overlooking the Great Salt Lake. In the foyer was a recent photo of the extended and extensive Huntsman clan. Anyone in Utah can tell you that Mormons

believe in large families and start them early, but when they put several generations together for a family portrait, it is striking. Their nine children were increasing the population exponentially with large families of their own. With all the in-laws, the picture required a wide angle lens.

A trip to the ski areas, still covered with snow even in May, was memorable and we promised to come back when we could do some skiing. Most impressive, too, was our personal visit with the lead-

A special presentation of patriotic music by the Mormon Tabernacle Choir in honor of Jake and his crew *(above)*. We are presented to the huge crowd by church leaders *(right)*.

Even in May there was snow on the slopes of the Utah ski areas.

ers of the Mormon Church. Elderly and frail, President Spencer Kimball didn't often meet with many out of town visitors, but because of Jake's faithful support of his church, we met with him briefly. And what could possibly top that? We were honored by an evening performance by the Mormon Tabernacle Choir in our honor. I have never heard a more inspirational sound than that huge magnificent choir singing patriotic songs for us and the congregation. Jake was rightfully proud.

All in all, it was exhilarating, inspirational, exciting and exhausting. Not until the end of summer would things quiet down enough for me to take on a new office assignment. Starting in the last half of 1985 I would be in charge of representing the Astronaut Office for all the crew equipment that was flown on the shuttle missions. From cameras, to experiments, to clothes, to duct tape, I became the Chief of Stuff. I also picked up the training for my next mission where I'd left off and resumed my *Mommy* job, my ER practice, and my spouse role for Hoot's next flight.

The crew of STS-61C for Hoot's second flight and his first as Commander *(above, left)*. The STS-61C crew patch *(above, right)*.

When I finally had a chance to catch my breath, I realized that Hoot's second flight, STS-61C, was fast approaching. Scheduled for December, he had been training with a wonderful crew. Whenever they went to the Cape for training they watched the movie Animal House in crew quarters. It wasn't long before they became known as the Delta House crew after the insane fraternity house in the movie. They even put the Delta Tau Chi insignia above their office door.

Hoot would be the commander of the flight. His pilot was Charlie Bolden, a remarkable man. President of his United States Naval Academy class, he had a distinguished aviation career in the Marines and became the fourth African-American astronaut. He and Hoot had been running buddies since Charlie came into the office in 1980. It would be his first flight and he had a lot to learn. During their training, Charlie discovered one of "Hoot's Rules" when he inadvertently turned off the wrong shuttle fuel cell during a simulator run when in a hurry. Hoot said, "Charlie, just remember that things are never so bad that you can't do something to make them worse."

Two members of our ASCAN class would be mission specialists. George "Pinky" Nelson was an astronomer who had performed a spectacular spacewalk the year before using the jet backpack on his first flight. Fellow astronomer Steve Hawley was married to Sally Ride and had a wonderful sense of humor. Steve wanted a nickname like Hoot and Pinky, so he dubbed himself "A²" (the Attack Astronomer) to poke fun at the military pilots who took pride in being either fighter pilots or attack pilots.

At first the third mission specialist, Franklin Chang-Diaz looked a little out of place with this raucous bunch. A rather unassuming young man, Franklin was a brilliant plasma physicist who had been born and raised in Costa Rica. He had come to the United States at 17 and became a citizen in order to apply to be an astronaut. When asked how he became interested in space, Franklin said he had gone to the American embassy in San José as a child to watch the early space flights. He spoke no English at the time but listened carefully to the communication. He told us he often heard Mission Control say "Roger, we copy." He thought it was an incredible undertaking, and he soon knew the names of all the astronauts. "However," he once said, "I never could figure out who Roger was." Given a short time with the crew, he began to fit right in.

Added to the flight were two non-astronaut payload specialists. One was Florida Congressmen Bill Nelson, a Democrat who represented the district that surrounded the

Because of the many launch scrubs, we made several trips to the Beach House in chilly weather. Here are the crewmembers and their spouses

PHOTO COURTESY OF NASA

Kennedy Space Center. I had gotten to know him when he brought his Space Science and Technology Subcommittee to my home town for our post-flight congressional hearing. Bob Cenker was an RCA engineer from Pennsylvania. They tried their best to become part of the crazy Animal House crew.

Their flight became famous for its inability to get off the ground and then the inability to get back to Earth. Crew and families went to Florida expecting a launch on December 18, 1985, but the paperwork for the orbiter wasn't complete and the launch was delayed a day. On the next day, the launch was scrubbed 14 seconds before liftoff because of a problem with one of the boosters. Since that couldn't be fixed quickly, everyone went home for Christmas and reconvened on December 31. We all spent New Year's Eve in the quarantine facility in Houston.

PHOTO COURTESY OF NASA

Bill Nelson working on science experiments.

Happy families unite at Ellington Field after the Shuttle landed unexpectedly in California.

On January 6, multiple problems stopped the count at T-31 seconds. The countdown was recycled to T-20 minutes for a second launch attempt, but that try was also scrubbed, as well. The crew was lucky they hadn't lifted off; a temperature probe had broken off during fueling and jammed in an engine pre-valve which could have damaged the engine on the way to orbit.

That problem fixed, another attempt was made on January 7 but was scrubbed because of bad weather at the emergency landing sites in Senegal and Spain. And on January 10, unrelenting rainfall in the launch area led to another scrub. The crew decided the delays were Steve Hawley's fault. He had bad luck on his first flight in 1984 when the main engines shut down seconds before the launch. On the next try on January 12, the fifth time they strapped in, Steve wore a Groucho Marx disguise so the orbiter wouldn't recognize him.

The flight went off without a hitch.

During the crew's months of training, through all the pre-launch preparations, and over the course of the many launch delays, we wives—Jackie, Sally, Susie, Peggy, Grace, Barbara, and I—had gotten to know one another well. Dutifully, we went out to the Launch Control Center for every attempt—drinking too much coffee and growing fat on too many doughnuts. We talked to relieve the tension. Our many children were about the same age, so they played together and became fast friends.

The crew finally reached orbit and got busy deploying a communications satellite. They performed a multitude of experiments, but the ground decided to shorten their mission from seven days to four because of the launch delays. On January 16 and 17, the weather at the Cape was terrible. More delays. On January 18, with the continued bad weather in the Sunshine State, they made an unplanned night landing at Edwards Air Force Base in California—a big disappointment for Bill, who had hoped to land triumphantly in his home state of Florida.

But Delta Tau Chi crew was home safe. Perhaps some of the problems they had were omens that there were safety issues lurking in the shuttle program.

It would turn out to be the only successful flight of 1986.

CHAPTER 9

★ ★ ★ ★ ★ ★

SWEET DREAMS AND FLYING MACHINES

The stars had not aligned well for the January 28, 1986 flight of the STS-51L on *Challenger*. There had been multiple launch delays. After the crew had been strapped in the day before, there was a problem with the side hatch. Technicians couldn't get the hatch latching apparatus off the door after closing it. They had looked a little ridiculous waiting around for a hack saw to be found so they could cut the thing off. As it turned out, it took a long time, the winds picked up, and the launch had to be scrubbed until the next day.

An old poem describes how little things can lead to bigger consequences:

For want of a nail, the shoe was lost;
For want of the shoe, the horse was lost;

For want of the horse, the rider was lost;
For want of a rider, the battle was lost;
For want of the battle, the kingdom was lost;
And all for the want of a horseshoe nail.

In the case of the *Challenger* and her crew, for want of a hack saw on a warm Florida day, all was lost.

The night of the 27th, a freak cold front descended on Florida. Usually balmy that time of year, the Cape had experienced a hard freeze with temperatures sliding into the low 20s and staying low all night. The morning dawned clear and bright…and still frigid. From the pad cameras came pictures of bizarre, thick icicles hanging from the launch tower. At lift-off would the ghostly fingers of ice break off and damage the shuttle engines or belly tiles?

Members of the Astronaut Office, even the flight crew themselves, were unaware that meetings had gone on late into the night between the NASA Marshall Space Flight Center managers responsible for the solid rocket boosters and the Morton Thiokol engineers who had built them. In question were the O-rings which, like washers in a hose linkage, sealed the blazing hot propellant inside the boosters from reaching the aluminum outer skin. The boosters had been tested down to 40 degrees F. The coldest launch to date had been at 53 degrees, and there had been some leakage past the first set of O-rings between the rocket segments at that temperature. But there didn't seem to be a direct correlation between temperature and O-ring leakage since there had also been some at warmer temperatures. And anyway, there was a second set of O-rings to back up the first. No one was sure what the extreme cold would mean. This was outside the engineering *experience base*. The Thiokol engineers at the working level recommended the conservative approach: wait until it was warmer.

What went into the decision to launch that day? NASA was trying to launch fifteen flights in 1986. Hoot's December flight had slid into January, so the schedule for the rest of 1986 was already in jeopardy. This flight had been delayed several times already. Halley's Comet was passing near Earth early in the year and both the *Challenger* flight and the next one scheduled for March had instruments to study it. Launching later in the year might mean these once-in-75-years opportunities would be lost. The State of the Union address was scheduled for that night, and with the morning's launch as a perfect backdrop, Reagan was to applaud NASA's accomplishments and the crew's first teacher in space, Christa McAuliffe. Were these factors in the decision making? Too much "go fever" as it was called in NASA's early days? Maybe subconsciously, but the tension was there. We were in a hurry-up mentality, pushing people and systems to the limit. Under pressure, the Thiokol managers overrode their engineers and convinced themselves the secondary O-rings would seal if the primary ones leaked. The Marshall managers gave their GO for launch. The Thiokol engineers prayed they were wrong about their worries.

Everyone remembers where they were on January 28, 1986 when a horrible confluence of tragic events came together. At 10:30 a.m. in Houston, my second flight's crew had a meeting scheduled with the support contractor in an off-site facility. We needed to map out the training required to prepare for Spacelab Life Sciences-1, as our flight was now labeled. As we all gathered we chatted about Hoot's recent flight which landed 10 days prior and all the delays that seemed to be happening. While we waited for everyone to arrive we turned on a television to check on *Challenger*'s countdown.

As we watched, Payload Specialist Millie Hughes-Fulford reminded us that when our Spacelab flight was assigned in 1984, our launch date had been set as January, 1986. This should have been our flight. Darn our bad luck for all the delays and rearrangements in the schedule. We were ready to go: put us onboard!

The television picture showed a crisp, bright, cloudless day at the Cape. The crew had walked out in the cold that morning looking a little pudgy from the long johns they wore under their flight suits. One of our 1978 classmates whom I regarded as a grown-up among us young pups, Dick Scobee

was the mature, calm commander, a real leader. Mike Smith, the pilot, was one of my favorites. A Southern boy from North Carolina, he had that easy drawl and lanky good looks that reminded me of my high school friends. Ellison Onizuka was one of Hoot's best friends and had been his first office mate. When we came to NASA in 1978, El was somewhat taken aback when

The crew of *Challenger*, STS-51L.

he was classified as a minority. Though a Hawaiian of Japanese descent, he hadn't considered himself one. Hoot always kidded him about liking fat Hawaiian ladies, though his wife Lorna was trim and elegant. When El was not in the office, Hoot would tell people he was on a *fat finding mission*.

Judy Resnik was the flight engineer. One of the first women in the Corps with me in 1978, this would be her second flight. Tough and capable, she relished her role of sitting behind and between the pilot and commander, watching their activities and helping with their checklists. Ron McNair rounded out the NASA crew of five. One of the three African Americans in our 1978 class, his first flight was on Hoot's first mission, so I'd gotten to know him and his wife, Cheryl, well. Since his son Reggie and my son Paul were close in age and attended the same preschool, we'd often compared notes about raising little boys. Greg Jarvis, one of the payload specialists, had gotten to know many NASA crews. Bumped from one mission to another because of our ever-changing flight manifest, he had for a short time been on my first mission until replaced by Jake Garn. When the *Challenger* crew had gone into quarantine, I had left him a bottle of fine champagne from our crew, wishing him well from all of us who were happy he was finally getting to fly. I wondered if he had decided to save it until his return home.

Of course, the best known crewmember was Christa McAuliffe, America's Teacher in Space selectee. Many of us had gotten to know her through our various job assignments. As the office crew equipment representative, I had made sure all the equipment she had requested for her school lessons from space was packed onboard. I also met her mother at the spouse party her crew had hosted for Hoot's launch the month before.

As launch time drew near, it was such a clear day in Florida that I commented that we'd be able to see the booster separation two minutes into the flight on the Cape's long range cameras. Since it looked like the launch was going to go at 10:38 a.m. Houston time, we delayed the start of our

A spectacular launch on a crystal clear day, January 28, 1986.

meeting to watch. Everything looked routine that day. No clouds, no high winds, no stuck hatches, no equipment failures to slow things down – just the bone chilling cold.

The main engines started up, the boosters lit, and the Public Affairs Officer announced joyfully, "We have lift-off, lift-off of the space shuttle *Challenger* and America's Teacher in Space!"

You couldn't see the puff of black smoke come out of one of the joints in the right booster. You couldn't see the tongue of flame as the propellant ate through the booster casing and then the strut that held the booster to the fuel tank. You couldn't see what was about to happen. The television was on a tight shot of the vehicle when it blew up.

"See," I said, "…there's booster separation."

"No" said Drew Gaffney, our other payload specialist, checking his watch, "it's too early."

A sickening feeling of incredulity swept over me as the camera panned back to show a big cloud of smoke with tentacle-like streamers arching downward. But something was still burning in the distance, still flying out of the cloud. Surely it was the shuttle, having for some reason popped off the boosters early. It took a few minutes to sink in that there was no *Challenger* anymore. The camera showed the surface of the ocean under the explosion. Large chunks of material started to hit the water, sending up huge sprays of water. At that point I knew with certainty that they were gone.

With tears welling up in my eyes, a lump gathering in my chest, I knew I had to get back to the office, maybe to find that the crew had survived somehow. I stumbled out of the meeting and dashed to my car before near hysteria overcame me. As I sobbed shamelessly on the five-minute drive back to the space center, I repeated over and over a phrase that later I'd feel great guilt about: "Thank God it isn't Hoot! Thank God it isn't Hoot!" It had come so close to his last flight, which had almost launched on a frigid day like this one.

Screeching to a halt outside our office building, I bolted out of the car in time to be met Hoot coming out the front door. He had been trying to track me down. I looked into his eyes searching for an answer. He shook his head, his blue eyes filling with tears.

"What happened? What happened?" I asked.

The break-up of *Challenger* as seen so many times on the television.

"It blew up – that's all we know now – it blew up."

"All of them gone?"

"Yes."

I stood sobbing in his arms outside Building 4 on a warm sunny day in Houston that January 28.

Tourists walked by the building staring at this strange vignette. There were no signs on us identifying us as astronauts. The tragedy had happened such a short time ago that people wandering around the center didn't know about it yet. Launches had become so routine that the world didn't stop to watch them anymore.

Scobee – Mike – Oh, Ellison! – J.R. – Ron – and poor Greg and Christa.

I couldn't believe they were gone. It was the first time in my life that a close friend had died and now so many at once. My colleagues from the military had dealt with this before, with airplane crashes and the reality of war, but in my safe little cocoon of life, friends didn't vanish. No one had ever thought that a whole shuttle would blow up. So deep was our denial that there weren't even any plans for dealing with such an occurrence.

After the initial shock and disbelief, no one knew what we should do. I had learned from Terry McGuire, the psychologist who interviewed us at selection, that in times of stress, workaholics are comforted by having work to do, and we were an office of workaholics. Bereft we walked up the stairs to our third floor office suite to find Bob Overmeyer giving orders in the hallway like the senior marine officer he was.

Were all the crew's children with their parents at the Cape? God forbid that one or more were in their school classroom without someone to take care of them. A call went out to aircraft ops to make sure there were T-38s available to take astronauts to the Cape to help. Every astronaut was tracked down to make sure they knew what had happened with orders to get them back to JSC. The wagons were circled.

Hastily a meeting was convened to solicit volunteers for tasks we knew had to be done and to tell everyone else to stand by for others. We were reminded not to talk to the press until we knew what had happened. We'd later learn that there was chaos at the crew quarters at the Cape as crew relatives gathered to deal with what had happened. The families were asked to stay at the Cape until Vice President George H. W. Bush arrived to speak to them—and it was late in the afternoon when his plane landed. He had brought Senators John Glen and Jake Garn with him who knew what it was like to venture into space. In a story told later, one of the most courageous of the day, we heard that June Scobee, the *Challenger* commander's wife representing all the families, asked the vice president not to stop space exploration because of *Challenger*'s loss. She was a remarkably strong woman and how incredible that she could focus outward and forward on such a day of loss.

It was after our office meeting that it dawned on me that my own three-and-a-half year old child was at preschool where they often watched shuttle launches. I called Chris LaChance, the headmistress (her own husband was a helicopter pilot) to make sure Paul was all right. She told me that by some fluke, they'd forgotten to turn on the television that morning. The staff had decided not to tell the children – many of whom had parents working for NASA, a few were astronauts' children – about the accident. They would leave it up to each family to explain it in their own way.

As soon as I could get away from the office, I headed for Monarch Montessori School, which was out the back gate of the Center. Paul's eyes were wide with surprise that mommy had come to pick him up so early – right after lunch. He may have been suspicious at my red eyes and sad face and at the extra big hug he got when he ran to greet me.

He was quiet as we started our ride home. Glancing first at me and then out the window, he fidgeted with his lunchbox. He was waiting for me to start the conversation. "Paul, I have to tell you something important – and sad," I began.

"Is Daddy okay?" was his worried response.

"Yes, he's okay, but the space shuttle *Challenger* blew up this morning right after launch."

He pondered that for a minute. "Blew up? What happened to the people?" he wanted to know. How could I explain this to a child whose parents had been on shuttle flights...and who might well be on them in the future? There had never been the grief and finality of death in Paul's young life. How should I put it so he'd understand?

"God took them all to heaven," was the best I could come up with. And then Paul gave me the only brief smile I'd had since 10:38 that morning.

"Why did She do that?"

Why did my little boy think God was a "she?" This was not the time to go into that; I tucked it away in my heart for a happier moment.

"Well, I don't think we know why. It just happened, and we are all very sad because they were our friends, and we'll miss them." I reminded him that Ron McNair, whose son Reggie was in Paul's preschool class, had been on the flight. That put a human face on an otherwise rather abstract event.

"You mean Reggie's daddy has gone to heaven and won't be back?"

"Yes," I said.

I knew he was struggling to understand what this all meant. He kept looking at me as tears dribbled down my cheeks. I realized what his main

The first of thousands of flowers and wreaths at the entrance to the Johnson Space Center.

PHOTO COURTESY OF NASA

concern was when he asked, "When will you not be sad anymore?" How do you answer a child's innocent question like that? I didn't know how long it would be before I wasn't sad anymore.

Hoot and I spent that evening feeling helpless. We watched the explosion over and over on the television news and were astounded to see all other programming preempted. President Reagan postponed his State of the Union address. Instead, he addressed the nation with a moving message about bravery and dedication. At the end, he excerpted from the poem "High Flight" by John Magee, so familiar to all flyers, saying the crew had "slipped the surly bonds of Earth...and touched the face of God."

It began to dawn on us that this was not a tragedy for NASA alone: this was a national—no, international—tragedy. Friends and family members began calling us to offer condolences. Many said they had been so frightened that one of us had been onboard. Did Hoot and I know all those people? They wanted to know. Yes, we told them, the five astronauts personally and closely, the others not as well. The astronaut families had partied together, supported one another, and loved each other. Our children played together.

Saddest of all was Hoot's dad, Grandpa Paul. Suffering from the last stages of a battle with cancer, his mind was often cloudy. Watching the television at home in California, he kept asking Grandma Rita time after time if Hoot was onboard. Oh, how close it had come to being Hoot, or even me. By what quirk of fate had Hoot not been on those boosters and my second flight had slipped, so this wasn't my launch date after all?

I had about cried myself out by the time I drove in to work the next morning, but what I saw started the tears all over again. At the entrance to our Center is a large stone sign proclaiming, "Johnson Space Center." Having passed it almost every day for eight years, I didn't notice it much anymore. On the morning of January 29, 1986 it was surrounded by hundreds of wreaths and bouquets of flowers. Oh, what a heart wrenching sight! People from all over the world, so saddened but not knowing what to do, had sent flowers. I would see that sign often in the years to come and always remembered the day that it was a memorial.

At work, speculation about what had caused the accident began to consume us. Where was the flaw? Was it something the crew had done wrong? Had it been preventable? So many of us suffered survivor's guilt, worried that perhaps it was something we had done or should have known about. There were more immediate tasks to take our minds off that. The families had to be supported. Since there were no bodies recovered, there would be memorial services but no funerals. It was soon announced that on Friday, January 31, President Reagan would arrive for a speech at our Center.

We were all farmed out to tasks to keep us busy. I had the job of calling the retired astronauts to ask if they'd like to come to the Friday service. Some had left the office in recent days and knew the *Challenger* crewmembers. They said they'd be there. A few of them, long gone from the Corps, were surprised to be asked. No, no reason for them to attend. Apollo Astronaut Rusty Schweickart asked if he could come and stay at our house: his old house. This was how connected astronauts were. We lived in the houses the earlier ones had built; we continued the work they had started.

I remember being surprised that many of the retired men answered their own phones. They were working out of their homes. Was there any exciting employment post-Astronaut Corps, or were these explorers sent out to pasture forever to be consultants about past glories? I would someday face this future. I hoped there would be a rich life after NASA.

I don't know why Hoot and I didn't go visit with the grieving families. Having never faced anything like this, I wasn't sure what to do. Hoot seemed equally unsure, so we played cowards. I have never, ever stopped feeling guilty for not going and offering my sympathies, especially to June

Scobee, Jane Smith, Lorna Onizuka, and Cheryl McNair. I have always hoped they would understand why some of us didn't come, but I doubt they were taking attendance.

In the military tradition, each family was assigned a Casualty Assistance Calls Officer from the Astronaut Office. These were astronauts who interfaced with NASA and got the families the help they needed, no matter what it was. Everyone was willing to do anything possible for them, though at the moment, it seemed the help they needed most was dealing with all the national publicity.

When the president visits a site, it must be modified to suit his needs. President Reagan's handlers were masters of visual effect. Although there were several open plaza areas around the central pond at JSC, it seemed that the lighting wouldn't be great at 11:00 a.m, or maybe it was the security. A small building on the west side of the pond which faced east was chosen as the back drop for the presidential address. For some strange reason some of the trees in front of the building weren't conducive to the best visual effect, so they were summarily chopped down. It seemed sad at this point in time to destroy other living things. Years later, a small grove of trees was planted near the front of the Center to commemorate lost astronauts. Perhaps that somewhat made up for the loss.

A podium was set up (without the usual festoons of crepe paper and balloons) and hundreds of chairs were put out in a semi-circle in front of it. We watched all the preparations from our grieving office area across the little pond. We supposed it was important for the president to express how the nation felt, for the families and friends to be consoled, to eulogize those lost, but at the time it didn't mean a lot to most of us.

Friday dawned, a beautiful day. No one was sure what we would have done if it had rained. Air Force One landed at Ellington Field and the entourage made its way down NASA Road 1 to our corner of the Texas coast.

The locals and all the visitors from near and far assembled at the appointed time. The astronauts were allowed to sit in a cordoned area near the front with the VIPs. Jake Garn, the Utah senator from my flight, and Bill Nelson, the Florida representative who had flown with Hoot, were there as members of our office's extended family and to represent the Senate and the House. Seeing Jake with reddened eyes reminded me that Mike Smith, the *Challenger* pilot, had been the person assigned to help Jake get ready for spaceflight, and they had become good friends. Hoot and I had walked the

The crowd gathers for President Ronald Reagan's remarks at a memorial service at the Johnson Space Center.

short distance to the service hand-in-hand. I would hold that same hand many times at memorial services in the future and was eternally grateful for its strength and warmth.

There were other dignitaries on site, but none seemed to matter. I could imagine how difficult it must be for the *Challenger* wives and children. If it had been my husband who had been killed, I'd have found the strength to bear up for his sake, but going through my head would have been the words *This doesn't help*. I would have been so bereft by the loss and so overwhelmed with helping my child cope that I'd have been on autopilot. Perhaps they were, too.

President Reagan gave a short talk that was well-written and, as always with him, well delivered. And then the planes roared overhead. I had read in books about the Missing Man Formation flown for fallen pilots, but I'd never seen one. I'm not sure whether it was the surprise of the aircrafts' roar, the fact that our joyful little jets were sounding a requiem, or pent up emotions, but that was when I lost my composure. Four T-38s swept low out of the west from behind the president in a V-shaped formation. As they passed overhead, one pulled up skyward as though climbing toward heaven. I couldn't help it; I didn't care who was watching—I buried my head in

313

Hoot's shoulder and wept. I never, ever wanted this to happen again.

The weekend was quiet. Letters poured in from our many friends. I talked to others over the phone. What had caused the accident? What would NASA do now? Would Hoot and I leave? These were all questions we were asking ourselves, too, and ones for which we had no answers.

Parts of the puzzle began to appear the next week. For each launch there were video cameras positioned around the pad to take pictures of the launch and to observe and record all the events. Pictures of the *Challenger* at the moment of booster ignition began to surface. There was a puff of black smoke from one of the joints on the right booster at liftoff. It had stopped, but in later frames a flame appeared in the same area in the first minute of flight. This had led to the explosion.

Was the cold weather responsible, or was there a defect in the booster construction? We would all come to know a tremendous amount about booster field joints and O-rings. The boosters were too large to transport in one piece to Florida from Utah, where the Morton Thiokol Company manufactured them. They were shipped horizontally on railroad flatcars in segments to KSC where they were put together. Where the segments were joined was called a "field joint" because it was assembled "in the field."

To make sure none of the hot gasses from the burning propellant escaped through the joints, there were rubber O-rings, like those that seal a faucet so it doesn't drip. The design had two around each joint circumference. If the gas got by one, the other served as a back-up. As a shuttle launched, there was a fair amount of bending of these boosters so the joints flexed some. Almost immediately, the accident investigation team began to focus on why the O-rings failed to seal.

The first thing that had to be done was to salvage as much of the *Challenger* as possible from the surface and bottom of the Atlantic Ocean. Large pieces of the structure began appearing along the shoreline around the Cape and were collected quickly. Experts from the National Transportation Safety Board (NTSB) were brought in because crashes like this fell within their jurisdiction. The chore of dragging the wreckage up from the ocean floor began.

Sometime during these first weeks a more ominous picture emerged from the hundreds of photos that were being analyzed. A grainy out-of-focus view of the wreckage falling away from the explosion showed a large piece of debris that appeared to be the nose of the orbiter.

"See," someone pointed out as he showed it to a small group of us, "here is the nose – it's facing us now…and here are the forward windows, rimmed in black."

Oh, what a gut-wrenching thought that was! Could the crew compartment have broken away and fallen into the ocean intact? I asked an NTSB investigator who was working out of our office what he thought.

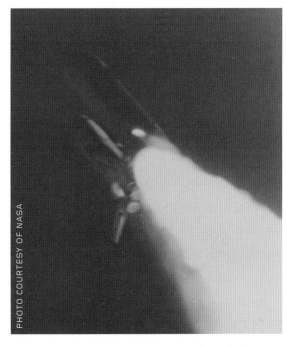

PHOTO COURTESY OF NASA

"What a hopelessly romantic thought, that the cockpit breaks free and turns to face the camera for one last goodbye before it plummets Earthward toward destruction. Ridiculous!" he told me.

The people who believed it could have happened wouldn't let the idea go, as awful as it was. They went back and looked at the radar tracks of all the major pieces.

The deadly flame that began to erupt from the booster.

There was the intact vehicle, there was the explosion. The fuel tank was gone, disintegrating into millions of tiny pieces as its hydrogen and oxygen tanks exploded. The two boosters has broken free and careened wildly out of control downrange before they were blown up by the Range Safety Officer. There were a number of other large chunks that arced upward and then took a ballistic trajectory downward. Yes, there was a piece about the size of the cabin forward of the bulkhead at the front of the payload bay. The spot where this piece hit the water was determined.

We had to know, had to see for ourselves however unpleasant the thought. Could the crew have survived the explosion only to be trapped in the cockpit as it ran out of upward momentum then dropped to the ocean below? They had no parachutes, no way to get the hatch open. This had been a design decision at the start of the shuttle program over the protest of the Astronaut Office. There didn't seem to be any way to get all crew members out of a falling orbiter that fit within the budget of the shuttle program. For mistakes made by any one of thousands of designers, builders, controllers, software programmers, or managers, it was the astronauts who would end up paying the ultimate price. As John Young often said with derision about the managers who made these decisions, "Ain't none of them ole boys ever died because a desk crashed." Yet in the years before *Challenger*, it seemed astronaut voices were listened to less and less.

A U.S. Navy salvage boat was sent out to scan the ocean bottom where the cockpit was predicted to have landed. It found a large mass of crumbled wreckage there on the ocean floor. Was it the final resting place of our fallen comrades? The year before in the Astronaut Class of 1984, we had brought into the Astronaut Corps a Navy SEAL, Bill Shepherd. Shep and some of the Navy divers went down in the relatively shallow water for a definitive look. They brought back the disturbing word: yes, it was the crew compartment, lying on its port side, a smashed wreck of metal and wires, all in one small area. It had broken free and fallen intact about 65,000 feet to the water below. The question of whether the crew was alive when it hit the surface of the ocean would occupy our minds and much of our time in the coming months.

By then it was springtime in Florida. The press had learned of our salvage operations and would watch and photograph the boats as they returned from sea. Of course, the first priority was to see if there were any remains of the crew. There were.

A big controversy arose as to who should be in charge of performing autopsies on the bodies. The Brevard County Medical Examiner thought since KSC was in his jurisdiction he should be in charge. After considerable argument and string-pulling, because of the national interest in the crash and because of their experience with similar disasters, members of the Armed Forces Institute of Pathology were called in to determine what had happened.

Bob Crippen, an astronaut from our office who had flown on the first shuttle flight, had been put in charge of representing the Astronaut Office in the operations at the Cape. When the first boat with crew remains onboard headed back to the Navy submarine docks at Port Canaveral, it did so under the cloak of darkness. Crippen had given explicit orders that there should be nothing to indicate that bodies were being transported. Bob Overmeyer was the senior astronaut on the boat, and he made the mistake of draping flags over the barrels in the stern. The picture made the papers the next morning. There was rumored to have been heated argument between Crippen and Overmeyer. Tensions were running high during these operations.

It was taking a long time to try to pull every bit of *Challenger* out of the water. Besides wanting to find even the smallest clue to discover what happened, the specter of souvenir hunters carting off pieces of fallen space debris was horrifying. As the astronaut in charge of crew equipment at the time, I was soon sent to the Cape to join the Investigation Task Force. My job would be to help identify the things that had been dredged up. I never could have imagined what that job would be like.

When I arrived in early April, I was given directions to a hangar near the huge Vehicle Assembly Building. Elliott Kicklighter was in charge of the operations. When I showed up, he offered to escort me around, and we went to see what they had in the hangar.

As we rounded the corner to the open hangar door on that warm bright spring morning in 1986, I was struck by the dockside odor of dead fish. Then came the sight etched forever in my memory. There stood the *Challenger* jigsaw puzzle: big pieces, little pieces, intact pieces, smashed pieces, barnacled pieces, shiny pieces— all assembled in a bizarre caricature of the shuttle's former self. It was up on stands with braces and scaffolding holding parts of it together, but there was no doubt what it was. I had no idea there would be so much of it and that it would be cobbled together so that it was a three dimensional view of everything recovered. In fact, there were almost no pieces missing.

"Want a closer look?" Elliott asked. I wasn't sure I did, a huge lump welling up in my throat.

"Yes," I lied. Some strange curiosity took over, and although I felt unmoored from reality, I tried to detach myself from the sickening sight.

There were recognizable things, almost untouched by the explosion, the crash, and their stay at the bottom of the sea. The titanium payload retention latches that held

Wreckage begins to be laid out in a hangar at the Kennedy Space Center.

the communication satellite in the cargo bay were pristine. Barnacles and sea creatures had made their homes over entire sections of the insulation blankets covering the fuselage and the tail, accounting for the fishy odor.

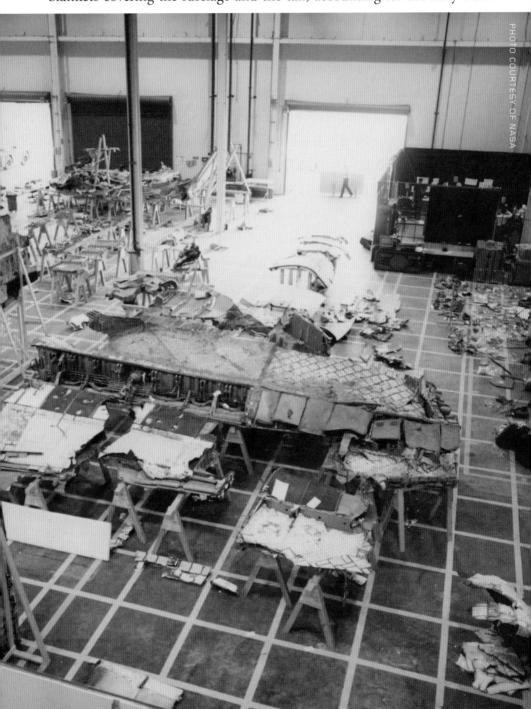

Since NASA had always been fanatical in its paperwork tracking of all the parts used to construct each orbiter, every piece that had an identifying part number on it could be fitted into the puzzle. Unexplainable things happen in these accidents. A small metal part from up near the nose was embedded in the trailing edge of the body flap at the back of the vehicle.

It was obvious that something had burned the back end of the right wing and that side of the tail. This provided evidence that a hole had been burned through the booster on that side.

The external part of the crew cabin was there, reattached to where it had been before the breakup. It was crushed on the port side around the hatch where it had hit first the water—then the ocean bottom. The space shuttle main engines were sitting outside under a metal roof on the concrete. I was fascinated by the fuel pumps on the top of them. These were the components that kept blowing up during their testing phase prior to the first launch. Of all our systems, we thought they were the most vulnerable to explosive failure. Other than having a few holes in them, all three looked almost intact. They had survived having their huge fuel lines violently wrenched free, the massive explosions all around them, and the force of smashing into the ocean. They were tougher than we ever thought they could be.

Then I was taken to a separate area to see the pieces of the external tank and the boosters. These had the look of a horrendous explosion. The tank had disintegrated when the torn-away booster had plunged its nose into the hydrogen and oxygen tanks inside. The boosters had continued to fly after the conflagration, and a ground command was sent to the explosive charges along their sides to blow them up. We had always known that the Range Safety Officer could issue these commands if necessary, but we couldn't imagine that would ever happen.

Out in another section of the hangar were all the pieces and parts that had once accompanied my friends in the pressurized front end of the shuttle. There were black boxes or instrument packages that housed computers, communication gear, and navigation equipment. There was a myriad of other paraphernalia that the crew needed on their voyage. Some were broken, others encrusted with sea creatures, and still more looking unaffected by their awful journey. The space suits needed for spacewalks, protected in the sturdy airlock in the middeck, looked brand new. All these things were arranged on metal shelves in the same relative positions they had occupied in the crew compartment.

Looking at the objects that had been recovered, I saw all sorts of articles I was familiar with: food packages, checklists, mementoes wrapped with care that the crew was carrying for friends and organizations, a deflated soccer ball for someone. As I lifted a tarp over one of the boxes, I was taken aback by a most surprising sight. Smiling up at me was a picture of Colonel Sanders, of fried chicken fame. This couldn't be something that came from the *Challenger*. On closer inspection, the face was on the top of an experiment package. A student experiment, sponsored by Kentucky Fried Chicken, contained fertilized chicken eggs that had been carefully packed to observe the embryos development in weightlessness.

There were the panels of switches and controls from the flight deck. Members of our office had been asked to come and look at the position of the switches. No one knew what it meant that some were out of configuration— that is, not where they should have been during the launch. Had they been knocked awry during the explosion and crash? Was there any logic to where they were now? Would the crew have started into emergency procedures if they had been conscious? All of us seemed to agree that there was no rhyme or reason or pattern to the anomalous switch positions. They seemed to be random enough that they must have occurred during the breakup of the vehicle.

The crew seats were there, and I spent a great deal of time studying them, trying to comprehend what it must have been like to be sitting in them. What could they tell us about those final moments? The NTSB experts pointed out some things I would never have noticed. The seats were all crumbled in the same direction. This meant that all of them had been occupied at the time of the crash into the sea. The crew members had died strapped into their seats. It meant no one had made an attempt to get out. Perhaps they were unconscious or dead already. But the search went on for more evidence of what had happened. I could imagine the *Challenger* crew at some great happy hour in the sky watching us in amusement as we poked around the twisted metal looking at shreds of what used to be.

A couple days after I arrived at the Cape, I was invited (as a physician) to Hangar L. To this day I have never forgotten what it housed, and I remember it every time I pass that building on the Air Force side of the Center. It had been set up as a temporary morgue in which the Armed Forces pathologists could work.

As remains of the crew were found, still in the wreckage of the crew compartment, they came to Hangar L. Autopsies were performed to find out what they could tell us about the accident. It was clear from the camera views and engineering analysis that the force of the explosion had not destroyed the crew compartment or the people inside. The destruction of cabin and crew had occurred when they hit the water. However, if the cabin had been ruptured at a high altitude and the pressure dropped rapidly, there might be signs in the remains of decompression. That would put our minds at peace that the end had come quickly for the crew. On the other hand, a small leak would have rendered them unconscious more slowly because the emergency breathing packs contained only air, not the pressurized oxygen required for high altitude survival. If the cabin walls had been split open during the explosion, there might be signs of the hydrazine fuel from the nearby reaction control jet tanks in the human tissues. These were the facts the pathologists hoped to uncover.

As hard as they sought to understand the scenario, many questions remained unanswered. No signs of decompression could be found, and no hydrazine was in the tissues. Several of the air packs had been turned on and some of the air used. It never could be determined whether the crew had been conscious, or whether they died shortly after the explosion or when they hit the water.

After the initial shock of the odor of the place (though the body parts were stored in a cold area, they had been in the ocean for several weeks), I managed to assume an air of detachment from the real meaning of what was going on. As a medical student during one three-month vacation I had worked in the Pathology Department at the John Gaston Hospital performing autopsies, but I had never known any of my *patients*. My natural curiosity about what was being done somehow allowed me to view the things being examined, not as my friends, but almost as their discarded clothes.

On my ride back to Crew Quarters (and after a good cry along the way), I analyzed these odd feelings. Somehow I didn't see the people in those pieces of flesh: their spirits were gone from here, and these were parts of the mystery left behind for us to use to discover the answers. Again, I envisioned them somewhere looking down on us as we scrambled about like sad ants searching and searching. It didn't really matter to them anymore.

I was surprised that the pathologists had to identify to whom each of the remains belonged. I learned from them that it wasn't enough to have a body with a name tag on the flight suit it was wearing. This was before DNA typing, and so other evidence had to be used. I suppose in aircraft accidents there is always the chance of foul play. like someone putting their flight suit on someone they've murdered and then having their wife claim the insurance. Interesting things could be used to give a positive identification. Bones could be x-rayed. Female pelvises are a different shape than that of males, and there is callus on a bone if it has been broken in the past and healed. Fingerprints, footprints, and dental records can be examined.

So total was NASA's denial that this could ever happen that they didn't have footprints or fingerprints from us. Old x-rays and dental records were found. Ever so slowly, the recovered bodies were identified.

It became obvious at some point that one of the crew members was unaccounted for, as though somehow gone intact to heaven. The salvage divers searched the scattered wreckage in earnest long after they might have called off their operations. It would have been too sad to have six funerals and lay six people to rest and tell one family their loved one was still out there, forever a captive to the vast and timeless sea.

At last the missing person was found. NASA declared an end to its ocean bottom operations and released the bodies to funeral homes. It was then that my most difficult task was assigned.

Some of the military crew members would be buried at Arlington National Cemetery where the military honors its dead. Jane Smith made the simple request that her husband be buried in the NASA flight suit he had been wearing that cold January morning. The flight suits had been kept at the morgue because they were declared crew equipment and, as such, would not ordinarily be returned to the families. I was asked to go retrieve Mike's clothing and make sure it got cleaned up to send to the funeral home, even though the casket would remain closed.

I had always regarded Mike Smith as a handsome man. He dressed like a Southern boy in khakis and starched shirts. Casually outfitted, he always looked dapper. In Hangar L was the tattered blue flight suit he had so proudly worn in anticipation of his first spaceflight, grimy and grungy from the destruction of the crash and its long stay in the sea. It had to be scrubbed clean. One of the security guards accompanied me to the holding area and got the suit for me. There was a a deep industrial style sink in the morgue area. I managed to locate some detergent and a scrub brush and went to work.

The more I scrubbed, the sadder I got. Why did this have to be happening? Why to a wonderful man like Mike? Why to a picture perfect family like the Smiths? The security guard was sitting next to the sink making small talk which I was answering with monosyllables. Soon tears began pouring down my face, splashing into the wash water. The guard noticed he wasn't receiving responses from me anymore and glanced at me for the first time. At this point he must have realized that Mike had been more than a distant acquaintance, that he had been my friend who was now gone. He left the room and let me scrub in silence until my knuckles were raw.

The flightsuit got cleaner and cleaner, but somehow I couldn't make it look like I wanted it to. So I cried even harder. Somewhere in my mind I heard Mike's voice asking me why I was making such a big deal out of this.

"Well, because Jane might want to see your flightsuit, Mike. Maybe because it will be with you forever. I don't know. Maybe I've just gone a little crazy or something."

He seemed to tell me it was okay—I'd done enough work on it—and that he appreciated the loving care. He asked me if there was anything he could do for me. At the time it didn't seem so odd that we'd be having this conversation, since I pictured him up there in heaven, able to ask God for favors for his friends.

"I'd like a daughter as beautiful as your two someday, Mike," I said to my absent friend.

"Sure thing; no problem," came the reply. I never lost faith, even though it didn't happen until long after it should have, that someday he'd see to it that my prayers were answered.

The funerals soon began, spaced apart so people from our office didn't have to choose between ceremonies. Mike and Dick went to Arlington, Judy and Greg to their families, Christa to New Hampshire, Ron to South

Dick Scobee and Mike Smith were buried with honors at the Arlington National Cemetery in Washington, D.C.

Carolina. Most poignant for Hoot and me was Ellison's. Hoot joined the contingent who went over to see him placed in a special area of The Punchbowl, the National Memorial Cemetery of the Pacific on Oahu. A crater formed 100,000 years ago by a volcanic eruption, it is a beautiful and peaceful setting. El's many Hawaiian friends made sure that it was a memorable occasion for all who attended that beautiful June day as he received a final *Aloha!* from his family and friends.

Somehow I missed every single funeral service. As my excuse I used my 3½-year-old son who seemed a little anxious to have either of us gone for too long, much less both of us. Hoot represented us at many of the funerals. That's the way it seemed to happen in our crazy lives. Hoot did the funerals; I did the weddings.

Those times were hard to get through. The accident itself, the memorial services, the travel schedules that kept us apart, the funerals. Weeks and weeks of unending sadness. The Rogers Commission had been formed to investigate the causes of the accident and what needed to be done to fix them. It became obvious that the commission would find more than simple mechanical failure. Yes, the faulty booster had a burn-through because of an O-ring that didn't seal on a cold day. It was also found that the booster segment where the leak occurred was the most *out of round* segment they had ever stacked, which might have put extra tension on the joint. Add to that the fact that the wind shear during the flight uphill was the highest ever experienced, probably causing some extra flexing in the boosters. As Hoot told me, it was always a series of failures that align to make tragedies happen. But NASA and the contractor managers had decided to try to launch that day. The boosters needed to be redesigned, but so did NASA

Ellison returned to his beloved Hawaii and lies in the National Memorial Cemetery of the Pacific on Oahu.

decision making. How would this affect our jobs, our positions, our future flight assignments? We didn't know.

Everyone said it would be at least a year before we started flying again. It had taken more than a year and a half after the Apollo fire, the one thing even remotely comparable that had happened at NASA. But in the Apollo program there was a race to get to the moon by the end of the decade, and the budget was almost unlimited as was the willingness to accept great risk. There was no similar sense of urgency following *Challenger*, and NASA's budget was tight.

After *Challenger*, many politicians in Washington took the opportunity to get on their soap boxes to say space exploration was too expensive and too risky, and that we might as well quit now. Scientists who felt unmanned space probes were the best way to explore the universe joined in. Were our jobs and futures in jeopardy?

Jake Garn, the senator who had flown with my crew the year before and who many had argued should never have been given a valued seat, paid back every cent NASA had invested in him. He spearheaded an effort to shift some funds from the Department of Defense to purchase a replacement orbiter. He got support from others in Congress to fund the whole amount up front, rather than giving NASA a little at a time over several years so they couldn't count on the funding until the yearly budget battles had occurred. The space shuttle *Endeavour* rolled off the Rockwell assembly line in 1991, ahead of schedule and under budget. That's the way to run a space program! And that is the way to lead it. One of the major training buildings at the Johnson Space Center was renamed the Jake Garn Mission Simulator and Training Facility, although I'm not sure most of the trainees who passed through its portals knew why.

There was a major overhaul within the management at NASA. Right before the accident NASA Administrator James Beggs had taken a leave of absence to deal with an indictment for fraud from his previous position at General Dynamics, and William Robert Graham, his deputy, became Acting Administrator. A rather quiet, intellectual man, we didn't see him leading us out of this morass, and soon former Administrator Jim Fletcher was called back to duty. Jesse Moore, who was head of the Office of Space Flight at Headquarters, had been named JSC Center Director replacing Gerry Griffin in January five days before the crash. Jesse was in transition from HQ to JSC when the accident happened and didn't assume his position until mid-year. He resigned the post in October. Aaron Cohen, a quiet, self-effacing older man from the engineering directorate who had been the Orbiter Project manager, was tapped to be our new Center Director. There was no hidden agenda with Aaron. He was devoted to the good of our organization and its people. Dick Truly, the astronaut who had been the pilot on the second shuttle flight and commander of the eighth, had been running the Naval Space Command. He was called back after *Challenger* to run the space flight office in Washington. John Young and George Abbey would soon be replaced as Chief of the Astronaut Office and Director of Flight Crew Operations.

The Rogers Commission filled our television screens for what seemed like an eternity. Sally Ride had been named as a member. This was a little disturbing to the senior astronauts in our office. Though bright and capable, a two-flight veteran by now, she was not the office expert on the space shuttle. She did have two characteristics that suited her for the job. She was out of the management chain so had no part in the decision to launch the *Challenger*, and perhaps more importantly, she was female. In the days of affirmative action, the Commission didn't want to look like an Old Boys Club. Sally was smart enough to tap into all the expertise our office had to offer, particularly her husband, Steve Hawley. Our office also sent a troop of people to staff an Action Center in Washington. Bryan O'Connor, Bonnie

Dunbar, Frank Culbertson and Sid Gutierrez fielded questions from the Commission, the press, and Congress. It must have been a crazy and stressful job. Yet we could see from the way things were going that the Astronaut Office was well-represented—finally!—in the recommendations about how the spaceflight program was going to be run.

Most of us plowed on, doing whatever big or small jobs we were given. At the Cape, decisions were being made about what to do with the wreckage once it had yielded up all its secrets. Everything was catalogued, photographed, and documented, and then buried in two old missile silos. Sad mangled dreams.

The Rogers Commission issued its report in June of 1986, and NASA set about implementing its recommendations. Hoot was already working with the Morton Thiokol people in Utah who were redesigning the boosters. It wasn't anything that was cutting edge technology. It was adding safety features that should have been there in the first place. Among other things they put heaters on the joints, tiny insignificant looking things, but they made it safer to launch in cold weather.

Once the design had been put on paper, it had to be analyzed, blessed by contractors and government engineers alike, and then tested. This seemed to take an interminable amount of time. Two years dragged by. What do you do with an idled work force of many thousands? No one knew when we'd start assembling and launching shuttles again, when we'd start training crews in earnest, when Mission Control would once again have a reason to exist. It made no sense to lay everyone off although lots of people saw the dry spell developing and took the opportunity to leave.

We lost several people from the astronaut office because their families wanted to move on. It had become apparent how risky our work was. During an interview a member of the press asked one of the wives why she was so nervous about her husband flying in space.

"He could just as well die driving on the Houston freeway," the reporter said.

"Yes," the spouse replied, "but the kids and I wouldn't be obliged to watch it happen."

Good point. A lot of astronauts got their noses

One of the many Challenger Learning Centers that commemorates the lives of the *Challenger* crew.

rubbed into what would happen to their families if they died in such a public way.

The *Challenger* spouses and Judy's brother bore up magnificently; they wanted the world to remember how their family members lived, not how they died. They asked that money which would otherwise be donated to memorials large and small scattered all over the country be donated to help start *Challenger* Centers for Space Science Education for children. Education was important to NASA and all the astronauts and there had been such interest in Christa McAuliffe who was to be the first teacher in space. June Scobee, the *Challenger* commander's wife, had her Ph.D. in education and became head of the campaign. This quest to bring something good out of a horrible event would become the subject of June's book, *Silver Linings*.

The Astronaut Office also lost people who didn't have flight assignments. Everyone knew it was going to take a year or two to start flying again. Then flights would start slowly at first, assessing the new booster design as we went. After an accident, an engineering organization tends to be conservative about everything. While there were already a number of crews in the queue, we were told that all assignments and the previous order of crews were off. But we still figured the crews-in-training would probably be scheduled before the others. So there were a lot of people who didn't want to wait for one more flight assignment down the line. I had been training for my life sciences Spacelab mission since early 1984, and I was committed to flying it. It was the one flight on the manifest that I had been waiting my whole career to fly. I would stay to fly it.

Hoot once again proved he led a charmed life. The people in the Mission Operations Directorate who planned flights, trained crews, turned out all our checklists, and manned Mission Control needed to keep up their skills. They decided to put together four crews to run generic missions for practice. Mike Coats and Rick Hauck would be the two crew commanders who would train to do missions that launched the Tracking and Data Relay Satellite (TDRS) System, a NASA communication satellite like the one *Challenger* had been carrying. Getting these two remaining satellites into orbit would be a priority once we started flying again.

They also wanted two commanders to practice military missions. Bob Crippen had been assigned to command the first mission to launch from Vandenberg Air Force Base. Located on the west coast midway between San Francisco and Los Angeles, this was to be the shuttle's second launch site. It would be used to put military satellites into polar orbit. When something launches out of Cape Canaveral, it flings itself eastward using the force of the Earth's rotation to help send it on its way. But launched due east from there, its path would go from 28 degrees above the equator to 28 degrees below the equator. Looking down, as I did on my first mission, I could only see around the Earth's *waistline,* crossing the Sahara, the Middle East, Southeast Asia, the Hawaiian Islands, and Central America. I'd see southern California, the desert southwest, Houston, and Florida but not much more of the U.S. It was possible to launch northward out of the Cape, but it took a lot more fuel to get to the higher *inclination,* as it was called. We were also limited to about 57 degrees north and south of the equator to avoid over-flying all the East Coast cities.

On the other hand, polar orbit would be spectacular for looking at the Earth. Launching due south out of Vandenberg toward the South Pole, the shuttle would orbit across the pole then head northward on the other side, crossing the North Pole. As it orbited, the Earth would revolve eastward so that on the next orbit another swath of Earth would be visible. As the astronauts' "day" went by, the entire Earth could be seen. The people interested in Earth observations were beside themselves imagining the spectacular pictures that would become available.

Their delight was bested only by the military who wanted to see things other than polar ice caps, geology sites, and ocean views. Most of the former Soviet Union, our Cold War adversary, lay well north of where the shuttle usually flew, so a polar orbit would be of significant military use. A great crew had been selected for this spectacular, but secret, military mission.

Things had not been going well at Vandenberg, however. The launch complex was way behind schedule. Then the engineers discovered that the flame trench beneath the launch pad wasn't designed properly. Also, launching due south put the densely-populated southern California coastline in jeopardy if the shuttle and/or its boosters went off track the way they had with *Challenger*. The Vandenberg launch complex was abandoned. Crippen in the meantime decided to retire from the Astronaut Corps and help run the shuttle program at the Cape. Dale Gardner who had also been assigned to the mission went back to the Navy.

Since the military had been persuaded to let the shuttle be its main launch vehicle, a backlog of military launches had developed during the down time. Both Crippen's old crew and one led by Brewster Shaw had been selected to train for the Defense Department missions. Who was there to replace Crippen? Most of the *old guys* who had commanded shuttle flights had left or were working on other things that prevented them from training. Of the 1978 class, almost everyone had some other assignment. Then there was Hoot.

He had just finished up with the booster redesign effort. He hadn't made a secret military flight. He was Navy like Crippen, whereas Brewster was Air Force, and NASA liked to divide military flights between the services. More importantly, he was an experienced commander. So even though he had flown the flight right before *Challenger*, he found himself assigned to another crew to practice military launches. There was no guarantee this crew would be assigned early after the return to flight, but everyone figured it would be. Bill Shepherd, the Navy SEAL who had been our office representative to the salvage operations, replaced Dale Gardner on the crew.

Not far into 1987, the launch manifest began to circulate. Everyone was pretty sure we'd be ready to fly again sometime in 1988. NASA had done away with the old numbering system based on launch site and order in the fiscal year and gone back to slapping sequential numbers on the missions as they were assigned. Sure enough, STS-26 would be the "Return to Flight" mission and would carry a TDRS satellite to replace the one lost on the *Challenger* flight. STS-27 would be a secret Department of Defense mission, then the other TDRS and DOD missions on 28 and 29. Because Brewster's crew had already been training on whatever secret thing was to go on 28, Hoot got the 27 mission. So he got to fly the last mission before *Challenger* and would fly the second after the shuttle started flying again.

We had watched luck play a role in flight assignments many times in our careers at NASA. I remember Tom Stafford and Neil Armstrong describe how one of them happened to be the first man to walk on the moon, and the other one never got closer than eight miles above the surface. It didn't have anything to do with superior skill, politicking, or personality; it was the way the program and the schedule worked out. It would not be the last time Hoot was in the right place at the right time.

On the other hand, my mission, SLS-1, was nowhere to be seen on the schedule. It was a NASA-funded science mission, and taking precedence were military payloads, important satellites, and a myriad of other things. Our crew had infrequent get-togethers to do a little planning, training, and to socialize, but all of us found other things to do.

I decided it was past time for me to get some refresher medical training. With a child at home, it wasn't reasonable for me to run off and do a real year of residency, even if I'd been able to secure a spot. I talked to the Department of Emergency Medicine in both Galveston and Houston, but it seemed to me that they were much like the training program I'd left more than eight years before in Memphis. There were no residency training programs in Emergency Medicine at either facility at the time. Their Emergency Departments were split between the "medicine end," covered by the internal medicine staff, and the "trauma end," covered by surgery. Resident physicians in all services rotated through, and there were great faculty physicians teaching on either end, but I wanted to work with a real Emergency Medicine residency program with a full-time Emergency Medicine faculty.

In my search I found that, at the time, there was one civilian program in the whole state of Texas, and it was in El Paso. As long as I was going to have to travel, I figured I'd widen my search. I noticed an ad in the *Emergency Medicine* journal for mini-sabbaticals, about a week in length, at Denver General Hospital. One problem was that they cost several thousand dollars. Okay for a rich doctor, not okay for a poor civil servant like me. But at least they were accustomed to having *visiting firemen,* so I took a chance and called the chief of their program, Vince Markovchik, and asked if there was something we could work out. He agreed to let me work there periodically at no cost.

So it came to pass that I spent one week a month for most of 1987 serving as a junior resident at Denver General and at the University Hospital. I learned a great deal during my stays there. I was 10 to 15 years older than the interns and residents and was not in town long enough to get to know many of them. I was much closer in age to the faculty physicians and enjoyed my time with them. The most important thing I learned was not how to use the latest medicines or perform the latest procedures, but that I didn't want to have to go back and do another residency when I left NASA. The number of hours required to care for the sick, perform research, and study for the boards seemed incompatible with a normal family life. While at NASA I had developed the habit of sleeping seven or so hours a night and having most weekends and holidays off. People get sick 24 hours of the day every day of the year. Life and death decisions must be made all the time in the ER. It is a tremendous responsibility, one that I didn't want to take back on when my NASA days ended. Doctors who care for people deserve great credit and every penny they earn.

In the meantime, many other things changed in the shuttle program besides the boosters. One obvious shortcoming was the inability to get out of the orbiter in case of an inflight emergency. The first four test flights of the shuttle had ejection seats for the commander and pilot, but it was impossible to put more than two of them onboard. So when crews grew larger than two, the ejection seats were disarmed and later removed. We wore helmets to dampen the noise of launch and provide communications and had an emergency air bottle to avoid breathing contaminated air as we ran away after a crash landing but little else.

The question kept coming up: could the *Challenger* crew have survived if they'd had the right equipment? At the altitude where the explosion occurred if the cabin had been breached the air pressure would have been low enough to have required a pressure suit to prevent the bends. Such suits were being worn by pilots in high altitude spy aircraft. They were big and bulky, but the spy plane pilots had to do little more than get in, be able to reach all their cockpit instruments, eject if necessary, or climb out at the end of the flight. While not perfect for the shuttle environment, the suits were available, so NASA went about adapting them for shuttle flight.

To be able to safely get out of a shuttle that was hurtling toward the ground, we also had to have parachutes. Unfortunately, analysis showed that if we jumped out of the side hatch of an intact shuttle that was in a dive, the airflow over the wings would smash us into the tail, killing or severely injuring us.

NASA engineers began to work out a way to shoot crew members out the hatch away from the vehicle. They developed something called a tractor rocket system. The side hatch would be blown off. Then the crew member would lie down on a slide, hook his or her parachute harness to a rocket device, and be fired out into the sky. Needless to say, there was great concern not only about the danger of being shot out of the orbiter but also about the wisdom of living inside a vehicle with multiple explosive rockets stowed aboard. Another group of people came up with a simpler system.

The alternative to being shot out of a disabled craft was to jettison the side hatch and deploy through the opening a long, curved pole which ended below the wing on the belly side of the orbiter. Clipping his or her harness to a ring on the pole, the crew member flipped headfirst out the hatch and slid down the pole. Tested by analysis then with aircraft and real parachutists, this low tech solution operated fine. What did the people who worked on this project call themselves? Naturally, the *Pole Cats* with special patches, T-shirts, and ball caps in the best of NASA traditions. This was NASA engineering at its best, coming up with a simple but ingenious idea, building it, and making it work.

It would be a few years before I was to learn the problems that these suits and chutes would cause, especially to the smaller members of our office. The first crew to fly with them would be all male. They'd surprise the public on launch morning by waddling out to the pad like astronauts of yore, in real space suits.

The other astronaut garb that changed during the *Challenger* stand-down was the inflight attire. Early shuttle inflight photos reveal the monotony of everyone dressed in light blue pants or shorts and dark blue polo shirts with NASA and crew patches on them. Standard issue, all alike. When I was working in the area of Crew Equipment, I found out about one of those weird things that *whistle blowers* often latch onto as a waste of government money. The contractor who supplied our inflight clothing was required to purchase the clothing, inventory it periodically, take old patches off shirts, put new patches on shirts, dry clean the shorts or trousers (fire retardant material which couldn't be washed), and pack them all for the individual missions. In the case of the shirts it turned out to be more expensive than purchasing new shirts for each flight and giving them to the crew afterward.

We began the process of trying to get the rules changed as a cost savings measure. It did occur to me, however, that people would be happier to have the freedom to choose the colors and shirt styles they liked, and it would add a little spice to our otherwise monotonous and impersonal clothing choices. So when we began flying after *Challenger,* crews began to appear inflight with bright colors, stripes, polo shirts, turtlenecks, and other choice items from favorite catalogues. Mary Cleave took over Crew Equipment after I moved on to another assignment, and she managed to persuade the higher ups that the Nomex used in our T-38 dark blue flight-suits which was washable was sufficiently fire retardant to be used for the shorts and trousers on the shuttle. So the *Columbia* blue ones from early missions were retired and may still be stored and inventoried somewhere as *important space equipment.*

There were other priorities in my life during these days. We wanted to have another child. After getting pregnant right away with Paul, we didn't think we'd have too much trouble. After trying much of 1986 with no luck, we consulted the fertility experts in Houston. Richard Jennings, one of our flight surgeons who was an obstetrician-gynecologist by training, sent us to all the best physicians. At 39 or 40 I didn't consider myself so old, but it sure took a lot of time, effort, stress, and money. Then in early 1988 I got a call from Mr. Abbey.

Jim Bagian, who was assigned to SLS-1 with me, was one of the last of the 1980 astronaut class to be assigned to flight. He had not flown prior to *Challenger,* and the SLS-1 mission was getting pushed further and further down on the manifest. Our office thought he should be on one of the earliest flights after we started flying again, so he was added to Mike Coats's crew.

Mr. Abbey was kind enough to figure I was going to have to wait a mighty long time for my second flight and hinted when he called that he'd like to put me on something sooner. There was an unwritten rule in our office that you'd better never turn down any flight assignment, but what was I to do? I knew if I needed to start training with a crew that I couldn't continue to try to get pregnant. Crews were well-integrated teams, each person assigned to critical areas of responsibility, and it was hard to change one person out close to flight if she became *incapacitated* with a pregnancy. And it was strictly forbidden to fly pregnant. I knew that if I flew this interim flight that I'd land and have to hurry back to training for SLS-1. It didn't take a lot of figuring for me to know that if I accepted Mr. Abbey's offer, I might be giving up any chance of more children.

What was more important to me? Turning down this flight might so anger the boss that there would be no further flight assignments after SLS-1.

Should I be honest about why I was turning him down? I was sure no one had ever said "No, thanks. I'd rather have a baby." Maybe we wouldn't be able to get pregnant anyway. But in my heart of hearts, I still had the same priorities that I had when I came to NASA. After my tenure there was completed, I knew I'd rather have a good marriage and a couple of kids than have the most and best shuttle flights and only one child. It was the balance that I would be happiest with. So I told him, honestly, that we were trying to have a another child, and I felt SLS-1 needed someone to continue to ride herd on it even if it was several years in the future. He seemed perturbed but left it at that. This is why on my resume there is a long gap of 1985 to 1991 in my flying career.

As 1988 moved into the dog days of summer it looked like we were on the road to getting our programs, management, and hardware *fixed*. September of that year looked like the right time for the "Return to Flight," STS-26. Hoot's flight, STS-27 would take place later in the year, after the boosters (the SRBs) had been recovered from STS-27 and all the changes evaluated. Hoot, who never liking to be second at anything, loved to give the 26 crew a hard time. He always referred to them as the "SRB Test Flight."

We had turned the corner on one of the darkest times in space history. Hoot and I had gone through a difficult time with the loss of so many friends, too much travel, worry about our future careers, and the death of Hoot's beloved father in April of 1986. But we knew it was nothing compared to what the *Challenger* families had faced.

After a couple of awful years, things began to brighten. The shuttle would soon be flying again. We both had flight assignments. And I found myself pregnant with our second child.

CHAPTER 10

★ ★ ★ ★ ★ ★

RETURN
TO FLIGHT

No Southern lady like me could ever imagine she'd be called Bubba, but in 1988 I became Bubba. When astronauts were not assigned to a crew or were more than a year or so from flight, they worked on technical assignments to support ongoing missions such as in the Mission Control Center or serving as the Safety Officer overseeing the operations of our T38 jets. There were myriad areas where an astronaut's help or oversight could be invaluable, and there were detached assignments working in other areas of the Center or off-site.

One of the more coveted detached positions was strange, but it was important. When our group of 35 entered the Astronaut Corps in 1978, George Abbey was the head of the Flight Operations Directorate, and he liked having a pilot fly him around in the T-38s wherever he wanted or needed to go—a perquisite of his office. In order to have someone always available, he created a position called the Technical Assistant to the Director. Since the work entailed doing every odd job Mr. Abbey could think of (in addition to the flying duties), the job holder was known as the Bubba. In return for being chauffeur and horse holder, the Bubba also got to see how our Directorate was managed and how it interfaced with the rest of the Johnson Space Center and NASA. It also allowed the delegation of various tasks to the other astronauts.

"Mr. Abbey would like you to find out the answer to the following question..." the Bubba would request from the eighth floor corner office of Building 1.

Known among us by his initials of GWSA, George William Samuel Abbey didn't select any astronaut for this job who he didn't like. That meant if you got the job, unless you made a terrible mistake, you knew you might be on his list of favorites for further flight assignments.

After *Challenger,* Dick Truly, a former astronaut, left the Navy and went to NASA Headquarters to run the spaceflight program. Mr. Abbey went to Washington to be his deputy. We all hoped that Dick would name an astronaut to fill Mr. Abbey's role as head of what was now the Flight Crew Operations Directorate, or FCOD, which included the Astronaut Office and Aircraft Operations at Ellington Field. I think we were all surprised and a little dismayed when Don Puddy was tapped to head FCOD. Don was a former Flight Director from the Mission Operations Directorate. As boss of Mission Control, the Flight Director ran a spaceflight from the ground; the astronaut commander on a spaceflight was in charge of that mission in the spacecraft. There were bound to be disagreements. Each side of the fence thought the other wielded too much power.

"Darn jet jockeys! They don't have all the data we have, so how can they make the right decisions?!" was a theme in the Control Center.

"Darn Flight Directors! Sit there at a console deciding whose butt to risk!" was the occasional feeling on the other side.

While almost all the time things were handled in a professional manner, the people who flew the vehicles would have preferred one of their own at the helm.

Don Puddy carried on with most of the traditions of FCOD. Having joined the United States Air Force in his youth hoping to fly, he found himself too tall to fit in the military's cockpits. I think we all expected him to go through the training to qualify in our T-38s (for which he was not oversized) and select a Bubba to fly him around. His first technical assistant was Brian Duffy, a pilot. But Don ended up too busy with other things and never got checked out to fly in the jets.

It didn't occur to me that the Bubba job was available to anyone other than a male pilot. Like not being allowed to sit in the surgeons' lounge at Baptist Hospital in Memphis during my internship, it was something I was excluded from because of my sex. I decided not to buck the system by asking for the Bubba slot so as not to be perceived as a trouble maker. However, I did want to get management experience. I went to see Dr. Carolyn Huntoon who had taken over as the head of the Space and Life Sciences Directorate which put her on the same level as Mr. Puddy. Life Sciences included the people who poked and prodded us for our medical exams or for medical experiments on our flights. Though there had always been some friction between our two groups, I had worked well with many of these scientists, physicians, and managers in my training and on my first flight. Carolyn agreed to take me on as an assistant in the spring of 1988.

At the time, Dan Brandenstein was Chief of the Astronaut Office. When I approached him with the idea of getting some management experience by working in Dr. Huntoon's area, he didn't like the idea. It had never been done. I suppose he felt I was too much like the life scientists already and a stint in their office would pollute my brain even further. That wouldn't have been good for our office or for my future.

In May of 1988, I was offered the Bubba job. I was stunned. I didn't know how Dan had arranged it. Mr. Puddy was thinking about doing away with the job altogether but was persuaded to let a female serve in the role. Quite a break for me!

When I took up the job, we were several months from the launch of the Return to Flight mission, STS-26, and preparations for it were in full swing. I was given several projects to work on dealing with the protocol for the flight, like which important people needed to be invited and what the post-landing ceremony would entail. Not long before, I had been one of the few women ever to orbit the Earth, and now I was a party planner. The astronaut job required many talents.

I was also asked to work on several major policies with the Space and Life Sciences Directorate. Thorny issues had to be addressed, such as who should have access to astronaut psychiatric records, how much examining was necessary to clear someone medically for return to work post flight, and whether subjects were required to volunteer for experiments. The physicians did a number of post flight tests based on tradition that appeared no longer necessary, and the Astronaut Office wanted justification for them. The scientists felt that astronauts had a responsibility to serve as experimental subjects as part of their jobs, but the astronauts felt it was unethical to be required to do whatever tests were on a flight without knowing what they entailed. Mr. Puddy respected my opinion on the issues and my recommended compromises, but Dr. Huntoon sometimes didn't want to compromise. The Flight Crew Directorate's positions would languish on her desk for months with no response until Mr. Puddy would be ready to tear his hair out. He once said he thought she had taken up the motto that indecision was the key to flexibility. Sometimes he gave up; sometimes we managed to hammer out a solution.

When I found out in the late summer of 1988 that I was pregnant again, I was struck by the humor of it. Not only was the Bubba a Bubbette, but she was also soon to be visibly with child. It was the perfect job, however, since it involved little travel and had regular hours. The new baby was due at the end of March 1989 which would give me almost a year in that technical assignment which was the usual amount of time. Then I could take a couple months of maternity leave before training picked up in earnest in the summer for my next flight. How happy I was that I had not taken on an interim flight assignment when one was offered to me! I would have a second child before my second flight.

STS-26 took on much of the hoopla that had preceded the first shuttle flight. Since there hadn't been a flight in over two and a half years, the excitement began to build. The crew of Rick Hauck, Dick Covey, George "Pinky" Nelson, Mike Lounge, and Dave Hilmers were interviewed and re-interviewed. They became media stars, heroes. The press wanted to know if they thought this flight was risky because of the new booster design. The rest of the astronauts all giggled about that since we knew the boosters would be safer than ever, and the mission—to launch a NASA Tracking and Data Relay satellite—was not demanding. We had all learned, however, that the press and the public were fickle and often cheered loudest for the simple things, missing the important stuff because they didn't understand it or it wouldn't fit into a sound bite on the evening news.

Hoot's crew of STS-27 was training for a much tougher assignment, but the world would never know about it because it was a secret military mission. As such, there would be no discussion of what would be done and no pictures of the payload before or during the flight. The crew couldn't even discuss what they'd be doing with their spouses. The Department of

Defense hadn't been able to launch anything on the shuttle in the almost three years since *Challenger*, so we all surmised that STS-27 was carrying something crucial because it got an early slot on the manifest. If a tree falls in the forest and no one is around, does it make a sound? If you have a spectacular shuttle mission but you can't talk about it or show it on television, did it really happen?

As the September launch date for the STS-26 Return to Flight mission drew closer, I began to focus on how it was going to affect Paul, my now six year old. He had seen the *Challenger* explosion many times on television, he had heard us discuss the good and bad things happening in the booster redesign at the dinner table, and he was old enough now to understand the risks. He saw his father training for a mission that was to take place soon. Even though we explained over and over that his father would be on the second mission after we started flying again, he still seemed to be confused and not reassured.

Anna Fisher and I talked a lot that summer about how to get our youngsters through that difficult time. Anna's daughter, Kristin, was a year younger than Paul and was going through the same uncertainties. Also pregnant with her second child that was due the following January, Anna and I decided we wanted to be with our children when STS-26 launched. As it turned out Mr. Puddy had to be at the Cape for launch, so we commandeered his large office and brought the two children with us to see it on television. We could watch and listen to what was going on in Mission Control away from anyone else, so we could explain to Paul and Kristin what was happening. We also had access to information if things went wrong.

The kids enjoyed sitting in the big 8th floor office with its great view of the space center and Clear Lake, listening to the countdown. As the launch grew closer, Paul began to spend more time at my side looking at my face and peppering me with questions.

"Are the boosters really fixed, Mommy?" he asked. "Are there any other things wrong?"

"We think everything has been fixed, and the flight will be very safe," I told him confidently.

"Where is Daddy? Are you sure he isn't on the shuttle?"

"I'm sure, Paul. He is just in Florida to help the people who are flying. I promise."

As the shuttle rose from the pad that morning, I was glad I could sit with him on my lap, my arms wrapped around him, and provide reassurance. It also allowed me to focus on him and not on my own fears and memories. As soon as STS-26 was launched, however, I knew that Hoot and his crew were next up or Prime Crew, and I'd have to deal with watching him prepare to fly. Would my fear show through when his was one of the lives at stake?

It was always more difficult to be the one staying at home. When I was on a crew I was too busy to do anything but focus on getting ready for my flight. The pilots always said they were good at compartmentalizing. They had their job which was separate from their family which was separate from their other interests. When they focused so much on the job compartment, they didn't spend much time worrying about the other compartments. I'd been there, and I understood that...although I was never good at it. Being the support crew back home gave me more time to worry.

I was serious about my job as an astronaut's spouse. As the commander's wife, I was supposed to get all the other wives organized to serve our social roles and our support roles. There were pre- and post-flight parties to plan, decisions about launch and landing guest lists, relatives to consult about their plans. Hoot again was gone much of the time: on travel to visit contractor facilities he couldn't tell me about, in simulators, and flying the training aircraft at landing sites in California, Florida, and New Mexico.

Being unable to talk about what he was doing on this flight made him seem remote even when he was home. Luckily, the pregnancy was going well even at my advanced age of 41. Paul was busy enjoying Mr. Ritchie's kindergarten class at a school near the Center. I tried hard not to show my fears. Too much to do, no time to worry, best not to think about the "what ifs." Yet I knew it was going to be difficult to get through this one.

We finished all the planning, I took some leave from the Bubba post, and we headed for the Cape for the launch of STS-27 in late November. The traveling part had been made easier by the new Family Support Plan. NASA saw to it that all the families got down to the Cape on a NASA plane and put them all in the same condominium complex. No more worrying if the kids could make it to the launch or be home with a babysitter if the worst happened. No more tension about whether there would be a place to stay if the launch slipped. The family escorts didn't have to round up people from different locations to take them out to crew quarters for visits. Decreasing the stress level for families was one of the finest things NASA had ever done for astronauts. Pinky Nelson had worked it all out and presented it to upper management, and Don Puddy pushed it up the chain of command for approval.

It was finally time to go. *Florida Today* carried a picture of a pregnant me kissing Hoot hello as the crew arrived at the Cape in their jets. It was difficult that time to spend those last few days with Hoot before this flight. The horrible memories of *Challenger* kept working their way into my consciousness. Knowing what their families had gone through haunted my thoughts. Intellectually I knew that the booster problem had been fixed, but how many other things could go wrong? Perhaps it had to do with the hormonal turmoil of pregnancy. I always found myself feeling more dependent during my pregnancies. I felt in need of protection, yet Hoot couldn't fill that need now. I knew I had to be strong for Paul. What if

A very pregnant me with my father at the prelaunch reception.

the baby I was carrying never knew his father? I was an emotional wreck inside, unable to show it.

Saying goodbye at the crew quarters the day before launch was hard. Hoot was not one to want sad partings. So we both pretended he was going off on a business trip and parted with a brief hug, a quick kiss, and final wave. I watched those sky blue eyes disappear behind an elevator door as all the wives were whisked out of quarters to go back to town.

On launch morning, Hoot called me as usual before he left for the pad. We went through our usual little litany of happy things.

"Have a great flight."

"Take good care of my babies until I get back."

What more could be said? Paul, Julie (now 12), and I were picked up at the condo and taken to the Launch Control Center. I had put on a brave front for the kids. Of course, everything would be fine. Daddy would be home in a few days. We watched reruns of the crew on television as they walked out to the Astrovan, waving and smiling. At the launch pad, they finished suiting up and climbed into the orbiter as we watched. My heart was about to burst. Would it be the last I saw of him alive? Could I go on alone without him?

At nine minutes before launch we were all herded up to the roof to watch the launch. I trembled standing looking eastward toward the pad, hoping the gleaming white craft would hold together long enough to carry this crew to orbit. Paul didn't want to hear the loud roar of the rockets which had scared him on previous launches so he asked me to stand behind him and put my fingers in his ears so he could take a picture with his little camera.

The tension was almost more than I could stand. 10.9.8…Please, Lord, keep them safe! 7.6.5… The smoke from the main engine billowed out. Please, please be okay! 4.3.2.1 – And there they went. That's when I lost control. I must have been a pitiful sight, sobbing with my fingers stuck in Paul's ears, unable to stifle my feelings. Mae Jemison, a fellow astronaut, happened to be nearby on the roof that day, and she looked away from the launch at me with surprise. Later, she would be on one of Hoot's crews, but that day with her arm holding me steady, she served as a shoulder to cry on. Julie leaned over to hug us both. I don't think I stopped boo-hooing until two minutes later when the boosters separated, having performed without a flaw, and I realized Paul was wiggling to get loose from the fingers in his ears. I didn't completely get it together until a half hour later when the orbital engines put the flight into a safe orbit.

There was little news from the flight, as expected. Department of Defense flights couldn't transmit pictures of what they were doing. They

Paul was six years old and put his fingers in his ears as he watches for the launch.

couldn't even show pictures of the Earth out their windows since that might give away how far north or south their orbit was. That seemed silly because the Russians could track the

PHOTO COURTESY OF NASA

Hoot in the Commander's seat. He claimed this secret flight was really a test of duct tape.

shuttle from their ground control facilities as easily as they tracked their own spaceships. At the time there was fear that our enemies might find out what we were doing, as if they didn't have spies who told them everything. There was one picture of Hoot in the cockpit commander's seat. A large roll of duct tape was stuck on the wall behind his head. As one of the few photos from the flight he could show, he told audiences that the flight was really a top-secret mission to test duct tape in space.

In Houston after the launch, Julie, Paul, and I went out after sunset one evening to watch the shuttle pass over. To see the shuttle at night, the craft had to be sunlit because it was high above the Earth where the sunlight could still strike it. We went to the park at the end of our street to get away from the neighborhood lights and trees. Never good at spotting lights passing through the sky, I was surprised when I saw it rising above the trees to the west. As the spaceship passed overhead, it looked like there were two lights flying in tandem. Years later when information about the flight was declassified, we discovered that, indeed, there were two objects

The crew inspects the damage to the heat shield tiles after landing.

there: the shuttle and a huge military satellite that they had released but were still flying close to. Rumors later would surface that there had been a problem with the satellite that the crew had to help repair.

I didn't know that my husband was under considerable stress dealing with another problem. The ground had asked the crew to verify if there was any damage on the heat shield tiles from debris that had been seen hitting the bottom of the orbiter moments after launch. Using the mechanical arm, the crewmembers discovered all kinds of divots in the tiles on their underside and told the ground so. They also downlinked pictures, but because all their mission data had to be encrypted, picture quality was poor. Mis-

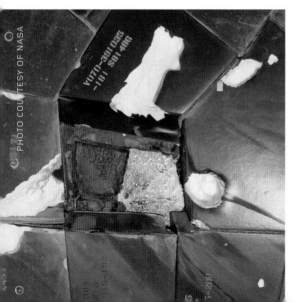

sion Control told them not to worry, that those were lights and shadows on the underside. Hoot knew different, but even after several attempts, he couldn't convince the ground controllers. He was worried the vehicle wouldn't survive

An entire tile had come off, charring the aluminum underneath.

the heat of re-entry. On inspection after the flight, over 700 tiles had gouges, and one tile was missing with the underlying aluminum charred, luckily in a non-critical area. Because of the secrecy surrounding the flight, this damage wasn't something that became news at the time. It was a harbinger of a later disaster, a lesson NASA should have learned about debris impact.

Hoot would remember this flight for the fun the crew had. My fellow spouses and I all agreed the men came from the Planet AD – the Planet of Arrested Development. Hoot, Guy Gardner, Jerry Ross, Mike Mullane and Bill Shepherd were like kids determined to have fun training for and flying this very serious military mission. Since they frequently made pig-snorting noises when pretty girls walked by, they had become known as Swine Flight. The office secretaries, joining in the silliness, gave them rubber pig noses to wear and, as a send-off before the flight, did a ballet routine in pink tutus at an office party to music titled Swine Lake. Had NASA really entrusted a multibillion dollar vehicle to this bunch?

The crew as Swine Flight had their picture on posters for Health Stabilization, the quarantine-like program that kept germs away from them.

There was always good-natured banter between the Navy guys – Hoot and Shep—and the Air Force Guys— Mike, Guy and Jerry. One topic that Hoot brought up was that the Air Force passed out medals for frivolous operations the Navy wouldn't have considered worthy of an award. During the flight a water leak had developed under the middeck floor. The crew pulled up the floorboards, isolated and repaired the leak and cleaned up the water. Hoot said that for such courageous action, the Air Force guys would probably get *Incredible Service Medals* (fictitious, of course). Not long after landing, at the astronaut Christmas party, Mike and Guy showed up in formal attire with bright green satin sashes across their chests adorned with gaudy, bejeweled brooches. They swore they had received these Incredible Service Medals for the awe-inspiring in-flight janitorial work.

When STS-27 landed safely that December, I felt a wonderful sense of euphoria. Once again, death had been cheated; the astronauts were safe. We had time to make quick Christmas plans to go skiing and relax with Bennie and Dixie Wright, friends from Mississippi, at Steamboat Springs. I managed to do well on the slopes even though six months pregnant. Hoot said it was because of my lowered center of gravity. It was wonderful to do something that was physical after all the brain work of my job and the emotional work of supporting Hoot.

After the holidays, we planned in earnest for our second child. Since I would need a C-section, we knew by March this little boy would be a big one at "8 pounds or so," and we needed to pick a birthday for him. It was great to invite guests to the party. Dr. Richard Jennings was an ObGyn who had joined the Flight Medicine Clinic and had given us lots of advice on the pregnancy, and he wanted to be there. Dr. Winnette Wimberly was our wonderful pediatrician, and she didn't want to miss the fun. Of course, Dr. Powell, my obstetrician, had to be available. The date we chose was Monday, March 27. My father could fly in on the weekend and be there to tend to Paul while Hoot took me to the hospital. It didn't occur to me until later when I wrote out the birth date that, by coincidence, it was the same as Hoot's office phone extension – 3-27-89.

At work, I wanted to give up the Bubba-ship two weeks before the baby's birthday so I could get everything ready and have a chance to finish up things at the office before my maternity leave started. As usual, everyone in the Astronaut Office had multiple important projects going on and giving me time to get ready for a baby wasn't a big priority. As the delivery date drew closer and closer, it became clear that I was going to have to work full time right up until the weekend before the birth. On Friday afternoon on March 24, I turned my job over to Ken Bowersox who'd been appointed the new Bubba that morning. I waddled around that weekend buying tiny diapers and crib sheets.

A name had to be chosen for our new addition. Since Paul was named for Hoot's father, I wanted this son to be named for mine, Edward. Yet we wanted to call him something other than my father's name to avoid confusion. My mother had the odd name of Clayton, which Hoot didn't like. But her maiden name had been Dann, which we both liked.

Edward Dann Gibson came squalling into the world at 8:01 a.m. on Monday, the 27th of March, 1989. At 8 pounds, 10 ounces he was bigger than expected. But Dann was perfect in every way, and we felt blessed to have our second—and what we were sure would be our last—child in our

Our second Astrotot, Dann, was born on March 27, 1989. He is welcomed by his big brother.

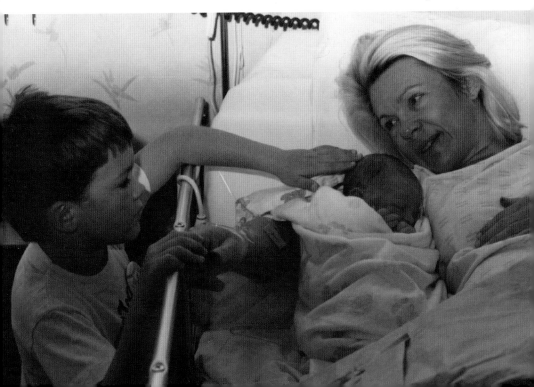

arms. At 41 and after all the trouble we'd had getting pregnant this second time, I decided that it was probably out of the question to even hope for a little girl in our future.

And yet…

I had three glorious months of maternity leave saved up. We had done some redecorating and rearranging in our house, and I was sure I'd have time to do lots of things. As it turned out, I raced around at the last minute to get the spare bedroom ready for our new nanny.

I read a story once about a lady who swore that whenever she was in need, an angel in disguise would appear to help her. It might take the form of a truck driver who changed a flat or a stranger who gave her critical advice. They were angels all the same. I came to realize that there were angels in my life, too. One of them arrived in May of 1989.

One of the biggest worries for any working mother is finding good

Joann, our nanny, became part of our family.

childcare. Our situation was difficult because our job hours were so strange. Since Hoot and I also had to travel for work, we were sometimes out of town at the same time. Paul was now in school, but with the new baby we would need a lot of help. Evening sitters were available, but trying to find one that could come at 5:00 a.m., allowing me to get to a 5:30 a.m. simulator run, was beyond difficult. Secretaries from the office, young pre-school teachers, and neighbors had all been wonderful about helping with Paul when we had to be gone. Nonetheless, there was tremendous stress worrying about whether everything could be organized before we left town knowing that the best laid plans might fall through at the last minute. We decided to try to find a live-in nanny.

I contacted several nanny-finding agencies and put ads in the local papers. After interviewing several ladies who I couldn't envision living with us, I started praying hard to find the right person. So did Joyce Westfall, the lady who was helping me keep house. As she tells it, it came to her (I think of it as divine intervention) that a friend of hers who lived near Waco might be that person. She talked to the friend then broached the subject with me.

That is how an angel named Joann Powell appeared on my doorstep with Joyce one sunny morning in May. At the time Joann was in her early fifties and a widow. She had raised five children, the youngest of whom was soon to marry. She had lived most of her life in Texas and was working as a teacher's aide in the small town of Meridian. The fact that Joyce knew her and could vouch for her honesty and integrity meant a great deal.

Joann arrived for her interview, and we chatted about the requisite items. She was a nonsmoker, able to cover strange hours for us, and willing to live with us and at the salary we could afford. As we visited, I began to like her more and more. She was a mature, intelligent, cheerful person. I had been holding Dann on my shoulder as we talked, and he was being his usual gurgling two-month-old self. When I asked Joann if she had any questions for me she did something that sold me right away on her. She asked, "Yes. May I hold the baby?"

That is how an angel came to live in our house and take care of not only the baby but all of us over the years. She stayed with us for twenty five years, a permanent, loving, and loved part of our happy family, an answered prayer.

Even with Joann's arrival in late June, it was not going to be easy to face going back to work. With Paul, I had gone back at six weeks, neither enough time to get to know that tiny person, nor enough time to develop little routines. After three months caring for Dann full time, we had become wonderfully bonded. He was a good, if wakeful, baby and had established his own patterns of living. When Joann arrived I still had a few days of leave, so after I briefed her on his schedule one morning I left to run some errands. Halfway down the block I started to cry. Never again would Dann be so much my own baby. I was happy to have Joann, but would he be closer to her than to me? Would she be a better mother than I was? I knew this made me part of the sisterhood of many, many mothers who had faced these issues, and it gave me greater sympathy for all working mothers. I was lucky; I had the means to find the best possible solution but knew others were not as lucky. I said a prayer that the closeness I had developed with this baby would not disappear. Again, my prayers were answered.

While we had been working part-time on my next flight since that awful day of the *Challenger* accident, training began in earnest in the summer of 1989 since the flight had been assigned to mission STS-40 and had been given a launch date of May 1990. There were many things to accomplish and learn before liftoff. Jim Bagian, the other payload Mission Specialist had flown in March, so in July when I returned from maternity leave he had completed his post-flight duties and we were ready to pick up where we left off. Drew Gaffney and Bob Phillips had been named as the flight's prime

Payload Specialists, and Millie Hughes-Fulford had been designated as the back-up. The rest of the crew had also been named. Bryan O'Connor would be our commander. A veteran of a flight which flew two months before the *Challenger* accident, he was a mature and well-respected member of our office…despite being a Marine! In the pilot's seat would be Sid Gutierrez, a humorous Air Force pilot from New Mexico. Dr. Tammy Jernigan was a bright young astrophysicist with degrees from Berkeley, Stanford, and Rice and she would complete the orbiter crew. Sid and Tammy were members of the 1985 class of astronauts, and this would be their first flight. While life sciences missions were not the most sought-after flights, they seemed to be happy that they would be flying with us.

The payload crew, meaning the life scientists onboard, had been training together since early 1984. It seemed like we should have had everything pulled together and been trained by then. But training a few hours every month since January of 1986, often with several members of the crew off on other assignments, didn't make for optimal efficiency. Also, Jim and I now had some flight experience and saw we needed to organize the checklists and timelines better.

The flight itself had been reconfigured several times. I understood that the investigators started out requesting everything they could think of in the way of data collection on the crew. They wanted many repetitions of their experiments to be performed on us before flight to establish our normal baseline physiology. For instance, they might ask that a crew member have six sets of lung function tests or five blood draws within the six months prior to flight to define without a doubt how our bodies worked on Earth. This would give them excellent data on what we were like prior to being exposed to weightlessness and how things would change due to the removal of gravity. If they had been doing these studies in their lab back at the university with volunteer subjects without much else to do and who didn't have other experiments being performed on them that would have been appropriate. It couldn't be done with the time the astronaut crew-members had available.

The scientists also wanted multiple measurements inflight to see how we adapted to space and how far that adaptation went before it leveled out at a new space normal. The more measurements, the surer they could be that they had statistically correct data. Then they'd want the same studies repeated as soon as possible after landing and several times during the week or so after flight as we readapted to being back on the ground.

The crew had a somewhat different perspective. In flight we would be doing multiple different experiments, and we would have many other responsibilities keeping the lab in working order. Plus, several of the experiments interfered with each other. For instance, we couldn't do a lung function test right after doing a heavy exercise test. And, worst of all, we had to be off all caffeine and alcohol for many days before several of the tests. Add the requirements for a dozen or so human studies together and we began to see ourselves as pithed frogs pinned to a dissecting table in a high school biology lab. Everyone—crew, principle investigators (PIs), NASA engineers, flight surgeons, and managers—had to work out compromises that would get good data without killing the subjects.

When first proposed our flight was overbooked with experiments. Somewhere along the line it had been split into two missions, Spacelab Life Sciences 1 and 2, with a different complement of experiments on each flight. On a previous Spacelab flight in April of 1985 rat waste got loose within the lab and floated up to the crew cabin, eliciting descriptive expletives from Bob Overmeyer, the crew commander. So the rats had been removed from SLS-1 until the cages could be redesigned. As the flight was delayed multiple times and the redesign of the cages progressed, the rats were added back as an engineering test of the hardware. No hands-on experiments would be performed on the furry creatures. However, issues about how to care for the animals and how to answer questions from the animal rights activists remained to be worked out.

Most importantly, each of the payload crew members had to learn how to operate each of the experiments, no mean feat. Each principle investigator had to train us to work his or her equipment in the right way to obtain useable data. We had to learn how to obtain ultrasound images of each other's heart. We had to learn to work a newly-designed zero-G gas analyzer that would reveal how much oxygen we used and how much carbon dioxide we produced while exercising on a bicycle with shoulder boards to keep us from floating away. A neck collar that squeezed or sucked on the blood pressure sensors in our necks had to be mastered along with the computer that analyzed our heart rate responses to this torture. We were serious about the responsibility of learning each study, every piece of equipment. We would be the eyes and hands of a multitude of scientists back on the ground.

We did persuade some other people to share our pain. One of the skills we had to perfect was inserting intravenous catheters, small plastic tubes, into each other's arm veins and drawing blood from each other. Our blood vessels were much too valuable to use for practice (we'd be stuck multiple times for the real studies), so volunteers were paid to come be our venipuncture, or vein sticking subjects. It was neither pleasant nor well paid, but many of the people who let us practice on them had never met an astronaut and were full of questions as we played vampire. Many of our trainers and engineers also volunteered. They told us they felt like they were contributing to the success of a space mission, which we greatly appreciated. All said they'd be watching us on television knowing they were part of a team effort.

We knew that learning to operate all the hardware when it was in normal working order wouldn't be enough. The second half of an astronaut's training was in what was called malfunction procedures. What would we do if the equipment didn't work properly? We couldn't call in the engineer who built the machine to look at it when it was up in orbit. So predictions had to be made about what could fail and what the indications of failure would look like. Some equipment had failure detection signals (or messages) that appeared when something wasn't right, sort of glorified Check Engine lights. Other machinery would begin operating erratically or not at all. As we practiced on our aging training hardware, more and more real failure modes were identified. Sometime the failures were not in the experiment machinery but in the connections of the science equipment to the Spacelab systems. Longer and longer procedures had to be worked out, written down, verified, and trained on.

For Jim and me, the Spacelab systems had to be mastered. Spacelab was a canister that sat in the shuttle's cargo bay. Its electrical, cooling, atmospheric control, and computers systems connected to the similar systems in the orbiter but had their own operating modes. We had to learn how to activate the lab when we got to orbit, how to check that the systems were working, how to do routine maintenance on them, and how to recognize and correct malfunctions. My brain felt ready to explode.

I had come into the office for a few hours each week during my maternity leave. Often I parked Dann in his baby carrier down the hall in Lucy Lytwynsky's office. As the person who handled all requests for astronaut interviews, Lucy always had a few minutes to cuddle everyone's baby. She would keep an eye on him as long as he wasn't fussy so I could run around, return phone calls, and check on my in-basket. This way I didn't get too far behind in what was going on at work.

When I returned to work after the Fourth of July holidays, I was ready to begin work full time on SLS-1. The bosses had other plans. The little smack to the side of my head came in a memo listing me as one of the astronauts who would serve on the upcoming Astronaut Selection Board for the next few months. I had to admit it was an honor. It meant my superiors had enough confidence in me to let me help select the astronauts of the future. I also knew that they wanted to have at least one female and one physician on the board and that I filled both squares.

About every two years (sometimes longer, depending on the number of astronauts leaving and the spaceflight rate), NASA would open up its application process for a new class of astronauts. Announcements were sent to universities, research labs, the military and contractors along with various news organizations. Inquiries would begin to come in from all over the world, several thousand applicants for fifteen to twenty positions. The military services had their own prescreening boards and sent their top candidates. For non-military applicants, members of the Astronaut Office did the screening and looked over each of the thousands of applications that came in. Some of the Screening Board members would serve on the Selection Board. Several months were devoted to weeding down those interested to about a hundred or so of the best qualified people to interview. It was never an easy task.

The applicants were grouped according to their backgrounds: life sciences, Earth sciences, astronomy, materials, engineering, and so on. The pilots were in a separate group.

Screening Board members assessed those who fell into their own areas of expertise. I looked at life scientists and medical doctors, for instance. Many applicants weren't what we considered highly qualified. Perhaps they had only bachelor's degrees, they had worked in a narrow field, or what they did had little applicability to spaceflight. I would present the best qualified in my pile to the other people on the Screening Board who could ask questions and critique the qualifications. We'd then decide whether we would be comfortable interviewing them and perhaps having them in our office.

All the applicants had to list three people who could recommend them, as I had done during my application process. NASA sent out a form that was a multiple choice rating sheet. The recommender checked off boxes in various categories, like "On a scale of 1 to 5, rate this person on ability to initiate important projects." Then a short space was given to write any other comments. I was often amazed that applicants who otherwise seemed intelligent could mess up on this part of the application. Great recommendations couldn't make up for lousy qualifications, but bad recommendations could ruin even top candidates.

One mistake was to choose a person with an important title to write the recommendation. If a senator, the governor, or the president of your university was indeed a close personal friend who played a major role in your life, ask him or her to recommend you. But it was the kiss of death when that famous person jotted a note on the NASA form that said he or she didn't know the applicant well enough to give an adequate assessment. Another terrible mistake was to misread a supervisor who didn't think enough of the applicant to give a good recommendation. It was tough to get one of the three recommendations back on someone that said something like the person "was difficult to work with" or "never showed initiative." Granted, it was one person's opinion, but maybe it showed some poor judgment to ask that person for a recommendation. This isn't to say we wouldn't interview an otherwise stellar performer based on that one piece of data, but we would be wary.

There were also stringent medical requirements. Pilots had to be between 64 and 76 inches tall, Mission Specialists (MSs) from 60 to 76 inches. There were vision requirements for pilots, which were relaxed somewhat for MSs. Blood pressure and heart rhythms had to be normal. The candidate had to be free of chronic diseases and not have anything in his or her past medical history that might indicate some future problems. People were always surprised that there were no specific fitness requirements for astronauts, although almost all of the people who were selected were fit of their own accord. This was a form of self-discipline most other fit people, like those on the Selection Board, admired and could assess during the interview.

The screening of large numbers of applicants, the narrowing down to the interview list, the five weeks of interviews, the endless meetings discussing what we thought of the applicants—all this dragged on into late in the year. I tried hard to work my other duties during the few days we didn't interview. Early in the morning and late after the interviews, I'd go to my office and plow through the papers that came to my desk requesting this or that decision. On Saturdays and on Sunday mornings before church I'd get up at 5:30 a.m., work out at the gym, and then swing by the office to study workbooks on experiments or Spacelab systems. I'd draft replies to proposed changes to our training, data collections, inflight timelines, or onboard procedures. I'd compile massive to-do lists of things that had to be done the following week. The other crew members were working hard on their particular areas, but we needed more time to train as a crew.

At last the Selection Board duties were over, and we announced the selection of the 1990 class of new astronauts who named themselves the Hairballs. Then, more training time for our crew became available. A hydrogen leak was found on one of the flights ahead of ours, and that caused a delay that rippled down the manifest to us. Certain flights had to go at a certain time or had higher priority, so we were pushed further and further downstream. We went from being behind in our preparations in the summer of 1989 to having to figure out how to spread out our training as the flight slid into 1991. The strain was beginning to get to everyone. There were more unresolved disagreements, more polarizing of crewmembers, less camaraderie.

When crews were assigned to shuttle flights, for the most part they knew they would be together for a limited amount of time, perhaps a year or two. Any differences could be put aside for the good of the mission. Any personality quirks or differences of opinion or work style could be ignored in the short run. The crew for SLS-1 had now been training for over six years. Stress was building like between two tectonic plates, and earthquakes were threatening.

Bob Phillips, our veterinarian payload specialist from Colorado, developed a health problem that the flight surgeons and the experiment investigators could not ignore. Not only was he no longer qualified according to the medical rules, but his problem made him a poor subject for several of the experiments. It was a heartbreaking loss for all of us. Being the wonderful, stable, helpful man we all adored, he agreed to stay on as our Backup Payload Specialist even though it would have been difficult to qualify him for flight. He helped immeasurably in the preparations for the flight and served an invaluable role as our ground liaison with the investigators during the flight.

Bad luck for one person often creates good luck for another. Millie Hughes-Fulford who had been serving as our backup (with the opportunity to fly on SLS-2) now became a bona fide member of our crew.

Two members of our crew began to have difficulty working together. Each thought the other had taken inappropriate actions that jeopardized the success of the mission. Things got worse as the pressure to get ready for the flight increased. Our commander, Bryan O'Connor, did a masterful job of trying to help us all cope with the difficult situation. He asked NASA's psychologist consultant Terry McGuire to work with us.

Terry sought to help us understand differences in personality types, which type we each were, and some of the ways each of these types responded to stress. Based on work by Taibi Kahler, Terry said there tended to be six personality types: rebels, dreamers, reactors, persisters, workaholics, and promoters. Everyone has a base mode, the natural first personality a person was born with. As people went through life, according to this theory, they could either stay in that mode or move through others as they gained experience and matured. The more modes gone through, the richer the personality, since many of the good things were retained from each mode as new ways of dealing with the world were learned.

Based on interviewing applicants for the Astronaut Corps for many years, Terry could say that dreamers were almost never selected. These tended to be artistic people who were creative but didn't follow the usual technical and analytical paths necessary to achieve the qualifications needed to get into our field. Nor would they find fulfillment in doing the somewhat unimaginative work we often had to do.

Few rebels passed our screening process. People out to change the world often didn't progress up their career ladders and sometimes lost jobs or alienated superiors, and the Selection Board frowned on those perceived to be troublemakers, even if what they were trying to accomplish was admirable.

A few astronauts were reactors, more so now since women were now a part of the office. Reactors were sensitive to everyone else's feeling and often spent time trying to please someone or to make everyone happy. I recognized my base mode. Southern girls in the 1950s were taught to be this way, although I was happy that I had moved into another mode as I pursued my career.

Promoters were people who were trying to sell something, including themselves. They had a cause or a product and devoted themselves to proving that everyone else should buy it. There were a few ambitious people in our office who had these traits.

Most astronauts were persisters or workaholics. Persisters were those people with strongly held beliefs who often stuck to them despite great pressure to change. Highly religious people had a streak of this. I thought that many of the military folks fell into this category. Hoot believed strongly that the military did the right thing in Vietnam (although sometimes not enough of the right thing) and never understood arguments to the contrary. How could someone talk young men into going to war if the soldiers didn't believe in the rightness of what they were doing?

Workaholics were the people who measured their own value by the things they accomplished. It was easy to see why it was necessary to be a workaholic to make it through medical, graduate school or test pilot school. I had traversed this mode myself.

There were interesting theories as to how these different types handled stress. Persisters became "equal opportunity perfectionists," according to Terry. Under pressure they expected everyone to shape up and march in the "correct" direction. They expected perfection of themselves…and everyone else. Workaholics felt all problems could be solved by working harder and expected everyone to do so. Reactors became emotional – angry or sad – and did whatever they could to help everyone get along. We all began to see some of our tensions as stress responses as we got busier and busier and the flight kept being delayed. It helped some, but it didn't solve the crew's problems entirely. I wondered if there would someday be a better way to put crews together. Would overcoming personal differences always be harder than overcoming gravity?

There were happy memories to be had. When crews got close to flight, they were invited over to the NASA photo lab to have their crew pictures made. There were the formal pictures, all stiff and proper, with only minor variations on the theme allowed. But most crews also had an informal picture done for friends and families. We decided we wanted to look like the crazy people from the television show M*A*S*H in ours. Millie wanted to be Hot Lips Houlihan. Radar O'Reilly and I had a lot in common. Sid was a shoe-in for Father Mulcahy. Of course, no one wanted to be Corporal Klinger, the soldier who tried to get a psychiatric discharge by wearing women's clothes. We decided the fair way to assign this duty was to draw straws. Drew lost. Jim and Bob took the roles of Hawkeye and Trapper John, and Tammy became Frank Burns. We all elected Bryan as the patient.

Crews must also design their own crew patch. For this flight of life sciences we couldn't resist putting da Vinci's Vitruvian man in the center with one foot on the Earth and the other in space. Since Drew and Sid were from New Mexico, the sunrise designating the first mission of its kind morphed into the Native American symbol of the sun. The space shuttle orbit formed the double helix of DNA

Our funny crew picture shows us as members of the MASH unit from the television show and movie *(below)*. The STS-40 crew patch *(above)*.

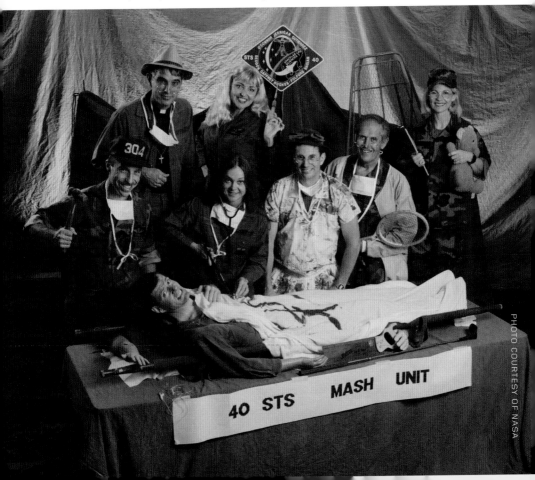

of all living creatures. There are seven stars representing the seven crew-members whose names are around the periphery of the patch. Most patches have some secret meaning. On ours, the stars form a "P" for Bob Phillips, the crewmember who trained for so long with us who didn't get to fly.

Then came the day I almost died, not in the shuttle, but in training. I found myself once again in a swimming pool, unable to breathe, flailing about with my heart pounding. It was like a horrible dream from which I couldn't awaken, and no one seemed to be there to help. NASA and I kept finding that equipment that worked well for normal-sized men sometimes didn't work well for little women. It was part of an exercise labeled "suit training" but which I always thought of as "suit wrestling."

One of the most daunting tasks for my second flight was learning to operate the new emergency escape equipment. During the investigation of the *Challenger* accident there was some evidence that the crew might have survived the breakup of the shuttle when the forward cabin broke free of the rest of the vehicle. There was a chance, though slim, that had they been able to get out and had the appropriate survival gear that they might have survived. So NASA found a way that might be possible

Changes had been made to allow the crew to jettison the side hatch of the orbiter. Everyone would now wear special suits like those worn in high altitude spy planes. The newly designed escape pole was incorporated into the middeck ceiling ready for deployment if needed. With time everything came together that might protect us someday but practicing for all the eventualities proved dangerous.

The new equipment attached to each crewmember included a para-chute, a life raft and other survival gear, oxygen bottles, the full body par-tial pressure suit called the Launch and Entry Suit or LES, helmet, and boots which altogether weighed about 75 pounds. In a high altitude plane and wearing similar gear, pulling the ejection seat handles and being rocketed out was pretty simple. But bailing out of the orbiter during an inflight emergency required unstrapping from a seat harness, standing up, climbing over other seats and down a ladder, and getting out the hatch. Encumbered this way, it was an almost impossible task for a 120-pound person. But I knew that one of the Astronaut Ten Commandments was to make survival look easy, and so I learned how to do it.

For other escape scenarios we could leave the survival gear behind but still had to get away in the big bulky suit. In the event of a landing in swampy land like that around the Florida runway we had to climb out one of the cockpit overhead windows and rappel fifty feet to the ground. In practice runs, I had to hook myself to a rope in the simulator and shove off for the fifty foot drop. It was more than a leap of faith for me; it was almost impossible to talk myself into, but I did it. Yet another involved exiting the side hatch on the launch pad and running over to slide wire baskets that would, in theory, zip at 55 miles per hour to a restraining net 195 feet below and 1200 feet away. From there we'd run some distance to a bunker before the vehicle exploded. Maneuvering around in a sealed multilayered suit designed to keep a person alive in freezing north Atlantic water for 24 hours was more than a little uncomfortable when it was 95 degrees outside in Florida.

During one exercise we were hoisted above a pool to practice parachuting into the water. It required wearing a training suit and helmet, and the one given to me must have been meant for someone larger. While suspended by a crane about 15 feet above the training pool, the instructor told me to close my helmet visor and pull the green knob below my right arm that would activate the air bottle. I did those things, gave him a thumbs-up, and was dropped into the pool.

The next task was to swim under a parachute and work my way across to the opposite side to simulate what to do if my chute landed on top of me after landing in the water. About halfway across, I became short of breath,

Crew escape training in the bulky Launch and Entry suits wasn't easy.

and my heart was racing. I tried to figure out whether I was getting exhausted or was having some kind of anxiety attack. As I popped out from under the chute and grabbed the side of the pool, I raised the faceplate of my helmet and realized that I had been slowly suffocating. My short arm hadn't pulled the activation knob out far enough to start the flow of air. The back-up system, an anti-suffocation valve on the helmet that should have opened to pull in fresh air, hadn't worked. Had I been under the chute and gone lifeless in the pool, there were safety divers who were watching and could have fished me out once they figured out what was going on, but still...

Whenever something went wrong during astronaut training, there was an investigation. The next time I would need to make sure I pulled far enough on the air bottle knob, and I found I had to stretch hard to do that. The anti-suffocation valve was another matter. The idea was that if I inhaled deep enough, then that would create a negative pressure inside the helmet and that would pull air in through the valve. However, with the ill-fitted suit, the suit neck ring that was supposed to fit snug and seal off the helmet from the suit was too loose on me. I had sucked air out of the lower part of the suit, and it was soon low in oxygen. The suit techs assured me that with a snugger neck seal in my real suit that wouldn't happen.

The next time I was in my own suit, we tried it. It turned out the volume inside the helmet exceeded the volume of my lungs. I couldn't inhale enough to get air to come in from the outside. The solution was to fill my helmet up with padding, and that seemed to work...sort of. When I inhaled hard, I could pull air in. Would it have saved me if I'd parachuted out and gone unconscious? I didn't think so. But there seemed to be no other fix and that was as good as it was going to get. The idea that we could get out of the shuttle after it exploded or were gliding down to the ocean seemed so far-fetched that I couldn't imagine it happening anyway. So I lied and said the fix was fine. On my third flight, I found other ways these monstrous suits could hurt me.

Another task required before each flight was to decide on some mementoes that NASA would allow us to take on the flight with us. All had to be stowed long before launch in the bowels of the spaceship. We were allowed to take personal items for friends and family in our Personal Preference Kit. Usually we took jewelry or medallions with our crew patch. We could pack away a certain number of things for groups we belonged to as long as they were small, lightweight and passed NASA inspection. They went in the Official Flight Kit. Organizations got creative when asked to provide things. I flew a long roll of paper with school children's signatures, a membership pin, school insignias and many others. We were allowed to take only two personal items with us in the cabin. Almost invariably that was a bumper sticker from our university or state and a family picture. Mark Lee, a single man on one of Hoot's flights, took a picture of the cows on his farm. NASA did allow us to wear a "reasonable amount" of personal jewelry into space. Sometimes crewmembers were literally festooned with it since it made wonderful gifts post-flight.

Our flight slid into May of 1991, and it began to look like Hoot and I might spend our tenth wedding anniversary on May 30 separated by a few hundred miles of space. After a couple of launch delays, however, it turned out we'd have a chance to celebrate at the beach house at the Cape. The spouses, Susie O'Connor, Marianne Gutierrez, Tandy Bagian, Sheila Gaffney, and George Fulford, decided nothing would do but that we have a renewing of our wedding vows on the beach. It was all a big surprise for Hoot and me. A bottle of champagne, plus glasses, plus a cake and tulle for a bridal veil appeared. George Fulford, being the sole male spouse, was there to give the bride away. But who would serve as the minister? Bryan, as a Marine colonel, said he was qualified to marry people at sea. So into the surf we stomped.

The male crew members had been given jams by their wives, long baggy shorts that they hiked up to their armpits to look nerdy. Somehow Bryan acquired a green pith helmet to round out his costume. A ring made of a pipe cleaner and a wad of aluminum foil was produced, and we promised to love and cherish each other for at least another ten years.

When we went back to the beach house to share champagne and cake, Hoot gave me a real anniversary present. He had designed a new wedding ring for me for the occasion. It incorporated the astronaut symbol of a star shooting through an oval band. The center of the star sported a diamond, and the oval had 10 diamonds, one for each year of our marriage. The tail of the star had three streaks. Paul's birthstone, a ruby, and Dann's, an aquamarine, sat at the end of two of the streamers. Did I dare hope that someday the third would be filled? It was a wonderful gift. Mine to him was a set of gold cufflinks with two astronaut symbols entwined. The ring and cufflinks had been designed by a wonderful jeweler in Los Angeles named Paul Dimitriu who had made several unique things for people in our office.

Another lasting reminder that we spent many hours at the beach house was placed on the mantel. It had become a tradition to leave an empty wine bottle with a sticker of the crew's patch affixed to it to remember last minute toasts. Our payload crew wasn't supposed to imbibe much alcohol. An anniversary toast was okay as long as we recorded it on the log we were obliged to keep of all our food and liquid uptake for the scientists looking at our metabolism. So we didn't have a good wine bottle. Besides recording everything we ate and drank from well before we entered quarantine, we also had to collect every drop of urine. We were dispensed large blue carrying cases containing multiple plastic bottles to hold the urine. On the mantel at the beach house among a vast array of classy wine bottles we put a large white urine container (empty of course!) with the STS-40 crew patch attached with pride.

We rode out to the launch pad on a steamy summer morning with swamp bugs smashing themselves on the front window. As he disembarked from the Astrovan at the Launch Control Center, the chief of the astronaut office, Dan Brandenstein, asked us to bow our heads for the Astronaut Prayer. Strange, I thought, I don't remember that from my first flight. "Crew of STS-40," he said, and paused. "God help you if you screw this up." It was a perfect send-off—and reminder.

The flight rocketed into space on June 5, 1991, over seven years after we started training for it, thirteen years after NASA had sent out a request for research proposals for it. No wonder it was difficult to get serious scientists to participate in space research. It was taking far too many years of work to get any results.

My own first launch after the horrors of the *Challenger* accident was

more frightening than I had thought it would be. I had lettered a part of a song by Michael Joncas from our Methodist hymnal on my kneeboard to assure me:

"And He will raise you up on eagle's wings,
Bear you on the breath of dawn,
Make you to shine like the sun,
and hold you in the palm of His Hand."

I still feared the boosters because I realized the power that they had to blow us to smithereens. My seat this time was on the middeck facing the lockers. For this flight I would be flying blind, unable to see any instruments or computer displays to reassure me of the health of our vehicle. When we launched it sounded like a cataclysm in the making. As the boosters ignited to carry us aloft, I reached over to my right where Drew sat and he was kind enough to hold my hand during the roughest part of the flight.

It was Drew who should have been afraid. Not only was it his first ride into space but he had what was called a central venous catheter lodged just above his heart. It was a long, thin plastic tube, inserted into a vein in the crook of his right elbow into his superior vena cava, the large vein that carries blood to the heart from the upper half of the body. Threaded out a port on his suit and attached to a sensor box in his pocket, it detected changes in the pressure in the column of blood as it entered the heart. As every astronaut knew, on arrival in weightlessness, the face would get puffy and neck veins would stick out due to a shift in body fluids in the absence of gravity. The pressure in those veins must be elevated, but no one had been able to measure the pressure directly. Drew was one of the scientists who had proposed the measurement as part of a study, back before he knew he would be the subject on it. Many people regarded it as a risky thing to do.

STS-40 finally launched on June 5, 1991. We had been together as a crew for seven long years.

There were several failure scenarios of this experiment that could cause problems. If the catheter somehow slid further up his arm and into his heart, the irritation of the heart muscle could cause a rhythm disturbance. The fear I had was that the connections on the end of the catheter might work loose and air get into the line. Air entering the heart could get frothy due to the pumping action of the heart and impede blood flow through the heart valves. Then there were other remote but possible complications: a clot forming on the end of the catheter and migrating into his lung, a major clot stopping blood flow in the vein in his arm, or an infection developing at the insertion site. The experiment had to pass multiple safety reviews.

One of the big surprises of the flight, however, was that when we got to orbit and the main engines cut off, Drew's central venous pressure dropped to almost zero. While there was still an enlargement of his neck veins above his collarbones, apparently the major veins emptying into his heart were not over-filled. Was that possible? Surprised, he was sure some part of the equipment had failed. So he changed out the sensor box with a spare stowed in one of the lockers on the middeck. It, too, read close to zero. Scientists would have to go back and revise theories and textbooks on this one.

As Drew was fiddling with his equipment, I went about doing my jobs to get the middeck ready for on-orbit operations. Struggling out of the monstrous launch suit while floating about weightless was a difficult task but one I hurried to perform. It had been a hot June day in Florida when we launched, and I felt like I was in a sauna before we even got off the ground. The cooling fan attached to the suit pumped warm humid air from the cabin into my suit. The only way the air could circulate at all was to create an outlet for it by pulling the rubber neck ring away from my body. When I tried to let the air out of my neck ring it was so steamy that it fogged up my glasses. I was heat stressed before we even launched. I was glad to be rid of the suit as early as possible after we got to orbit.

The most important early task I had to perform was to get the toilet working. We'd been lying on our backs on the launch pad with our feet up for several hours before the launch. Most of us had urinated in the diapers we wore under our suits by now but needed to go again. Usually, getting the space toilet working was a matter of pushing a few circuit breakers, throwing a couple of valves or switches, and making sure the air was being pulled into the urinal. On this flight, however, a piece of equipment called the urine monitoring system (UMS) had to be attached so we could measure the volume of each of our urine voids and then take samples for the research studies. The UMS had not performed well on its previous flight with urine globules sometimes backing up in the hoses and floating like amorphous yellow puddles in the bathroom area. Its design had been improved, but whether it would work well in weightlessness was still an unknown at that point.

Several hoses had to be attached, a fitting had to be precisely aligned

The Urine Monitoring System in the side hatch near the toilet.

PHOTO COURTESY OF NASA

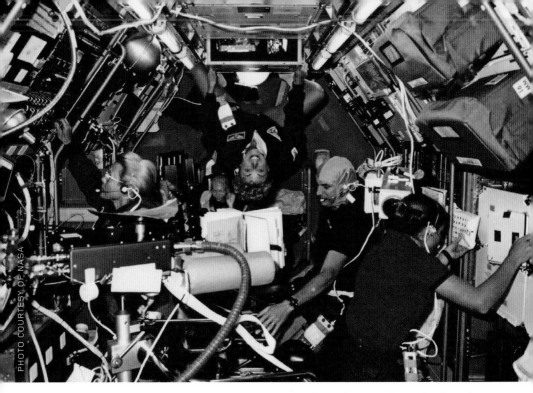

and connected, the electrical power attached, and everything had to be done right, or it wouldn't work. I giggled at the thought of having to announce a NO GO toilet. As I struggled and sweated to get the UMS set up, I became aware that my bladder was getting fuller and fuller. I thought the equipment was ready to use. Air was flowing into the urinal funnel, ready to suck urine into the tubing. I had gotten out of my wet diaper and sweaty long johns I had worn under my launch suit and put on fresh clothes before I began the task. I remembered from my last trip into space that if I pulled my pants down and any urine escaped from the funnel, I'd get wet underwear, and a clean pair was all the way across the middeck in my stowage locker. The bathroom had a curtain that I pulled closed because it was best to strip naked below the waist. It was a great relief when all the urine went down the hose like it was supposed to. My first major milestone of the flight accomplished!

As we got further into the day Jim and I activated the lab, and Drew and Millie got started on setting up the experiments. Our duties were carefully

The Spacelab was a busy place with everything that wasn't tied down floating, including the people *(left)*. Drew and Jim measuring blood flow to the leg *(right)*.

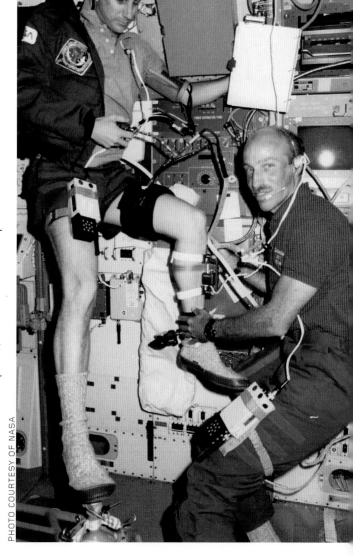

choreographed, and we flew about getting them done. We had more than our share of space motion sickness sufferers that day, but injections of promethazine, an anti-nausea drug, from the medical kit (a great discovery since my first flight) kept everyone functional.

Little and large things began to crop up that put us behind in the timeline. It became obvious that we had been too optimistic when we planned our day's activities. We got behind by the end of the day and worked into our sleep time. This would be the rule for the next eight days. Not enough sleep, getting up early, staying up late, having to fiddle with balky gas analyzers, freezers that always needed defrosting, and broken connectors.

One of the big unknowns was how the rats and their redesigned cages would fare. Facing the specter of being attacked by space-crazed rats—or their poop, we knew that animals might never fly again if the hardware didn't perform better on this flight than the previous one, a significant loss for the science world. Each day we had to peer in at the little white critters and make sure they were getting water and food. At first they clung to the bottom rungs of their cages and looked back out at us with frightened eyes, not understanding why they were floating. Did they have motion sickness, too? Soon they relaxed and seemed to enjoy this new freedom as much as we did, slithering around and peering out at us upside down or sideways or sleeping in a furry ball. They were well fed and content and no waste made its way into the cabin.

We also did a checkout of a large, glass enclosed work bench. Once we were sure it held whatever liquids or solids we released within it, we asked Mission Control permission to put one of the cages inside the workbench and turn one of the rats loose to see how it reacted. As with many space unknowns, some scientists had dire predictions about what a freed animal would do. Would it become frightened and unruly? Would it bite its han-

Drew checks on the rats in their cages.

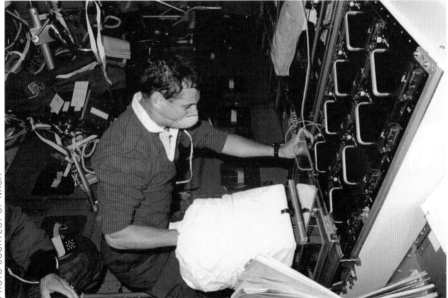

dler and be difficult to get back into the cage? We all knew trying it out would give us valuable experience for the next life sciences flight when the rats would be removed from their cages for testing.

To our surprise, when Drew got the cage into the workbench and opened the door, the rat hung onto Drew's hand for dear life. When released, the white furry creature did a pirouette in order to grab onto the nearest structure. We needn't have worried that he would choose to fly off like Superman, or Super-rat. He went happily back into his cage when we put him near it. There were so many routine activities on Earth that were new in weightlessness and had to be worked out, like handling rats and peeing. That was the challenging—and fun—part of being an astronaut.

The little creatures we had great fun working with were Dr. Dorothy Spangenberg's jellyfish. Dorothy's enthusiastic belief that all mysteries of the living world could be answered by understanding her jellies was contagious. Learning how to swim about in the sea required jellyfish to develop gravity sensors, and Dorothy wanted to know if these gravity detectors, something like portions of the human inner ear, could develop in a gravity-free environment. We took small flasks of the tiny jellies which were barely big enough to see, activated them with a hormone, and then filmed their growth and behavior. It was fascinating to watch them swim in circles in zero-G, but it turned out that once back on Earth, they detected up and down and did fine. Forming the sensors was hardwired into their DNA.

We plugged away, exhausted, until midway through the flight when we received a half day off. Deciding that the Spacelab would be the largest zero-G playground we would ever see, we put the bulky science equipment away and declared it was recess time. First we had our fill of gymnastic stunts. Then we played "Can you do this?" – like bouncing off the floor and ceiling hopping down the length of the lab. The whole crew (except Bryan who had to be the grownup and babysit the vehicle from the cockpit) played snake. Grabbing each other's ankles, the leader of the snake pulled all of the rest of us around the lab like a giant whip. Sid proved that he could do a push up with the rest of us stacked on his back. It was good for our psychological well-being to take a break.

As we drew near the end of the mission, I read to the crew the poem Jeff Hoffman had read to my first crew about the responsibilities that went along with the opportunity to see the world as we had seen it "from the top of the mountain." Somehow everyone was too busy to pay attention, and I didn't feel like this crew was as close, so it didn't mean to them what it had meant to my first crew.

On the morning of landing day we faced one of our toughest challenges. After wakeup the orbiter crew went to the flight deck to prepare for entry. The payload crew was left to button up the lab. In addition we had to get the big orange launch and entry suits and all our landing equipment out of the airlock and from behind bulkheads, where they had been stowed, and get the seats set up for landing.

The problem was that the orbiter crew had put away all the suits, seats, and ancillary equipment like helmets and boots after launch so the payload crew could get to work in the lab. Now the payload crew had to find everything and get it all sorted out while the orbiter crew was busy. We decided the best thing to do was to pull all the stowed equipment out into the middeck.

What a sight to behold! Drifting about were seven empty orange suits, seven bulbous helmets, seven suit fans, seven parachutes, fourteen boots, and fourteen gloves like bizarre disconnected hands reaching for us. Everything had to be routed to its owner or set up on a seat. Several pieces of equipment seemed to be missing, but they had to be there somewhere. It wasn't like anyone could have taken them somewhere else or they'd mistakenly gone out to the curb with the trash.

The clock was ticking. It wouldn't do to ask the ground to give us an extra orbit or two to get everything sorted out. We were once again late in our timeline since we'd had to stay late in the lab to make sure the payload bay door closed over some torn insulation. It was a wild time that morning, and I wasn't sure it would all get done before the wheels hit the ground. At last, everyone had every piece of equipment.

I managed to stuff myself into my suit one more time and then sweat and swear until all the harnesses and straps to my seat on the flight deck were fastened. Tammy and I were seated behind Bryan and Sid, crammed shoulder to shoulder. I didn't see how in the world two big shouldered men could ever fit into that space with their suits on. This spot would allow me to watch the entire re-entry from the fireball stage through the S-turns to dissipate energy to the approach to touchdown and roll out. Since I had been on the middeck for landing on my first flight, I had often imagined what it would look like.

The deorbit burn started right on time. The orbiter was turned tail-for-ward and was upside down to the Earth. We could feel the push of the Orbital Maneuvering System engines when they fired. I knew that it was because we hadn't felt any major acceleration since arriving in orbit, so we were more sensitive to it. There was a low pitched rumble when the engines lit and then a gentle feeling of being pushed along. In this case, we were slowing down. I held my breath a little as the desired burn time ticked off on the computer screen. If the engines quit midway we could have completed this slowing down with the smaller reaction jets (enough propellant was always saved for them, just in case), but the entire deceleration had to be completed. A partial burn would slow us down enough to fall out of orbit but not enough to allow us to reenter the atmosphere. We'd skip back out into space and be unable to get home.

After a successful deorbit burn, the orbiter flipped over so that its nose was forward again. The nose had to be cocked up about 40 degrees so that the heat shield tiles on the underbelly would get most of the heating during re-entry. As we sank deeper and deeper into the atmosphere, an orange glow began to appear out the windows. Behind my head, heated air molecules struck the tail and created bright flashes of light on the backs of Bryan's and Sid's helmets. We were in a thin skinned protective cocoon in the midst of a fireball as hot as the surface of the sun. If there were any breaks in our vehicle's skin, we'd soon be incinerated.

As we were slowed down by the ever-thickening atmosphere, we began to feel the pull of gravity once again. The checklists that we had watched for days floating like lazy kites on their tethers settled down onto the console between the pilot's and commander's seats, our hands once again rested in our laps. After the fireball faded, we became aware of wind noise. Up above the atmosphere there is no air so rushing along at the breakneck speed of 17,500 miles per hour was silent. As we got closer to Earth the air molecules created a wind around us, and it began to sound like the air whooshing by the window of a fast moving car. Since the orbiter was a glider with no engine noise at this point, the wind noise was more obvious.

There also seemed to be some disturbances at various points in re-entry. A couple of times up high and then again as we slowed down, the ride was a little rough for a few seconds. It was almost like hitting a bumpy spot in the road, and the shuttle shuddered a bit.

"Not to worry," said our experienced commander. "Happens every time."

Soon we passed over the lakebed at Edwards Air Force Base. Bryan and Sid spotted it even though we were at 60,000 feet above the ground. It was a familiar and welcome sight. As the orbiter slowed below Mach 1 and we felt the transonic buffet, we knew the guests on the ground would hear the double sonic booms that announced our arrival. Bryan took manual control and began the slow sweeping turn that would align us with paved Runway 22. As a heavyweight orbiter—we hadn't dumped anything off in

Two year old Dann watches the Shuttle landing.

orbit and were bringing our fully-outfitted Spacelab home—we couldn't land on the more commodious lakebed runway since our tires would dig in to the surface too much and perhaps damage the landing gear.

As we began our final approach, a steep dive from about 30,000 feet, we could make out details on the ground. There were people out at the end of the runway. We knew this was the spot reserved for families only. I craned over Sid's shoulder but couldn't see who was who. Hoot, waiting there, managed to take the most fantastic picture of little Dann, a bit over two years old, in his tiny blue flight suit watching as *Columbia* crossed the runway threshold.

Bryan's landing was perfect. Whoops and hollers could be heard from everyone aboard. Mission Control welcomed us home at wheels stop. We began the job of buttoning up our fine spacecraft so others could come aboard and take over her care.

A couple of people onboard felt unsteady after landing, which was about the average. Called postflight orthostasis, there is instability in maintaining normal blood flow to the brain when seated upright or on standing. In part,

Columbia was met by the landing convoy and the crew was escorted into the new Crew Transport Vehicle.

it was due to having gotten rid of some fluid on orbit (for which we took salt tablets and drank a liter of water before re-entry) and in part to messed up blood pressure control mechanisms. It was almost like we had been at bed rest for nine days and had not exercised those regulatory reflexes, and they got out of shape. Although we wore military-type G-suits to compress our legs and abdomen to help push blood upward toward our head, these didn't completely solve the problem. Given a little time and a little help everyone made it to the recliners in the Crew Transport Vehicle which was set up for this flight. Then we were taken back to the clinic to begin a full week of testing to see how we re-adapted to being back on Earth.

A precious, not-to-be-forgotten event happened as we got back to the lab for testing. We had to walk (with assistance) from the transport vehicle over to where stretchers awaited us. This was where our families gathered to greet us. Dann, my two years old, stood in his little flight suit holding onto Daddy's hand. I ambled over to him and squatted down to look him in the eye. He hugged me, and we said a few words, but I could tell he didn't understand what was going on. As I stood up, I was asked to get quickly onto the stretcher so my body wouldn't start getting used to gravity before the testing started. When I was laid out on the gurney, Dann peered up at me through the rails with worry on his face and tears in his eyes. Some kind soul saw what was going on and quickly hoisted him up and put him on the stretcher beside me. He snuggled close, and we were both glad to be back together.

The decision to land at Edwards had been made long before we launched. The post-flight readaptation testing on the payload crew was a crucial part of the research we were doing. There were not enough researchers or pieces of equipment to set up the testing lab in two separate landing sites. Everyone knew that the weather at Cape Canaveral was unpredictable and when assessed, the chance of good weather at Edwards was better. Despite some increase in the cost of the flight associated with flying the shuttle back to Florida, NASA had agreed to land the flight in California where all the researchers and their equipment would be positioned.

Since the payload crew had agreed to stay in the desert for a week of tests after landing, we got the NASA management to let us stay at the Silver Saddles Resort about an hour's drive north of the base. Our fam-

The crew was allowed to spend nights at the Silver Saddle Resort with their families while undergoing post-flight testing.

ilies were allowed to stay, too, although we had to pay for them. Joann, our nanny, had come along to help look after the boys and also to see the sights. Launch had been her first trip to Florida, and this was her first visit to California. Lest she think California was all desert and Joshua trees, on my partial day off, our family drove about an hour and a half southwest to Malibu so she could see the coastline there, which was so different from the one she had gotten to know in Florida. She was excited to be able to dip her toes in the chilly water of the Pacific.

Although we spent most of our time dedicating our bodies to science that week, the crew had a chance to go over and visit *Columbia* as she was prepared for her trip back to the east coast atop the NASA Boeing 747 Shuttle Carrier Aircraft. There she was, our mother ship, which had carried us safely to space and back, suspended in the large structure called the Mate-Demate Device. We felt awe and a special closeness to her as we climbed up on the scaffolding. As we crawled around and looked at

the nicks and dings on her surface, I kept thinking of her as a slightly middle-aged woman, a little worn in places but a fine, fit specimen all the same. Millie and I stood in front of her, looked her straight in the eye, and had our pictures made with her. We both felt we could identify with this magnificent lady.

PHOTO COURTESY OF NASA

The "face" of *Columbia*.

It was late June 1991 by the time we finished up testing and debriefs on my second flight. Almost immediately we were whisked off to Washington D.C. for our *Hill visit*. We went soon after our return from space rather than waiting a few weeks, as was customary, because there was a great battle underway over the space station funding. Since the current thinking was that life sciences would be one of the major fields of study on Space Station Freedom, we were trotted out to stress how important studying living organisms in weightlessness was—as though we were Columbus bringing samples of gold to our benefactors.

We told congressional committees, senators, and congressmen (sometimes their aides) that studying human beings in space allowed us to better understand gravity's role in many human organ systems. The changes that took place in astronauts looked much like disease processes here on the ground (osteoporosis, anemia, and balance disorders, for instance) and held promise for helping to treat those illnesses. I always hated trying to convince legislators who weren't supportive of the space program to change their minds. My congressman at the time for the 6th District of Tennessee, Bart Gordon, was a high school friend, and even he had concerns about funding for the station. NASA funding came from the same pot of money as that for the U.S. Department of Veterans Affairs, and we had a large Veterans Health Administration hospital in our district. Bart always said that he wasn't against space exploration, but couldn't justify large outlays for it given the other priorities of the budget.

On the other end of the spectrum were the members of Congress who were our staunch supporters. We had to be careful that they didn't go overboard in making associations between what we were studying in space and other pressing problems. A hearing of this type might go as follows:

"Tell me about the white blood cell studies you did, Dr. Seddon," one senator would say.

"Well, sir, one type of white blood cell, the lymphocyte, doesn't seem to function well in the test tube in weightlessness."

"Hmm. Isn't that the same type of cell that is defective in AIDS?"

"Well, yes sir, it is, but…"

"Then you may someday find a cure for AIDS if you understand these cells better?"

"Well, uh…," I'd say, trying to think how to get off that track.

"Wonderful!" the esteemed NASA supporter would shout. Then we'd be off to another line of conversation. I would picture tomorrow's headline, "Astronaut Finds Cure for AIDS."

I wished we could have said that space research would soon give the human race cures for cancer, AIDS, the common cold, and brittle bones, but drawing those parallels wasn't that simple. The study of medicine and life sciences in space was still in its infancy. We had performed many studies on SLS-1—lung function tests, red blood cell survival studies, calcium loss measurements—that had been routine tests in doctors' offices or labs for decades, but we'd never been able to do in weightlessness. The things we found out added to our understanding of how these systems worked without gravity, but it would be a long time before we would be performing full-up, sophisticated research in space. SLS-1 was a good beginning, but we couldn't do great science when it took over seven years to prepare for a flight and, after nine days in space studying a mere four subjects, the lab had to be dismantled and brought back home. Yet we were discovering such interesting and unpredicted information about how gravity affected living systems. I felt as if those were strong enough selling points, but in a fervor to help us have a future in space, some supporters wanted to make it look more spectacular than it was.

The highlight of the trip was a get-together with President George H. W. Bush. Several shuttle crews before us had Oval Office visits followed by a nice tour of the West Wing's living quarters with Mrs. Bush.

It didn't look like we were to be so lucky.

We were scheduled to meet the president at a rather large reception in the Treaty Room, the president's private study often used as an audience or waiting room. Beforehand we were shown through the formal areas of the White House by a pleasant and capable aide. Several other groups were already in the meeting room when we entered, and we didn't feel too special. President Bush arrived at the appointed time and greeted each of the groups. When our turn, we presented a montage of flight photos that we'd brought for him, including a crew picture.

At the end of the session, President Bush came over and invited us into the Oval Office: a surprise! We were like school children invited

To Robert Gibson and Rhea Seddon
With best wishes,
Cy Bush

It was a thrill for our STS-40 crew to visit President George H. W. Bush in the Oval Office during our post-flight visit to Washington, D.C.

into a secret inner sanctum. He inquired about flying the shuttle and what her systems were like. Since he had been a Navy fighter pilot in World War II, he was knowledgeable and interested. Standing in that calm, solemn room, I got shivers reflecting upon all the historic events that had taken place there. He showed us his favorite spot outside his office: a putting green. What a nice man the president was, making us feel comfortable, important, and unrushed! He apologized that Mrs. Bush was out of town and couldn't share with us their quarters. Each of us had an individual picture made with him. A staunch Democrat, even Drew considered being a Republican that day.

July was a time to wrap up debriefing and publish our post-flight report. I finished those in time to serve on another Astronaut Selection Board that summer and fall. I also asked for and was given my dream job of Capsule Communicator, or CAPCOM, in the Mission Control Center or MCC. I would now work in Mission Control: where the huge screen in the front of the room showed the grainy pictures of the first moon landing. Mission Control: where brainy people fashioned an air filter out of cardboard and duct tape to save the crew of Apollo 13 crew and wept as they saw the capsule hanging beneath the landing parachutes.

I had spent the last few years isolated from mainstream shuttle activities. So tied up with the science flight, I'd lost track of what other things were going on in the orbiter world and with other flights and programs. There was no better way to be in the thick of things than to be a CAPCOM.

A flight crew couldn't monitor all the spacecraft systems, the weather at launch and landing sites, the flow of data to the ground—the thousands of things that the army of flight controllers in the MCC monitored throughout every flight. When things went wrong, it was the MCC that figured things out for the crew: how to silence unimportant alarms so the crew could sleep, how to salvage a failure-plagued mission, or how to get home alive.

Mission Control Houston was where the people on the ground kept track of the Space Shuttle and its crews in flight *(previous spread)*.

The *front room* was the Mission Control the public experienced on tours or in the movies, like *Apollo 13*. The flight controllers at those consoles were the top people in their particular areas. Each monitored a system or group of systems and had a unique call sign. EECOM had environmental and consumables systems. GNC was guidance, navigation, and control—indicating where the shuttle was, where it was going, and how it was going to get there. FDO (called "Fido") was the flight dynamics officer who monitored vehicle performance during launch and landing, the *dynamic* parts of the flight. MMACS (or "Max") watched the mechanical and crew systems parts of the orbiter. Max was also in charge of inflight maintenance or IFM procedures, the fix-it person. Max determined how to fix a toilet that quit working, build a satellite-snagger out of plastic book covers for my first flight, or find a way to keep carbon dioxide below lethal levels like on Apollo 13. The Flight Activities Officer or FAO was in charge of the crew's daily schedule, including when meals and sleep would occur. And there were many more.

CAPCOM was always an astronaut. The name and tradition came from the early Mercury days when someone in Mission Control or MCC had to be responsible for communicating with crew members in the capsule. It was crucial to have someone to talk to the crew who had done the same training as those on the flight, who knew the same things, and who spoke the same language. There wasn't a lot of banter between ground and flight crews. In the old days communications went through ground stations and the time to talk was limited, so everything had to be transmitted rapid fire. By the time I sat at that console, we communicated via satellites, so we were in voice contact with the shuttle almost all the time. However, communication needed to be crisp so the crew was not tied up with talking too long and there would be no confusion over what was said.

Behind each of the controllers in the front room of MCC, there were many people in back rooms. They handled the details, analyzed the plots and data trends, and tracked down facts and figures from thick tomes of flight rules or computers. They reached out to experts in other buildings, at other centers, or at contractor facilities—observing everything in anticipation of someday being expert enough to propel themselves to the front room.

The boss of all these people was the Flight Director, call sign: Flight. (The first was Chris Kraft who wrote a book, titled *Flight*, about his early days setting up the MCC and all the other flight ops needed to get into space.) He was the focus for all the information. He had to gather it, synthesize it, ask the right questions of the right people, and decide what to do. Hundreds of decisions had to be made during each shuttle mission. The flight director was a flight controller who had first staffed a back room position, then a front room console. Flight did those jobs well enough to be moved up to the pinnacle of controller-dom.

Some of the flight controllers and directors were people I had grown up with at NASA. One I would never forget was Milt Heflin. At the beginning of my career I had flown somewhere in a T-38 with one of the pilots. The plane developed a problem, and I needed to fly home on a commercial flight into the tiny airport in Clear Lake, Texas near the space center. It never occurred to me that there was no taxi service in the area. After calling every friend I could think of with no success, I stood there in my spiffy blue NASA flight suit pondering how I was going to get the three or four miles down the dusty road to my house. A nice young man with a couple of little kids had dropped someone off and overheard my conversation with the airport desk clerk. He walked up and said, "Hi, Rhea. I'm Milt Heflin, and I think we met during a meeting over at NASA. Can I give you a lift?"

If there was ever an angel sent to me that day, it was Milt.

It was a small favor and one I doubted he would even remember, but it was so thoughtful. I never forgot it. It was wonderful to watch his career progress as he achieved the lauded position of flight director. MCC folks were all terrific people. They and astronauts had occasional arguments but also a real shared camaraderie based upon shared responsibilities and goals. Flight and CAPCOM sat side by side, working together to keep the crew alive and the mission on track. Flight was the boss, but he or she often relied on CAPCOM for the best solution or the best way to voice it up to the crew.

Real flights were easy compared to preflight practice. It wore everyone out. NASA wanted to verify that all those controllers and crew members were ready to handle any problem. It did this on a regular basis by staging flight simulations, also known as sims. *Generic* sims were crewed by astronauts (often ones not yet named to a flight) and teams of controllers-in-training who would use flight simulators and Mission Control—all connected by massive banks of computers to simulate a shuttle mission. *Flight specific* sims began when a crew preparing to fly was teamed with the flight control teams that would support their mission. There would be several MCC teams for every flight: one for Ascent and Entry, ones for the two orbit shifts, and one for the planning shift. All would need to practice and become experts on a particular portion of the flight.

Ascent skills sims were wild- and were sometimes referred to by the crews as "Ascent Kills" lessons. Everything was crucial during the launch phase, and things happened fast. The crew was strapped in at the Shuttle Motion Base simulator in the training facility and controller teams in MCC were connected via comm lines. The astronauts were tilted backwards to mimic launch position. The simulated countdown would proceed, and the simulator would lurch and feel as if it was lifting off.

Then the fun began.

From the start, things went wrong…or pretended to.

A red light illuminated on the dashboard and alarms began to go off: *one of the main engines had malfunctioned.* A row of lights above the commander's face would flash on: *a computer was down.* Each failure required certain actions or procedures, all written on cue cards or in checklists nearby. Some failures weren't obvious to the crew, so the controllers in MCC had to pass the messages up in a hurry.

"Flight," Fido would say. "Stronger than expected upper level winds. Their trajectory will be lofted."

"Roger, Fido. Okay," said Flight, looking at the CAPCOM. "Tell 'em."

"*Columbia*, Houston. High upper level winds will loft your traj," the CAPCOM would radio.

Crews learned how to work as a team to handle problems during simulations in realistic cockpits like this one.

"Roger, Houston."

It was a calm and beautiful ballet, with the shuttle belching fire and hurtling away from Earth at an ever-increasing speed, the crew always in imminent danger...except that they were in a simulator. There was a term "suspension of disbelief" applied to simulation that meant that things weren't real, but they felt like they were. NASA tried to make simulations so believable that the astronauts worried they might die and controllers worried their error might kill someone. Both scary and exhilarating, it was much like a well-designed video game.

Once a crew and its flight controllers proved they could handle individual malfunctions, the simulation supervisor or SimSup who dreamed up and planned all the training scenarios would complicate things. One failure would mask another. An electrical failure might keep a main engine failure warning light from illuminating. A computer failure might make something appear as if it had quit when in fact, the computer wasn't there to hear its signal anymore. The crew rushed to coordinate their activities, flip multiple switches and check all the systems. The controllers were occupied monitoring computer displays and consulting with their back rooms. The flight director often had several controllers talking over one another and had to know the systems well enough to prioritize the problems. CAPCOM kept frantically jotting down the controllers' instructions for the crew; the final solution would be approved after considerable discussion and many proposals. When Flight gave the go, the CAPCOM would press the Ground-to-Air mic button and say in short bursts of words what to do. Sometimes in the mad frenzy during ascent, with no time to explain why an action had to be taken, the crew had to trust MCC and the CAPCOM. *Entry* sims were the same as the orbiter plummeted toward Earth. The skills took a CAPCOM a while to master, but it was lots of fun, especially being part of this incredible team.

Sometimes SimSup would bring Mission Control and the crew to their knees. Whether an oversight on a controller's part, a slight delay in noticing something was going wrong, poor communication on the part of the CAPCOM, or improper steps taken by the crew, the shuttle wouldn't make it to orbit or couldn't reach a runway to land. All runs of the simulator were debriefed with the unsuccessful ones being discussed at length. Everyone was careful not to rub it in too bad when someone screwed up. To the one who made the mistake, it was painfully obvious. The purpose of the sims, though, was to make those errors on the ground, not during a flight. Well-trained flight controllers, CAPCOMs, and crew members were the best of the best: they learned from their mistakes and didn't make the same one twice.

Orbit sims were less hectic but often more interesting. SimSup had at least one failure for each controller with the failures requiring several controllers to collaborate to solve a problem. As in Apollo 13 (and my own first flight), when one thing went wrong, it could impact many parts of the vehicle or cargo. Sometimes a piece of equipment would fail, and there would be no backup system. That was when Mission Control got creative. Was there an opportunity to rig up something to serve the same purpose? It was amazing to see what could be done with duct tape, spare batteries, odd pieces of stuff...and a few brilliant and creative minds.

There were special things that had to be learned about each particular flight payload, its requirements and rules, and its shuttle interfaces. For instance, communication links had to be shared to ship vehicle performance information and massive amounts of science data to the ground for Spacelab missions. If an orbiter computer failed before a satellite was ready to be launched, the deployment would have to be stopped until there could be a reboot.

As ever-increasing degrees of difficulty were built into the sims, all involved gained confidence in their system knowledge and in their ability to handle whatever materialized during the flight. Compared to the simulations, everyone knew that the flight itself would be easy. There might be three or four minor malfunctions, maybe even a major or unexpected one, but never would it be as bad as the sims. As the commanders would say during actual launches as the main engines cut off and the shuttle reached orbit, "Well, there goes half our training down the tubes."

Between September of 1991 and June of 1992 I gained an appreciation for how the ground could help a crew and how the crew could help the ground – and I wished I'd had this experience before I first flew in space. MCC was manned 24 hours a day, and crews were often busiest when the rest of the U.S. slept. (Thank goodness for Joann, our nanny!) Except for the long hours required for major simulations and the often strange mission hours it was a great job. I was sorry to leave it to train in earnest for my next flight.

After returning from SLS-1, I had begun to look ahead to my next flight. There were several spacewalks planned, but I wasn't spacesuit qualified. There were some missions using the mechanical arm, but I wasn't excited about retraining to operate it. There were a few flights involving a rendezvous, but that was pilot stuff. I wanted to use what I'd learned on SLS-1 to make SLS-2, the second dedicated life sciences mission, even greater. When I spoke to the chief of the astronauts, Dan Brandenstein, he liked the idea. It wasn't as if there were lots of people vying for that mission. Physicians in the office were few, and most were either assigned to something else or didn't want to do that flight. The payload commander position had been created so that there would be one point of contact for the science crew. It was a nice title, carrying with it the responsibility for heading up the onboard science team. In October of 1991, I was named payload commander for Spacelab Life Sciences-2—STS-58 on the shuttle manifest.

In the midst of being a CAPCOM and getting preparations for SLS-2 started, I once again had to play astronaut spouse. Hoot would be commanding his fourth flight, a cooperative mission with the Japanese Space Agency, dubbed Spacelab-J or SL-J. His pilot would be Curt Brown, the flight engineer Jay Apt. The science crew consisted of Mark Lee (as the payload commander, the one member of the payload crew who had flown before), Jan Davis, Mae Jemison (with Stan Koszelak, a biologist as a payload specialist back up), and a payload specialist from the Japanese Space Agency, Mamoru Mohri.

During the training for the mission, Jan and Mark married each other. This put NASA into a quandary. The unwritten rule was that married

The Japanese sponsored Spacelab flight, called Spacelab J, sits on the pad ready for launch.

couples shouldn't fly together to prevent an accident from leaving orphans. Jan and Mark had no children, and had both trained for a considerable length of time for the mission. Who should be removed? Neither could be spared. Many thought the rule was there to avoid the question of whether astronauts had sex in space. The newlyweds learned to field questions on this subject before and after their flight. For anyone who had lived in the cramped quarters of the space shuttle, it would be hard to imagine that a couple could find a spot private enough for lovemaking.

Everyone enjoyed getting to know the Japanese astronauts. Mamoru would be on the flight. Chiaki Naito-Mukai and Takao Doi would be his back-ups. All were the nicest, most hardworking people we had ever

known. They were fluent in English. Well, almost fluent. One word that they had trouble with was Hoot's name. There is no "h" sound in Japanese, and Hoot got used to being called *Foot*.

When it came to spouse duties, we were short-handed. Curt and Mae were both single, and Mark and Jan were married to each other. Mamoru's wife Akiko was new to this country and had never been involved with a spaceflight before. Since Mamoru was the first Japanese citizen to fly in space, she also had many social duties for the Japanese Space Agency. Jay's wife was Ebe Apt. She was a jewel and a delight to work with. A graduate of Columbia, she had been a social worker until her daughters Sarah and Rachel were born. Since Ebe wasn't tied down to a job, she was able to accomplish things that

I could not. Jay took on the job of organizing the post-flight party at Villa Capri (our favorite Italian restaurant) and assembling the guest list before the flight. That was a huge help.

Spacelab-J launched right on time in September of 1992. After being involved in several delayed flights, I was almost flabbergasted when the crew went out the door of crew quarters at the appointed hour on September 12, climbed aboard their shuttle, and when launch time rolled around—*launched*. Standing on the Launch Control Center's roof with three children in tow, I realized that this launch was not as difficult for me as Hoot's launch right after *Challenger*. The tears were tears of joy, not of terror or relief. I'd become more confident in the shuttle's capabilities.

The Spacelab J crew doing a shift changeover in the lab.

Inflight picture of the crew.

The rest of the flight went off like clockwork, too, without major problems. We returned to the Cape for a right-on-time landing. Hoot's touchdown was so smooth the crew wasn't sure when the wheels hit the pavement. "Are we there yet?" was a strange thing for his passengers to say after a space shuttle landing. He'd done a great job making a well-functioning team out of a diverse group, and the flight had gone well. I asked him if he wanted to leave NASA after this one. He wasn't ready to stop. I wasn't surprised but wondered if he'd ever want to begin another phase of our lives.

Spacelab Life Science-2 had become the focus of my career in early 1992. We had learned a number of lessons on SLS-1 that I hoped would help us on that mission. One was that the astronauts objected to being signed up as

PHOTO COURTESY OF NASA

subjects for experiments without knowing what they entailed. Voluntary participation in scientific research had been much in the news, including the story of experiments in the '50s in which people had unknowingly been exposed to radiation. The term *bioethics* had been coined, and it was a sensitive subject. I had discovered that it was considered unethical to force someone to be a research subject without obtaining informed consent, and it was illegal to coerce someone into participation in research as part of a job.

We'd had a problem on SLS-1 with people *unvolunteering* for some experiments after assessing all the risks. This was within their rights, but being limited to a few subjects for each experiment sure threw a monkey wrench into some of the investigators' plans.

I discussed these problems with Dan Brandenstein, chief of the Astronaut Office, who was in charge of assigning the crew to SLS-2. I thought it important that he let potential crew members know what they were getting into before they were assigned to the flight. I gave him a synopsis of the riskier experiments, the ones which had caused difficulties on SLS-1, and told him I'd be happy to explain them in detail to anyone who needed clarification.

Dave Wolf put together the echocardiograph for my first flight, and he had been selected in the astronaut class of 1990. Eager to be a part of this life sciences flight, his skill as both a physician and an engineer would be invaluable. Shannon Lucid, my 1978 classmate and a biochemist, would bring considerable experience (this was her fourth flight) and additional expertise to the group. Dan said these were the two people he was considering adding to the crew and asked me to brief them to ensure they were willing subjects.

Since the crew needed to start training soon, I was asked to expedite the process. It wasn't a formal consent briefing, which should entail having each investigator describe the study, including its risks and benefits (which did happen later), but Dave Wolf and Shannon Lucid were given more information than previous crews. They agreed to participate in all the studies. Dave was assigned as Mission Specialist 3 and Shannon as Mission Specialist 4. I would come to realize that each person has his or her own level of acceptable risk: some risks that wouldn't bother one person would be unacceptable to another. Although the experimenters and some NASA managers felt it an astronaut's duty to participate in any assigned research, federal law stands against making that a job responsibility. Astronauts had always willingly participated in most research. Henceforth, though, they couldn't be signed up for studies without knowing what they entailed.

The PSCs or Payload Specialist Candidates for the flight were soon selected from a group of scientists proposed by the principal investigators, also known as PIs. Two of the three I already knew. Dr. Larry Young was a MIT professor in vestibular physiology, the study of balance mechanisms. A bit older than the rest of us, Larry was a senior, much respected scientist who had been involved in space research for years. Jay Buckey was a bright young doctor who worked in the same cardiovascular lab in Dallas as Drew Gaffney, my crew mate on SLS-1. He had developed much of the equipment that had been used in the heart and blood vessel studies on SLS-1. The third member of the group came recommended by Bob Phillips, our back-up payload specialist on SLS-1. A veterinarian, Marty Fettman was something of a child prodigy. He had started college at 16, vet school at 19, and had his Doctor of Veterinary Medicine degree at 23, as well as a Ph.D.

in physiology at 25. He was a professor at Colorado State University when he took a detour and applied to the space program.

Their help would be essential in preparing for the mission, Marty's in particular. One of the thorny issues with this flight was animal research. There were many procedures to be conducted on the rats we'd carry to orbit (almost 50!), culminating in full dissection of five or six animals near the end of the flight. The scientists who had requested tissues from the dissections had evaluated the best way to dispatch the animals: decapitation with a guillotine was preferred. While the crew would rather have given the rats injections to put them to sleep, the chemicals interfered with some of the changes caused by weightlessness.

Having a veterinarian as a teammate would help everyone be sensitive to the concerns of those opposed to animal research. He would also help us assess the procedures to determine whether they could be accomplished in weightlessness.

The difficulty with having three great candidates train with us was that we knew only one would fly. Some felt it cruel that we made them compete, but choosing a crew member based on how they'd worked in their own labs and how they performed in the short one hour interview for the job was hard to imagine. Much of what was important to a space mission was teamwork and an ability to perform all parts of the payload science well. An evaluation period was helpful.

In the summer of 1992, the rest of our crew was named. John Blaha would be the commander. Since SLS-2 would be a fourteen-day mission with considerable time between the last of the simulated landings and the real thing, the commander needed to be someone with experience landing a shuttle. And it would need to be someone who enjoyed staying in space for a long time because this would be the longest shuttle flight to date. After serving as the pilot on STS-29 and 33, John had commanded a nine-day

flight and landed the orbiter on STS-43. He would later prove his love of long duration flight by living on the Russian Mir Space Station for four months. He was perfect for our flight.

First in his class at the United States Air Force Academy with a master's degree from Cal Tech, Rick Searfoss was our pilot. It was his first shuttle flight and he wanted to become our expert in Earth observations. Since our flight path would take us further north and south of the equator than most missions we would have more of the Earth to see so Rick was happy.

The crew of Spacelab Life Sciences 2 or STS-58 including the two back-up Payload Specialists *(below)*. Our crew patch with the double helix of DNA and the medical and veterinary symbols *(above)*.

Bill McArthur would serve as the flight engineer. A graduate of the United States Military Academy at West Point, Army helicopter pilot, test pilot, and all-around good-ole-boy from North Carolina, Bill was one of the most courteous and helpful people I've ever known.

As our training progressed the investigators on the flight were polled and Marty was selected as our prime payload specialist. Larry and Jay would play major roles in the Payload Operations Control Center in Huntsville, Alabama. They would serve in the same capacity as the CAPCOMs in Mission Control, but they would talk to the payload crew working in the Spacelab about science operations—coordinating lab activities with the CAPCOMs. They'd also have to continue training with us so they could take Marty's place if he was unable to make the flight.

Our training load was heavy. Even though many of the human experiments were performed on SLS-1, there were several new studies and the timeline was different. I knew that for workaholics like me the work would expand to fill the time available. I was the science commander, and I was determined that all would go well.

Then there was suit wrestling, Round Two, this time with potentially catastrophic consequences for me. Every crew on every flight had to practice evacuating the shuttle in an emergency. I hated it more than any other part of our training. The launch and entry suits were heavy, bulky, and hard to maneuver. With the helmet closed, they became a steamy fishbowl. One scenario involved exiting via the orbiter's side hatch after an emergency landing. On the day of this exercise in the full scale simulator, the SLS-2 crew first talked through our plan. The crew members on the middeck—Dave, Shannon, and Marty—would open the side hatch, throw out the inflatable escape slide, and zip down to the ground. The flight deck crew—Bill, John, Rick, and I—would unstrap, climb down the ladder to the middeck, exit the hatch, and follow the others to the ground. Our training

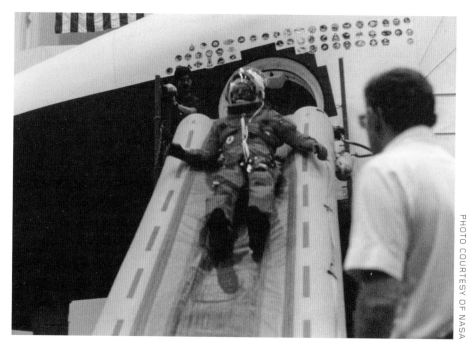

The Escape Slide out the side hatch of the Shuttle trainer.

team warned us of a difficulty that previous crews had encountered. As the commander and pilot unbuckled, unfastened all their connections to the vehicle, and struggled out of their cramped seats, their lines sometimes became entangled with their seat backs. With the restricted view through the closed helmet faceplate, they couldn't see where they were caught. It was the job of the MS1 sitting behind the pilot on the right side of the cockpit to be their spotter and ensure they were clear of the seats. That meant MS1 would be the last to leave the ship. I was MS1 on this flight.

With our plan worked out, we strapped into our seats, connected oxygen and communications lines, and waited for a GO from the trainers. At the call "*Columbia* crew, you have a GO to exit the orbiter!" we began our escape. As those of us on the flight deck began detaching ourselves, we could hear the middeck crew scrambling about, and we could hear the hatch open and the slide whoosh out. Seated to my left, Bill watched the downstairs though the interdeck hatch to see when the middeck crew was out, and then started down the ladder.

This was the cue for John and Rick to work their way out of their seats and down to the side hatch slide. I kept my spot behind Rick and pulled all their straps and lines clear as they left the flight deck. Then I huffed and puffed my way across Bill's seat and down the ladder. *I hate this stuff, I hate this stuff!* I panted under the cumbersome load. Downstairs, sitting on the edge of the hatch I swung my legs around to line up to go down the slide. *This is the easy part,* I thought as I pushed off the ledge.

The ride down was fun until, near the bottom, when I felt a horrendous pain in my left foot. Trying to stand up at the bottom of the slide, my left foot collapsed under me.

"Ow, ow, ow!" I said as I lay sprawled on the floor. There was a flurry of people standing over me moving their mouths. "Left foot, left foot!" I kept saying. The crowd of trainers and medics grew, and I realized my helmet was closed. They couldn't hear me. I popped open my faceplate and shouted, "Left foot!" which even when they heard it seemed to cause consternation on their part. They figured out that I hadn't broken my neck or back and wasn't unconscious or paralyzed, and we all calmed down enough to begin a sane conversation.

After a painful extraction of my foot from my heavy flight boot and an even more painful removal of the bulky suit, I was taken to the Flight Medicine Clinic in my long underwear. The flight surgeon of the hour awaited my arrival. After a brief discussion and an even briefer exam of my foot and ankle, he assured me it was a sprain but we'd take an x-ray. As he turned to leave the room I glared at his departing back thinking, *I'm a doctor, you turkey, and something is BROKEN!*

Sure enough, on his return he put the x-rays up on the view box and pointed out that I had broken...not one...but four bones in the middle of my foot. The local orthopedic surgeon saw me the next day and said it would be fine after being in a cast for about six weeks. Bless his heart, my favorite flight surgeon (Dr. Richard Jennings) decided to get a second opinion from a specialist. It was less than three months until our launch. Dr. Jay Oates was a foot and ankle specialist up in Houston, and he confirmed I had a Lisfranc fracture, named after a French surgeon who described it during the Napoleonic Wars. He recommended aligning the bones well and affixing them with screws that would be later removed. He warned that I might have arthritis and pain in the foot as I got older. (Could he have imagined I would still be running half-marathons in my sixties?)

So, I had surgery, spending six weeks in a cast and another six weeks in a walking boot. I remembered the story of Ginger Rogers who did all the dancing Fred Astaire did, only backward and in high heels. That's how I felt during the rest of the training with my crew, dragging around a cast or boot. (I was exempt from further suit training.)

As with all significant NASA failures or mishaps, an investigation took place. I had assumed I had somehow messed up my ride down the escape slide, but the investigating team found that the slide had lost a little pressure with each crew member that went down it. It was slightly underinflated and a little buckled at the bottom when I made my ride, and my foot had caught at the bottom and had twisted backwards. I had also had my left toes pointed leftward, and the trainers thereafter reminded crews *Toes up* before they were sent down the slide.

I was surprised that no one called for my removal from the flight, neither the medics or my bosses, nor the scientists who would be using me as a subject and operator for the flight. No one from the training or equipment teams got in any trouble, and my foot healed. As they said at NASA, The flight was delayed a couple months for other reasons, and I was ready to go on launch day.

When it came time for our crew picture, it was easy to plan the formal one: orange suits, crew patch, American flag. Nice and simple. For our informal picture, we wanted to remember how much equipment had been crammed into our orbiting laboratory, as though we were

Our humorous crew picture as The Happy Campers.

on a family outing to the great unknown. Since we'd also be the longest flight to date, we dressed up in outdoor gear and posed as "The Happy Campers." Since this version of our photo would be restricted to our NASA team, friends, and families, we knew they would understand why we had chosen this vignette.

One of the major new ventures on this flight was the animal studies. Animals had been to space before, and there had even been some limited interaction with them. On SLS-1, we had taken one of the rats out of its cage in our enclosed work station to see its reaction to being in weightlessness. There had been no surprises; however, the extensive and detailed procedures that were planned for SLS-2 had never been performed.

There were many unknowns about working with the animals—and as Chris Kraft had described the first space flights—a lot of "unknown unknowns," things we couldn't imagine or plan for. Could we as operators stay stable enough around the work station to do delicate work for several hours? What could happen during an animal dissection that would be a surprise? Would we be able to secure our instruments so they didn't float away? How could we get tissues into the fixative solutions without letting the dangerous chemicals get out into the work station and perhaps into the Spacelab cabin itself?

The NASA Ames Research Center in California had responsibility for the animal work. Our trainers Chris Maese, Justine Grove, and Lynn Pickett, as well as other engineers, investigators, and mangers spent countless hours working out the details. The procedures were daunting, the various pieces of equipment extensive, the timing and coordination critical. They all regarded this as a momentous and historic event. Many scientists were depending on it going well.

Were the animals treated humanely? Most certainly. It was so much in the public eye, NASA worked hard to ensure we abided by all the rules of animal research. There was an Animal Care and Use Committee at Ames that always considered the Three Rs in approving animal experimentation: replace, reduce, and refine. Animals are replaced with cell cultures or computer models if possible. The number of animals used is reduced to as few as possible to get significant data. The studies are refined so that no animal suffers needlessly and as much good science as possible is obtained from each of them.

Our entire crew, all the investigators, and many NASA managers were briefed about the concerns of animal rights activists. These groups had raised the consciousness of all researchers working with animals and had improved the way business was done. On the other hand, there were people at the extremes who believed animals have the same rights as humans. They were strict vegetarians and used no animal products (including leather and silk). They believed that to own a pet was an act of "species-ism" and a form of enslavement. We learned not to argue with these folks for we could never convince them to change their minds no matter how rational our arguments. We learned to state our case and agree to disagree.

A big flap arose a few weeks prior to the flight. An Ames scientist said something insensitive in the press about our animal research. The NASA Administrator Dan Goldin (who was rumored to have a family member with ties to one of the animal rights groups) called for an investigation into whether NASA was doing the right things regarding our animal experiments.

This was typical of what seemed to be going on in our agency at the time. Mr. Goldin had replaced Dick Truly as NASA Administrator in the spring of 1992. No one was sure why Vice President Dan Quayle, then head of the National Space Council, urged President Bush to change administrators. At that time, George Abbey was the NASA advisor to Quayle's Council and became Goldin's special assistant at headquarters. He would soon be back in leadership roles at the Johnson Space Center.

Mr. Goldin came to us from the world of unmanned satellites. He was a "vision" kind of guy. He did a good job appearing before Congress, but it took him a long time to understand what shuttle missions were all about and to trust the people who were putting them together. He seemed to focus on the mission that was next on the launch pad. If any questions were raised about that flight, an investigation had to be undertaken, rather than ask the responsible people to talk to him. It happened on a couple of the missions before ours, so I suppose we should have expected it. Nothing was more disruptive to a massive endeavor like a shuttle flight than to threaten a change it in the six weeks prior to lift off.

Questions were raised about whether the animals should fly at all. Would the hysterics prevail and persuade our agency that Americans didn't want their space dollars going toward the demise of lab rats? Years of vetting the scientific benefits, preparation, equipment development, and training appeared in jeopardy.

It was during these frantic weeks that I learned a great deal about something called integrity. I got to watch someone take a difficult stand even when it put his job in jeopardy.

Someone in the NASA hierarchy requested that I look into what we could do to salvage some of the animal science if we were directed not to kill the animals in flight. I was told that this work should be kept secret. I was given clearance to work with Marty on this since he was the crew member with the most extensive animal research background. We tried to decide what tissues could be harvested without harming the rats too much. We knew the spleen could safely be removed from the abdomen. Taking out the leg muscles was not an option, but we thought we might be able to do a muscle biopsy and perhaps gather a bone marrow specimen.

The more we thought about it the more complex it seemed to get. What anesthesia would be used? How would we monitor the animals as they awoke from the anesthetic? Wouldn't the animals be in pain after the surgery, and how would we help them? The Spacelab had already been packed with our dissection equipment and fixative pouches for flight. How would we get additional medicines and instruments on board?

The next day we went back with a list of the things we thought could be done, along with our concerns. We stressed that our conclusions were our own and that the first thing we needed to do was consult the investigators who had proposed the original studies. No, we were told: we wouldn't bother them with this. It would slow things down, complicate matters. Marty and I looked at each other. Secondly, we felt that we'd have to put the entire proposal through the Animal Care and Use Committee (ACUC), which decided on whether these were proper things to do with the animals. They would have many of the same worries that we did about anesthesia, monitoring, pain, and so on. We'd have to address all their questions with a mere four weeks until launch. We were told that the ACUC would do what they were told to do. Marty and my eyes met again.

I was flabbergasted but couldn't figure out how to say what I knew to be true: doing this seemed unethical in so many ways. I had a huge knot in my stomach not knowing what to do. I knew Marty was in a difficult spot, too. He had been hired to make this one flight, and there were two other qualified people who could replace him if he got fired. He showed the kind of *right stuff* he was made of.

"As the onboard vet, I will be the veterinarian of record with responsibility for the overall welfare of the animals," he said. "I can't in good conscience sign up to pursue this line of thought outside the proper channels."

He said it looking straight at the NASA person who could have sent him packing. Then they both looked at me. I considered waffling a bit, trying to be the perennial peace-maker, to offer some sort of compromise or temporize. But Marty was right, there was no way around doing the right thing. I was willing to stake my future career on it, too.

"I concur," I said.

"This was all to help you salvage some sort of science from this fiasco. I don't want to hear any more about this," as if this mission was somehow our personal cause.

We skittered out the door, certain that the matter was over. We would later learn that our inputs were disregarded. Dave Leestma, the head of Flight Crew Operations and a former astronaut, was told to direct us to work on the alternate plan. Dave knew it was wrong and took no action until time ran out and nothing could be changed. The whole issue blew over.

We had a lot of fun in quarantine. Marty was dating John Blaha's college-age daughter, Carolyn. All of the other spouses—Brenda Blaha, Julie Searfoss, Cindy McArthur, Mike Lucid, and, of course, Hoot—were a relaxed fun-loving group, so we had raucous parties at the beach house. On one rainy October day we all lounged around watching the crazy movie *Groundhog Day,* about a man in a time loop reliving the same day over and over. The American public would have

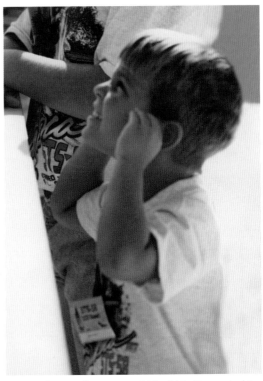

Dann who was four years old had his fingers in his ears during launch *(above).* Launch of STS-58 on October 18, 1993 *(right).*

found it odd that this was how people possessed of the *right stuff* would prepare to meet their fate.

The flight had the usual delays. We scrubbed one launch for a computer glitch and another for a malfunctioning piece of communication equipment. We were feeling like we were part of a new movie *Groundhog Day in Space.* But on the morning of October 18, 1993, Hoot, Julie, Paul, and 4-year-old Dann (with his fingers in his ears), along with the other families, watched from the roof of the LCC as Mom rocketed into space once more. This time, my kneeboard card had words from the 23rd Psalm on it:

"Yea, though I walk through the valley of the shadow of death,
I will fear no evil: for thou art with me."

It seemed apropos of this event and comforting during that awesome eight and a half minute rocket ride to space.

Dave Wolf even managed to get one of his favorite foods on board. He had worked before his flight assignment at the Cape (as a Cape Crusader as we called them), prepping the orbiters for flight. The cooks at the crew quarters loved to spoil this single guy by fixing his favorite foods. For breakfast he delighted in having cheese blintzes, those little folded over crepes with cream cheese in the middle.

When we got close to flight time, Dave tried to figure out a way to get blintzes on our spacecraft.

"They'd go bad if put in the food locker and you don't have a refrigerator," the cooks said.

"Sure we do. It's back in the lab," Dave said.

"But you can't get to the re-frigerator until three hours after launch which makes it more than six hours after you leave crew quarters for the pad."

"Can they be frozen ahead of time?"

It turned out that they could, so Dave carried a plastic bag of frozen cheese blintzes in his equip-ment sack as we went out to the launch pad. When he was busy transferring his goodies to the Spacelab refrigerator several hours later, he was kind enough to share them with me. It was undoubted-

The nice ladies in crew quarters had helped us sneak extra food on board.

ly a first and one that might never be known about: *blintzes in space.*

I was pretty sure this was to be my last spaceflight, so I wanted to gaze out the window at Earth as much as I could. When everyone started staking out places to sleep, I claimed the space behind the pilot's seat on the flight deck. Every *night* (that is, during the eight hours specified in our timeline that we were to sleep), I'd unroll my sleeping bag and hook it to the wall, positioning my face near the overhead windows. Since MCC allowed us to turn *Columbia* upside down, payload bay to the planet, during our off hours, I had a magnificent view of Earth. The trouble was, it was the same swath of the ground every night. I'd climb into my sleeping bag somewhere over the sands of the Middle East and watch the Himalayas drift un-

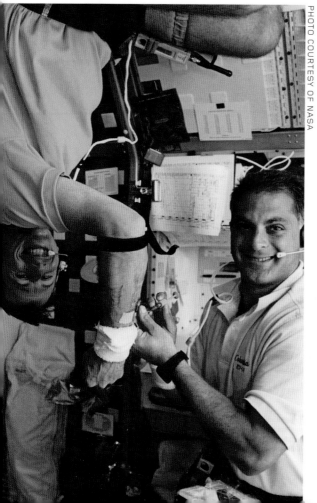

PHOTO COURTESY OF NASA

derneath me. By the time the coast of China went by, I'd be asleep. The continent of North America went by during the *morning* hours of our workday when we were invariably busy, but we did manage to take occasional breaks on clear days to press our noses against the window panes to oooo and aaaaah. I could never get enough of the view.

The human experiments went as planned.

Dave draws blood from Marty's arm for one of the metabolic experiments.

While I kept waiting for the equipment failures like the ones we had seen on SLS-1 to occur, they never did. It seemed we were hitting our stride in doing sophisticated human studies in space.

The animal cages functioned well, and we checked each day to make sure the rats had plenty to eat and drink. The studies on their blood cells and metabolism required drawing blood and injecting tracers into their tail veins. Rats' tails have a tough, scaly skin, and the tiny veins are located just under the surface. Poke the needle in hard enough to get through the skin, and it often went right through the vein. Shannon and Dave were the champs at doing this and were assigned most of these duties throughout the flight.

Since the surgeries were to take place as late in the flight as possible, on Day 13 (good thing I wasn't superstitious), I had the preflight period

The inner ear sense of movement was tested in a rotating chair.

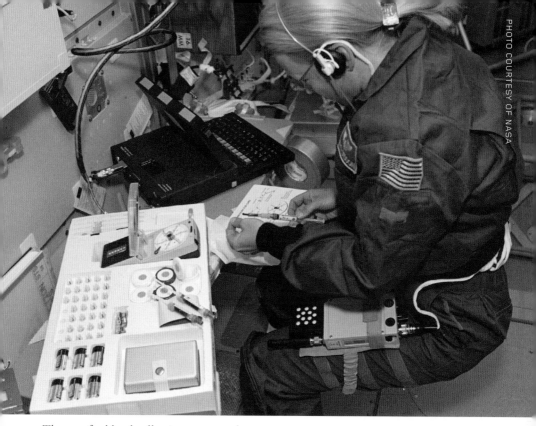

The tray for blood collection was complex.

and almost the entire flight to worry about it. One of my most challenging tasks would be to get the bony part of the rats' inner ears out of their skull and into the fixative within two minutes after decapitation or they would begin to degrade. The inner ears were a couple millimeters in diameter and were buried within ridges in the cranium. I was at an age when my close up vision was beginning to deteriorate, so I spent time finding glasses with the right magnification and focal length to do the task. Thank goodness for Dr. Bob Gibson, one of our NASA optometrists who worked with me on it.

Marty was tapped to dissect most of the rest of the body with me as his trusty assistant. The other difficult time constraint was for him to get muscles out of the legs and have me stretch them out on muscle holder clamps and get them into the fixative solutions in less than 10 minutes. The muscles were tiny, and the clamps were small and awkward to use. I constantly went through these scenarios hoping I could remember every well-practiced step.

On Flight day 13 Marty and I got up early to set up for the animal dissections. We Velcroed all our equipment near the work station. As we had done hundreds of times in training, we went over what we planned to do. We agreed we'd do the first rat slowly, and then debrief. On subsequent animals, we'd adapt according to any lessons learned.

We took a cage containing two rats from the holding facility and brought it into the General Purpose Work Station (the GPWS), an enclosed box with glass on three sides and portholes front and side for two sets of arms. Air flowed from top to bottom which would help pull any debris out of our field of view down to the bottom of the work area.

Marty opened the cage door and extracted one of the rats. He held it by the body and decapitated it with a small guillotine which was affixed to the back wall of the GPWS. He drew into a syringe some of the blood that welled up from the blood vessels of the neck, stretched the body out on a work table, slipped it beneath some straps, and got the fixative bags ready to receive the inner ear. In the meantime I took the head which had floated loose and pinned it to my end of the work table. Making a few efficient strokes with a scalpel and a few snips with a bone cutter, I removed the tiny nubbins of skull that contained the balance organs and slid them into the top of the bag Marty had waiting.

The plastic bags containing the fixative solutions were ingenious. About two inches wide and six inches long, they were sealed on three sides and open at one end. The chemical solution was at the bottom of the bag, and there were two clamps above it. When ready to receive a piece of tissue, the upper clamp was removed, the specimen inserted, and the clamp replaced. The lower clamp was then removed, allowing the fixative into the upper part of the bag where the tissue was. The bag was shaken so the solution had time to mix with the tissue, then tissue and fixative were squeezed back down into the bottom of the bag. Finally, the second clamp was reapplied to keep them there with as little air as possible.

Fixative chemicals like formaldehyde can preserve tissue specimens but are dangerous if they get into the operators eyes or lungs, so it was important to keep them contained. In weightlessness, of course, liquids tended not to stay in their containers, so this somewhat cumbersome method of operating had to be developed.

After both inner ears were in the bags (and the clock checked to document that it took less than two minutes to get them there), Marty set to work on the leg muscles. In well under 10 minutes they were out, stretched onto their holders, and bagged; we each went back for further tissues. The head yielded brain, pituitary gland, eyeballs, and the thyroid gland in the neck. Marty retrieved the heart, lungs, thymus gland, spleen, bone, bone marrow, kidneys, liver, testicles, and several other leg muscles. All of these had to go into either marked bags of specific fixative or into foil to be frozen. Someone likened our choreographed act to the cooks at a Benihana-type restaurant.

After the first rat, Marty and I knew that our lengthy training had paid off. There were a few minor improvements needed, and we had time to complete five additional rats. Due to the sensitivity of the dissections, no pictures or videos were taken. All the lessons learned and experience gained from this work would reside in two human brains.

When the dissections were proposed a few specific tissues were on the list for collection. It seemed wasteful not to use as much of the animals as possible, so NASA sent an announcement out to research groups all over the world to see if they could put the spare parts to good use. It turned into a massive undertaking, but I always felt that we made the best use possible of the animals we used.

Despite the spectacular view of Mother Earth, despite the science so

unique and well done, despite the pure joy of floating weightless for fourteen days, the most memorable moments of the flight were of a simpler nature. The complex and sophisticated communication equipment on the shuttle was always busy sending important systems and scientific data to mission and payload control centers, so there was no opportunity to talk to space fans on

Bill McArthur was our specialist in the ham radio operations and helped me speak to my son's class during the flight.

Earth. Earlier in the shuttle program, astronauts began using a ham radio mounted in the window of the orbiter to talk to ham radio operators on the ground around the world. A popular program allowed schools to schedule a chat with an astronaut in flight, and my son Paul's school applied.

St. Barnabas School in Houston was a small elementary school attended by several children from our neighborhood. It won a slot on my daily calendar late in the flight. NASA wanted this to be a learning experience for the students. The children had to study about the shuttle, the flight, the ham radio, and radio voice protocols. They each had to develop pertinent questions. Paul was eleven years old and when a reporter from the *Houston Chronicle* came to the school to interview some students and teachers, Paul finally understood that what his mother did for a living was unusual.

Paul learned how to use the ham radio that had been set up at his school and had his questions ready. As part of the homework for this event he had to practice his questions at home. I noticed as we worked on his part that he seemed apprehensive.

"Are you afraid you will forget what to do, Paul?" I asked.

"No," he said.

"You've practiced like you should, and you're doing a great job. Why are you nervous?"

"Mom, I'm afraid you'll say something mushy when you talk to me and my friends will laugh."

I smiled at that. He didn't want to be embarrassed in front of his classmates.

"Don't worry, Paul. I'll treat you just like all the other students, okay?"

"Okay, Mom. Thanks."

On the appointed in-flight time during a nine-minute pass over America, I established contact with the school, and the kids began their well-rehearsed questions, using the proper voice protocol.

"Hi, this is Jordan. Can you see Houston from space? Over."

"Yes I can, Jordan. It's a little hard to see much, but I can just make out the Astrodome and the runways at Intercontinental Airport. I can see Clear Lake near my house. I'm afraid I can't make out your school though. It is too small to see. Over."

When it was Paul's turn, he asked his question, and I answered without any mushy stuff. When I began to hear a crackling noise in our communications, I knew we had to wrap things up because we were about to lose our link with the ground.

431

"Thank you, St. Barnabas students. Your questions were excellent, but we'll need to close now. I hope I'll see all of you back on the ground soon. Good-bye."

As the sun-lit east coast of my home country slid beneath my window and I looked at the lonely blackness of the sky, a little voice came through my headphones as clearly as if spoken by an angel in heaven.

"I love you, Mom. Have a safe trip home."

As tears welled in my eyes, I knew that those mushy words would be the most memorable moment of my space career.

We wrapped up the mission and made our preparation for coming home. Having learned how crushing being overworked was on SLS-1, I'd made sure the timeline was not overbooked. We had built in time to handle any failures. We also had extra activities planned if time became available. Since getting the data was the main purpose of the mission, we'd even persuaded the or-biter crew members to serve as subjects in some of the studies. Unbelievably, all of the equipment worked, so we ended up getting 115% of the information we'd planned to collect: every-thing that was on the time-line and several things that weren't.

I was back downstairs on the middeck for landing, as with my first flight. John did a great job of putting us down smoothly on Runway

Dann watching his mother land again at Edwards Air Force Base in California.

22 at Edwards on November 1, 1993. I had never had any problems after landing with feeling faint and didn't anticipate I would this time even though, at 14 days, this flight was much longer than my seven- and nine-day missions. After stopping on the runway, it was my job to unstrap and stand up on my seat to turn on an overhead speaker, allowing all of us downstairs to hear the flight deck conversation after we took off our helmets. As I stood up and craned my head back, I had an *UH-OH* feeling and, after turning on the speaker, decided to sit back down until I felt steadier.

Later when we got back to the clinic I participated in a study called the "stand test". After my heart rate and blood pressure—along with various other parameters—were measured lying down, I was asked to stand up while these parameters were repeated every minute for 10 minutes. One of the machines beeped with every beat of my heart, and as I lay I could tell my heart was doing its usual rate of 50 or 60. When I stood up I was surprised to hear the beeping rise to over 120 beats per minute. My heart was fighting hard to get enough blood to my brain to keep it functional. My reflexes had forgotten how to fight gravity and keep my blood flow up. After a few minutes, my blood pressure began a slow decline. I felt woozy and had to sit down. This convinced me that the longer the missions, the greater the changes in the body and that could produce unexpected difficulties readapting to being back home.

The postflight dizziness and unsteadiness that I had experienced on both my other flights also persisted longer. My brain seemed to misinterpret my head movements. As I turned my head to the right, for instance, it felt like I was moving to the left instead. To compensate I moved to the right, often running into the wall as I went around a corner. On my first two flights that feeling was almost gone by the time I woke up the morning after landing. On this flight, it persisted a full two days until my inner ear got used to gravity again.

Most astronauts would say they felt almost back to normal three or four days after landing from a shuttle mission. It was fascinating, however, to see the data the scientists collected on us on SLS-1 and 2. It told them we weren't back to normal in some ways a week after landing. There were still subtle differences in our physiology that proved we were still trying to readapt to being back on Earth. We still had some trouble navigating in the dark. We hadn't gotten the red cells in our blood back to their normal levels. Exercise on the bike still showed we weren't as strong as we had been. We were still trying to replace the calcium in our bones that we'd lost in weightlessness.

Some people disagreed with doing animal research, but we learned many things we'd never have been able to find out by using humans. The nerve cells in the rats' inner ears that sense gravity were found to have changed in type and number when gravity was removed. This was evidence that the nervous system can rewire itself depending on its environment. The muscle cells of the rat's leg changed from the type used to resist gravity to the type used to move around quickly. Whereas there were four subjects for the human studies, we could carry 48 rats. The larger the number of subjects for any experiment, the more certain the findings.

We made our required Hill trip after the flight. Once again, the space station was in funding jeopardy and we needed to come save it, as if whatever we did would have any bearing on what was decided. I hoped to have a nice visit to the White House. Al Gore, who I had known since he had been my Congressman back in Tennessee, was now the vice president. I thought he might do something nice for my crew. It was disappointing to be ushered into a large meeting room between a Kiwanis Club and a contingent of preachers for a brief handshake and a short photo op with him. Al had moved on to bigger things. I, too, had to think about moving on.

CHAPTER 12

★ ★ ★ ★ ★ ★

SPACIBA,* Y'ALL!

How NASA got involved with the Russians in space was a strange story. When President Bill Clinton and Vice-President Al Gore came into office in early 1993, they inherited both NASA Administrator Dan Goldin and Space Station Freedom, which had been reviewed, downsized, and redesigned many times. (Due to much whittling down of size and capabilities, we began to call it Space Station "Fred.") Hoot and I figured that the Democrats would put their own man as head of NASA, and during the campaign the candidates had come out in favor of a space station. We didn't realize they had said *a* space station, not *the* space station, meaning the one that had already been designed.

*"Thank you" in Russian

In 1993 the Space Station became a post-Cold War foreign policy tool. This was a plan of the new Clinton/Gore administration. There was waning support for the station in congress. With the break-up of the Soviet Union there was concern that Russian space scientists and engineers would sell their nuclear expertise and services to Third world dictators. While NASA was working furiously to design a less costly station in mid-1993, Vice President Gore signed an accord with Russian Prime Minister Chernomyrdin to merge both countries' space stations into a single facility. It was a done deal at the highest level of our government. In the agreement NASA would pay $400M (subsequently $482M) for astronauts to spend time on the Russian Space Station Mir. In return, the Russians agreed to abide by a treaty not to sell rocket technology and know-how to India. Also, modified Russian modules would be at the core of the new, international station. Other components would be added by the U.S. and the space programs of our other international partners, Europe, Canada and Japan.

It was a chaotic time. How could NASA form a forward-looking strategic plan and propose a long term annual budget with ever-changing directives? No one seemed to consider the impact on the astronauts and the other NASA personnel who would be required to spend years doing their life's work in a foreign language and in a very different environment. Would Gore and Goldin themselves have signed on to speaking Russian and living in Russia and for two or more years?

For his part, the NASA Administrator would keep his job. Mr. Goldin liked to say this program would be "Faster, Better, Cheaper." It was hard to understand how that could be. Because the Russians launched their rockets from Baikonur in Kazakhstan, the flight path of the station would be required to go 51.6 degrees north and south of the equator, instead of 28 degrees if launched from Florida. In order to get to the station's orbit, space shuttles would lose a fourth of their cargo-carrying capacity, requiring more flights—at around half a billion dollars each—to put all the parts and equipment up there. Not to mention the additional time.

It might have been fathomable if we'd agreed to do a brief cooperative effort with our Cold War enemies, but we tied our whole future inextricably to a country that was falling apart after the dissolution of the Soviet Union. Born bargainers, the Russians had to do whatever they could to bring hard currency into their country. They would bargain hard for that $400 million...and more.

For those of us in the Astronaut Corps who suddenly had to face being shipped out to "The Gulag" as we called it, the entire program seemed to appear out of nowhere with little study of its feasibility. When our front line engineers began analyzing what we'd gotten into, they unearthed a different philosophy on the Russian side of the deal. The Russian motto seemed to be, "Better is the enemy of good" when it came to designing their space hardware. In a Communist society there was little incentive for radical innovation and risk taking. For instance, in the mid-1960s, they had developed the capsule Soyuz to take their cosmonauts into space. They were proud of the fact that a modified Soyuz capsule would transport people to Mir and to the International Space Station in the 1990s.

Their Mir station had allowed cosmonauts to remain in space for long periods, but it was built as a place to live, not to conduct sophisticated science. The Russians still returned to Earth in capsules. There was little room to bring back any samples from space. When a new piece of equipment went up to Mir, something else had to be ejected into space to make room for it.

Larry Young trained with me for my third mission. He had a European friend who sent to Mir a sophisticated piece of hardware to study the inner ear and balance. The European scientist who flew to Mir with it served as the first subject. Larry's friend hoped to get a cosmonaut on a later flight to agree to be another. Larry ran into the friend and asked if he'd gotten his second subject.

"Larry," he said. "I have good news and bad news. The bad news is that I won't get any more subjects. The good news is, I have my own satellite."

His equipment was pitched out the door and now circles the planet.

Being a proud people, the Russians found it impossible to concede that our technology might have surpassed theirs. As our NASA colleagues began working in Russia, they sent us Russian press clippings of articles in which higher ups in their space agency bemoaned the fact that they were being robbed of their advanced ideas to provide currency for the country.

Advanced ideas?

When our people went to Star City (the Russian equivalent of the Johnson Space Center) where the cosmonauts trained, they had to run phone lines out from Moscow. Mail was unreliable. A FedEx package might take several weeks to get to the addressee. The two apartments to which our astronauts were assigned shared a washing machine. There was no dryer. Wet clothes had to be carted through the freezing weather back to the other apartment to be hung on a line to dry. On a visit to the prestigious Institute of Biomedical Problems in Moscow, a friend of mine said she had to step over a dead rat in the hallway.

Star City, outside Moscow, is where the cosmonauts train.

With the fall of Communism, corruption was rampant. Someone described the country as a "kleptocracy," people trying to steal what they could. NASA would ship hardware to Russia, but no one on the Russian side knew who could sign to get it through customs. "Not to worry, comrade, we can store it for you – at a nice price." Money sent to support Russian scientists or purchase hardware often never reached the intended people.

"Yes, the Russian side agreed to write up the training material and the checklists, but we have no computers. Can you please provide them?"

"Yes, we have written up the material on our new computers, but—alas—we have no printers. Please send some."

On and on it went to the point that it was almost comical.

We never understood why an important general had to accompany cosmonauts when they came to train in the United States. Then we found out that he *handled* their money for them. NASA would give the general a certain amount of money per day for their hotel, food, and incidentals, and he would disperse money to the cosmonauts. Was it coincidental that the general soon began to build himself a Western style home in Star City?

The two cosmonauts who came to live in the United States in 1993 to train for a shuttle flight were nice people and did good jobs, but they weren't above milking the system. Initially housed in nice apartments near the Johnson Space Center, they soon decided they wanted houses like those the astronauts lived in. Given a car to drive, they requested another—allowing them to be two-car families like their American counterparts. It was rumored that one of them accepted money for public appearances. Astronauts and non-astronaut payload specialists were required to sign agreements not to accept money for speeches as long as they worked for NASA. The cosmonauts weren't required to sign such a document.

The cosmonauts did enjoy flying in the NASA T-38s with the astronaut pilots. One day John Blaha and I ran into them at Ellington Field.

Their English was pretty good, but John at the time spoke pure Texan.

"Where y'all headed?" drawled John.

His inquiry was met with quizzical looks on the cosmonauts' faces.

"Where y'all headed?" he shouted, utilizing the usual American technique to be better understood.

Having traveled a little in Europe, I saw right away what the problem was.

"Where are you going?" I said.

"Oh," said one of the cosmonauts. "We are going to El Paso today."

In late 1993 Norm Thagard was preparing to go to Russia to train as the first astronaut to live on Mir. Hoot had gotten in a little trouble when the topic of sending astronauts to Russia to train first came up. As chief of the Astronaut Office, he had said in a newspaper interview that he didn't think many astronauts would want to go train over there, and it was true at that time. No back-up for Norm could be found. Dave Leestma, who was the head of Flight Crew Operations, made a personal plea to Bonnie Dunbar in December of 1993 to take on this task. When they left for Russia in February of 1994, Norm had been taking Russian language lessons for almost two years. Bonnie was given two months to prepare. No one else, however, wanted

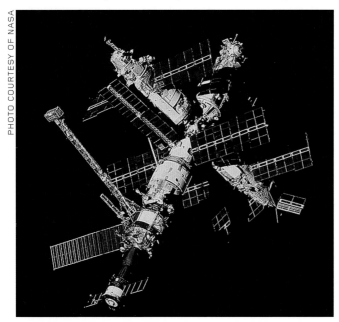

PHOTO COURTESY OF NASA

The Russian Space Station Mir.

440

the assignment. None of us came into the shuttle program planning to live in a chaotic country and do our work in a foreign language.

I offered to help follow the development of the science program planned for Mir after Norm and Bonnie left for Star City in early 1994. Since many of the experiments they were to take with them were life sciences studies, I felt I would be a helpful point of contact in the United States. Many hardworking and conscientious people worked endless hours to pull the Shuttle-Mir Science Program together, but it was planned backwards and was problem-plagued from the outset. Rather than asking the science community to propose an overall, well-thought-out science program and then determine how many flights it would take to complete it, NASA had signed up for as many as ten flights to Mir starting in 1995, and then told the scientists to generate requirements to fill up the flights.

Many people—Peggy Whitson, who would later become an astronaut, John Uri, Charlie Stegemoeller, and many, many others—put their hearts and souls into finding hardware for Norm's flight and finding scientists to design experiments that he could perform. The Russians had to do exhaustive tests on the hardware before it could be shipped to Russia. Of course, the Russian engineers had to come to the United States at our expense to oversee the testing. Then they had to test it again after it reached its destination. There were shipping and customs fiascos. There were problems with faulty power supplies in Russia that fried our equipment. There were no copy machines, viruses in the Russian computers, and the risk to personnel of contracting hepatitis, cholera, or plain old bad athlete's foot. At the launch site, Baikonur, there were no phones, and the water was not drinkable. Hands had to be washed in antiseptic solutions to avoid the diphtheria that had broken out in the area.

The one safe, comfortable hotel in Moscow was the Penta at $200 per night. The breakfast buffet was $26, the dinner was $46. Besides

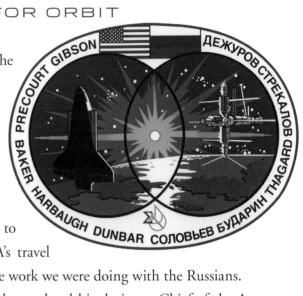

paying for many of the trips the Russians made to the United States, there were massive expenditures every time we sent NASA engineers or scientists to Russia. The Astronaut Office's regular travel budget was cut, and it didn't take a genius to figure out that most of NASA's travel money was going to support the work we were doing with the Russians.

In the meantime, Hoot had completed his duties as Chief of the Astronaut Office in early 1994, a job he had hoped to keep much longer. As chief, he had selected a fine group of folks to assign to the first flight to

The STS-71 crew. The unsmiling ones are Russian, two of whom will launch on the Shuttle for the trip to Mir and the other two plus Norm Thagard will return to Earth on it *(below)*. The crew patch for the STS-71 Mir docking flight with the names in English and Russian. The small symbols at the bottom honor the American and Russian Control Centers *(above)*.

rendezvous with the Russian space station which was to launch in 1995. Hoot had not put his name on that list; he had sworn as chief of the office that he wouldn't take the good flights for himself. The higher ups at NASA had other ideas, however. Before the crew was announced, Hoot was told that he would command the mission.

For the first shuttle flight to Mir (STS-71), Hoot's crew would take cosmonauts Anatoly Solovyev and Nikolai Budarin to Mir and bring Norm and his crewmates Gennady Strekalov and Vladimir Dezhurov down. The shuttle would ferry up new science hardware and logistics material and return Norm's samples and data. There would be a Spacelab in the shuttle's cargo bay with equipment to perform more extensive and intricate medical testing on Norm and the two cosmonauts who had been in space for a hundred days with him. Behind the shuttle's crew compartment, there would be a docking module, a large heavy tube that allowed the shuttle to attach to a port on the Mir, and which would serve as a tunnel between the two vehicles.

The rest of Hoot's crew was a great bunch. Pilot Charlie Precourt was a natural whiz at languages and was soon chattering away in Russian. Greg Harbaugh was the flight engineer. He was a specialist in spacewalks having performed an EVA on one of his previous missions, and he might have to do one on this one. When NASA engineers first saw the drawings of the docking module, they were surprised to see an unsophisticated pulley and bell crank design that would hold the two vehicles together. They were reassured by the fact that the design included small explosive devices called pyros as backups that could unlatch the mechanism if it failed. When the hardware itself arrived at the Cape, they found that the pyros had been removed. The Russians decided they didn't need them and hadn't updated the drawings. NASA wanted to have a backup capability to undock if the automatic system didn't work, so Greg had to develop an EVA to unhook the space shuttle from the Mir docking port.

The crew in Russia for training. In Red Square, on the left is St. Basil's Cathedral and on the right is Lenin's tomb.

Physician Ellen Baker would be in charge of the Spacelab testing that would be done on the Mir crew. After returning from Russia following Norm's launch to Mir, Bonnie Dunbar would undergo the shortest shuttle training template in history (three months) and fly along as the fifth American crew member. Having trained as Norm's backup, she was knowledgeable about the Mir and its systems and would help Ellen in the lab as a scientist and translator. I admired her willingness to go to Russia on short notice, to take on all the responsibility to train as a back-up Mir crewmember, and to accept the additional stress of a short training cycle for a shuttle flight. Add the two cosmonauts on their way up to Mir and this rounded out the crew of seven that would launch on STS-71.

In my role of prepping the scientific studies for the Mir missions, I had the interesting job of helping to train the Russian cosmonauts to operate the experiments that would fly. The NASA trainers, the scientists, and I all had experience doing the same thing for astronauts who were preparing to fly, but we knew this would be more difficult because everything would have to be translated from English to Russian. When astronauts trained, they would receive an overview of the science, a description of what data would be collected, and training sessions on how to operate the equipment. We were used to crewmembers working with the equipment for a while then bombarding the scientists with questions about possible failures, requests for more in-depth information about the science, and suggestions about how things might be streamlined in weightlessness. They always felt responsible to perform all the steps precisely and wanted to know everything

The crew visited the Mir mockup in Star City and got to see the simulated docking ring where they would attach to the Space Station.

about a study and its hardware by the time they flew. The back and forth often took a while, so we set aside plenty of time with the cosmonauts.

We were in for a surprise. The science overview was delivered.

"Any questions?" asked the investigator.

"Nyet," said each cosmonaut.

The experiment equipment was set out and each switch, button, and display described, followed by an explanation of how everything operated. The Russians listened but seemed detached. The investigator explained each step in the checklist.

"Any questions?" the trainer asked.

"Nyet," said the cosmonauts.

We Americans didn't understand the lack of interest, so we requested a break. One of the Russians traveling with the entourage had to explain why the cosmonauts didn't care to know much about the studies, the equipment, or the plan for inflight operations. As it turned out, they had a different philosophy of the role of the crew.

Cosmonauts were paid a modest annual salary in their homeland. However, unlike astronauts, they received a large bonus for flying in space. The amount of this extra money was determined by how closely they followed the rules for the flight. They were trained to do certain things, and those were the things their bonuses depended on. They even received additional pay for participating in the experiments. In America scientists weren't allowed to pay an astronaut for his or her blood or urine, but the cosmonauts expected compensation.

As far as performing a scientific experiment in space, the Russians were responsible for doing exactly what the checklist said. If a step was incorrect in the checklist or for some reason something went wrong, that was not their problem. They would abandon the thing or turn it off. They had no interest in understanding the purpose of the study, how to observe for

The crew meets Valentina Tereshkova, the first woman to orbit the Earth.

any interesting or unusual scientific findings, or assist in overcoming any problems that might arise. If the unexpected occurred, it was not like on the shuttle where the crew could make decisions in the heat of battle or in the interest of time. Cosmonauts had to ask for permission and await instructions from the ground. Or lose part of their bonus.

This prohibition for onboard decision making was a surprise and annoyance when it came to science, but it would be anxiety producing on later Mir missions. There were incidences in which astronauts were involved in accidents on the station where the necessary steps were obvious and the consequences of inaction were dire. In one case the cosmonaut, along with the astronaut, acted and was criticized when he returned to Earth and lost much of his bonus. In another, even when it was obvious what needed to be done to avoid a potential abort of the mission, the cosmonauts refused to act until they could receive instructions from the ground and left the astronaut scared and dumbfounded. These were some of the unintended consequences of trying to blend cultures with different ideas about responsibilities and command structure.

Norm is congratulated by a military official upon completing his training.

Hoot had some interesting experiences, too. The Russians were not required to be able to speak any English, so the astronauts began Russian language training. Even though Hoot was an engineer and phobic of foreign languages, he studied earnestly. He'd come home from a long day's work, have dinner, and retire to his downstairs airplane room to spend a couple hours with his head in a book, mumbling to himself. As always, he had the most fun learning phrases that would shock his Russian teacher but given a little time he got pretty good at Russian. He liked to say that there might be a time where he would have to say to a crewmember on the shuttle flight to Mir, "Izvenichya pojolista! Oo nas yest milyensky pojar na bortu priamo si chas." which could be translated as "Excuse me, please. We have a small fire on board right now."

Mastering the foreign language was minor compared to the flying task that faced Hoot. He liked to say he had to be perfect in many dimensions. The Russian docking module was mounted in the cargo bay of the shuttle, and it would have to be flown into a docking ring on the Mir with precision. Small jets on the shuttle were used to push the orbiter through space, and firing too many of them to brake while closing in would contaminate the surfaces of the solar arrays on the station. So he had to make the right jet firings to start a slow coast into the Mir, then minimize using the up-firing braking jets so that his closure speed was 0.1feet per second plus or minus .03 to latch, or he'd bounce away. He would damage the docking mechanism if he hit it at more than 0.2 feet per second. Of course, he had to be lined up fore and aft, left and right, and up and down, or he might get jammed into the docking ring crooked and be locked up. All this while circling the planet at 17,500 miles per hour.

Norm's launch from Baikonur, the Russian launch site in Kazakhstan.

There was one more thing. The Russians wanted the docking to occur over Russia so their ground stations and the Russian Mission Control Center could monitor it. So there were the three dimensions of location, a tight speed restriction, and a specific time window. Even for a great pilot like Hoot, it was a pretty sporting task.

My focus at that time was different. There was one remaining thing I hoped to accomplish before I left NASA. I wanted to try again to find that baby girl that I knew was out there somewhere. We had tried after SLS-1 and before I had been assigned to SLS-2 but had had no luck. At 46, it seemed hopeless, but Hoot humored me and let me give all our money to the fertility experts. He kept saying that with all the drugs involved I was sure to have three more boys. But in late 1994, I found out that I was expecting, and all of us began praying it was a girl.

Despite the craziness of trying to combine two different space programs, Norm and his crew launched from Kazakhstan in March of 1995, and the Soyuz docked with the Mir for a three month mission.

The spring of 1995 was a challenge for me. As if minding two little boys, working as a full-time astronaut and a part-time ER doctor, and playing astronaut spouse weren't enough, I was trying to make the best of being an old pregnant lady. When I got pregnant, the STS-71 launch date was in May of 1995. My due date was June 22. Going to the Cape eight months pregnant didn't sound like a lot of fun, but it was doable. As the pregnancy and the flight preparations progressed, however, the launch and due dates began to come into a strange alignment. For a while the launch was set for early June.

When the launch slid to June 22, things became clearer. With a history of a problem labor once before, I couldn't afford to risk going into labor in Florida at age 47, away from my physicians. How early would Dr. Powell be willing to deliver this baby? Since we had closely monitored this high risk pregnancy from its outset, we were sure of the maturity of the baby. Frequent ultrasounds and an amniocentesis not only showed that our prayers had been answered and it was a girl but that she was perfectly formed and at least seven pounds by the end of May.

For a launch on June 22, Hoot would have to go into quarantine on the

15th, and we'd all leave for the Cape on June 19. I wanted him to be by my side for the delivery and to get me home from the hospital before he disappeared into seclusion. We pulled out everyone's calendar: mine, Hoot's, Dr. Powell's, Dr. Jennings'—my flight surgeon who would assist in the delivery, and Dr. Wimberly's, our pediatrician. Friday, June 9, 1995 looked like the right day, and "Friday's child is loving and giving." Hoot's scheduler, Karen Flanagan, even managed to give him that Friday and the weekend off.

Miss Emilee Louise Gibson celebrated her birthday right on schedule. My sister, Louise, had died tragically at age 44 the year before, and we knew that the baby would have her name. The first name took us longer to figure out. There weren't any family names that we liked, so we had to choose something pretty. We both like Emily, and spelling it *Emilee* put Hoot's middle name, Lee, in there. At 7 pounds 2 ounces, she was the lightest of my three babies. Right after the birth when the nurses brought

Emilee is welcomed into the world by her big brothers.

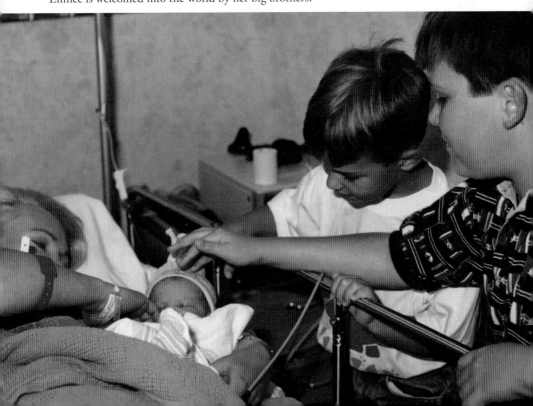

Tiny Emilee's first airplane flight going to Cape Canaveral for the launch.

us a little card with her footprint stamped on it, we had to laugh. She had inherited her father's long skinny feet.

She made her first flight on the NASA plane with us to the Cape ten days later. When Trudy Davis had put the manifest together for the flight several weeks earlier, we hadn't named the baby yet. We asked big brothers Paul and Dann what they thought we should name their new sister. Dann, who was six, voted for Sweetie. Emilee appeared on the official passenger list as "Sweetie Gibson."

In Florida we had our first opportunity to interact with Anatoly's and Nikolai's families. Communication was difficult because of the language barrier. I felt an obligation as the flight commander's wife to welcome

452

them and make them comfortable. As customary, I had some note cards made up with the crew patch on them and had some extra ones printed up for the cosmonaut wives. At our first get together I introduced myself, welcomed them to the United States, and presented them with the cards. They seemed somewhat taken aback but politely thanked me. They also congratulated me on my newborn whose name in Russian was "Amelia." After a few pleasantries, it was clear that small talk would be impossible because they spoke no English, and the two words I knew in Russian were pazhalusta for please and spasibo for thank you.

At our first crew dinner at the Cape, the families let the American and Russian crewmembers do what talking they could manage. Our daughter Julie, who was then 19, found that Anatoly's son Gennady (20 years old, blonde and handsome) had taken English in school, so they managed more conversation than the rest of us. Perhaps flirtation makes communication easier. All in all, the Russian families had their own entourage and spent only the time necessary to be polite with their American counterparts.

The crew's pre-launch breakfast.

PHOTO COURTESY OF NASA

Emilee was a good baby, and because little babies don't generally carry any diseases, she was allowed into quarantine. I got lots of help from spouses and crew members alike in taking care of her at crew quarters and the beach house. Julie was old enough to be a primary contact and could be around the crew, so she was a tremendous help. In addition she got to see the beach house she'd heard so much about. I figured traveling to Florida less than two weeks post-C-section with a newborn in tow got maximum points for *increased degree of difficulty*. Thank heaven for our nanny Joann, who tended the boys, and for the Good Lord for making me strong. I felt like one of those women of old who birthed their babies while working in the field and kept right on going.

Our family and Kirby Thagard, Norm's wife, in the viewing room of Mission Control awaiting the docking.

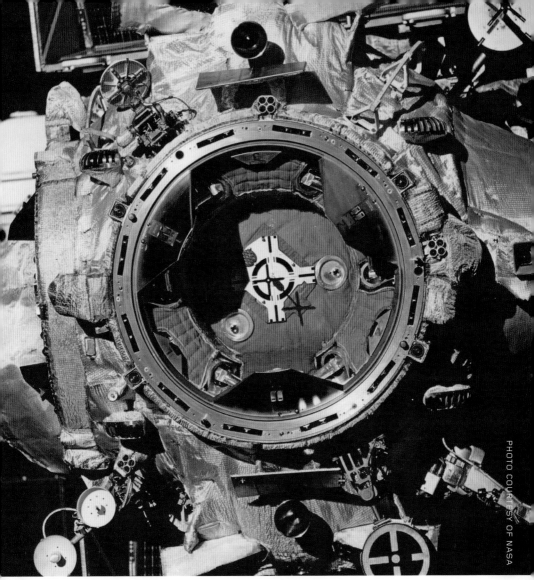

A Hoot's eye view of the targets on the Mir docking ring.

After delays on June 23 and 24 for bad weather, the historic 100th human space launch from the Cape rocketed skyward on a plume of smoke on June 27, 1995. Emilee slept through the launch as we stood on the roof of the Launch Control Center. She slept as Julie, Paul, Dann, and I watched in MCC ("Michigan Control" as Dann called it) as Hoot drove the shuttle over to a perfect docking with the Mir. (From the NASA data base: Closing rate was close to the targeted 0.1 foot per second, being approximately

455

Hoot peers out the overhead window at the space station.

0.107 foot per second at contact. Interface contact was nearly flawless: less than one inch (25 mm) lateral misalignment and an angular misalignment of less than 0.5 degrees per axis. Docking occurred about 216 nautical miles altitude above Lake Baikal region of the Russian Federation.) At landing 10 days later, Emilee stirred a bit as the double sonic booms announced that the shuttle was overhead. Her daddy would have to tell her about it someday.

The picture of Hoot shaking hands with Dezhurov across the Shuttle-Mir hatch was portrayed as the handshake that ended the Cold War. Hoot was a little afraid it wasn't going to come off. In Russia it is bad luck to shake hands across a threshold, and the cosmonauts wanted him to come into the Mir for the greeting. The NASA protocol people thought that was poor form. The cameras in the docking tunnel were set up to capture the moment right at the interface, and when the hatches were opened Hoot stuck his hand across into the Mir, and the handshake took place with him on the shuttle side and Vladimir on the Mir side. Nothing terrible happened.

After the flight, with great hoopla, the STS-71 crew was paraded across the land to describe their historic mission and tout how this was the beginning of a great partnership in space. The old Cold War adversaries would now work together to explore space. We all hoped so but only time and experience would tell if the "mongrel design" of our combined stations would work out.

Hoot shaking hands across the threshold between Mir and Atlantis.

A beautiful picture of the Shuttle docked to Mir.

I had saved enough sick leave to stay home with Emilee over the rest of the summer. Joann and I had a delightful time dressing her up in little girl things. I spent time trying to imagine what I would do when I returned to work in September. It had been made clear to all the mission specialists that we had to be willing to be assigned to Russia to be part of the Shuttle-Mir or space station missions. It required that we become fluent in Russian, a huge investment of time. I couldn't imagine asking Joann to spend a year or two in frigid Star City or dragging a baby, a six year old, and a thirteen year old over there. Nor could I imagine leaving them behind. And would they send Hoot at the same time or would he even want to go? In October of 1995 Hoot would turn 49, and in November I would turn 48. If we were to reinvent ourselves for our next careers, we needed to get moving soon.

Hoot was assigned to be the Deputy Director of Flight Crew Operations which was a higher management position that he had held before. Despite concerns with some of the NASA leadership and the worries about fickle Congressional decisions on NASA's budget, he wouldn't have minded staying at NASA or being in the contractor world in Houston until he retired. On the other hand, I didn't want to stay in Houston. There was the torrid weather and the bugs. The good, private schools for the children were an hour away in Houston (and admission was competitive). There was no job at the center that I wanted, nor could I envision working at the Houston Medical Center downtown. I knew there would be people who could open doors for me back in Tennessee.

A family picture taped to the Shuttle control panel

PHOTO COURTESY OF NASA

Inflight crew picture –a record number of people in space at one time.

PHOTO COURTESY OF NASA

When I considered applying for the astronaut program two decades earlier, I was at a different stage of life. I was not yet 30 and single, I had no children; I was at a good pause point in my medical career. Why not take a gamble on a fascinating opportunity? If I had been at that point in life in the 1990s, the cooperative space program with the Russians might have seemed an exotic, adventurous challenge. What fun it might be to have a job where you were taught a foreign language, could become a world traveler, and live in a foreign country! But with 20 years of life behind me, it didn't look the same with a husband, children, and an elderly father back in Tennessee to consider. The stars were not aligned in the same way.

When the shuttle was in its planning phases, NASA projected there would be considerable opportunity to do scientific work in space. Scientists were excited about being able to put complex experiments in Spacelab. In the life sciences field, animal habitats were being designed so that large numbers of rats and monkeys could be tested in both weightlessness and in partial gravity on a centrifuge. My third flight did some of the most extensive and sophisticated animal and human studies ever accomplished. But by 1995, the Spacelab was being phased out. There was little science planned for the space station until all the components had been built, launched, and constructed in space. As near as I could figure, that would be no earlier than 2004 if the ambitious schedule went according to the early planning. We all knew that never happened.

All that meant was that for the next eight-to-ten years, the primary mission of the shuttle would be to carry up large pieces of station hardware and assemble them all in low-Earth orbit. This filled all the people who did spacewalks with glee. Since I wasn't big enough to fit into the spacesuit, I wasn't sure where that left me. Perhaps I could help with the construction as a robot arm operator or plan out how to move tons of stuff between the orbiter and the station. The remaining spaceflight opportunity was to go train in Russia for a year or two, then spend six months in space with a couple of men on Mir. None of those options thrilled me. Nor did I want to move into a management position in medical operations or life sciences with NASA.

While I didn't know exactly how the things I had learned at NASA would translate in the *real world,* I knew there were some things I had discovered about improving the way organizations operated that might be helpful to the medical world. I didn't want to return to clinical medicine. While I had practiced emergency medicine in Houston,that was not the field I had intended to make my life's work. The idea of going back into a residency in plastic surgery or some other field at this point was beyond imagining. What I'd learned best at NASA was that I wanted my next boss to be a good boss.

Over the years in the space program I'd had the opportunity to work for and observe many *bosses*. I'd seen some great ones (Aaron Cohen, Gerry Griffin and Chris Kraft as Center Directors at JSC came to mind), as well as some that were awful. I had decided that whatever I chose to do I'd look for someone to work for who didn't play politics or favoritism, who was clear and transparent about decisions, who would provide support, encouragement, and honest feedback, and who would give me a choice in my own future.

When Hoot saw that I was serious about moving on, we talked about where we might go. Hoot's family was all in southern California, and we had spent considerable time visiting there. We found it modern and exciting but crowded with a lifestyle that could get kids into a lot of trouble. Anyway, we couldn't afford to live there. Then we'd visit my hometown of Murfreesboro, Tennessee —no longer the small town I grew up in and *country* by California standards, but so welcoming and friendly. It also looked like a good place to raise children. Hoot was impressed by the politeness and straightforwardness of the children of my friends there. There were good schools, and Nashville was 30 miles away.

Hoot knew that he didn't want a job where he sat behind a desk 40 hours a week. Several of his friends flew for Southwest Airlines and encouraged him to apply. He acquired the necessary flight certifications, retired from the Navy, and was accepted for their next class of trainees. This flying job would give him about half his time to pursue other work and keep him in the air in a different brand of airplane.

Was it hard to leave NASA? In some ways yes and some ways no. I didn't want to get stale in a job I didn't enjoy and be disappointed all the time because the exciting space future we could envision was not happening. NASA leadership had a way of changing with every new administration, and some of the choices that were made were astoundingly mediocre.

As the NASA budget shrank, fewer good people wanted to hitch their wagon to that star.

On the other hand, there were wonderful people working at NASA, both in the Astronaut Office and other places, who were so bright, fun, and committed. There seemed to be nothing they couldn't do. To them, it was still a great adventure. The bright new faces of the astronauts who had recently been selected were eager to add their names to the list of people who had flown in space.

It was time for them to have their chance.

No one could take away from me the experiences I'd had. No one could negate the contributions to understanding about how humans could live and work in space that I'd made. No one could any longer say that women couldn't be astronauts. It seems strange looking back that it was ever doubted.

NASA Administrator Dan Goldin greets the crew at the landing site.

PHOTO COURTESY OF NASA

A post-landing family picture – Julie, Hoot, Emilee, Paul, Dann and me.

Our years in Houston were blessed. We were coming out of it healthy and alive despite taking great risks. Including Julie, we had four beautiful children. We had been fortunate to experience life in space which so few people had ever gotten to do. We had seen the Earth—our home—from orbit, in all its beauty and vastness. We had seen stars more plentiful than anyone could imagine. We worked with some of the finest people in the world, many of whom would be friends for life.

Hoot and I left NASA with the confidence that once again the stars would align in our favor and bring many more adventures to our lives.